HOME EDUCATION

·Teacher's Edition·

for Christian Schools®

Second Edition

BJU PRESS

GREENVILLE, SOUTH CAROLINA

SCIENCE 2 for Christian Schools® Home Teacher's Edition
Second Edition

Authors of Classroom Edition
Teresa R. Barnett
Kimberly A. Pascoe
Dawn L. Watkins
Gail H. Yost

Author of Home Teacher's Edition
Peggy Davenport

Editors
Carolyn Cooper
Ellen M. Gildersleeve
Rebecca S. Moore

Design
Elly Kalagayan
Duane Nichols

Illustration
Tim Davis
Jim Hargis
Mary Ann Lumm

Composition
Typo-Graphics, Inc.
Peggy Hargis
Carol Larson

Project Manager
Vic Ludlum

Photo Acquitition
Susan Perry

Photo credits appear on page 221.

for Christian Schools is a registered trademark of BJU Press.

© 1991, 2003 BJU Press
Greenville, South Carolina 29614
First Edition © 1976 BJU Press

ISBN 1-57924-910-8

20 19 18 17 16 15 14 13 12 11 10 9 8 7 6 5 4 3 2

Contents

Introduction vi

Suggested Daily Schedule vii

Summary of Correlated Skills and Instructional Materials viii

General Lesson Plan Format xiv

Instructional Materials xv

Lesson Plans xvii

   How Long Do Plants Live? 1

   The History of Earth 19

   Forces 39

   Your Bones 55

   A Round Earth 71

   Light and Shadows 85

   Living and Not Living 101

   How Long Is It? 123

   How Earth Moves 137

   Your Muscles 151

   Layers of the Earth 167

   Where Things Live 179

   Motion 195

   Ocean Shorelines 209

   Little Things Count 219

Supplement 223

   Concepts 223

   Materials List 226

   Bible Action Truths 231

   Bible Promises 234

Appendix A1

dis•cern•ment
(dĭ-sûrn′mənt)

n. 1. Clear, accurate perception. 2. Sound judgment and keen insight.

The fact that your student has this BJU Press product is evidence that you have exercised not only discernment in your choice of the finest state-of-the-art materials available, but you have also exercised trust—something we remember here every single day. You will not regret choosing a BJU Press Science textbook.

- **Enjoy** interacting with your student to discover the amazing secrets of God's world through daily activities that go beyond reading and include doing.

- **Relax** at test time—your student will be ready and the test prepared for you.

- **Watch** the subject take hold of your student as the process of learning for life begins.

a program designed to teach science skills by

1 Developing a knowledge of God
- Creation tells us about God (Psalm 19:1; Romans 1:20).
- By studying the universe, your student can see illustrations of God's wisdom, omnipotence, sovereignty, and benevolence.

2 Encouraging Christian growth
- Your student learns discipline in his attitude and his fulfilling of responsibilities.
- He should be prepared to evaluate and reject "science falsely so called." In certain ways, the study of science can do more for him spiritually than the study of most other subjects.

3 Promoting scientific knowledge, skills, and attitudes in order to identify and solve science-related problems
- Short statements of scientific knowledge are given for each lesson.
- The practical experiences which involve action ("hands-on" or "learning-by-doing" activities) use process skills such as classifying, measuring, predicting, and experimenting.
- Your student will develop a positive attitude about science by being an active participant.

4 Focusing on the inductive approach to teaching
- This method of teaching enables you, the teacher, to stimulate your student to learn through observations, experiments, questions, and discussions.
- Using any of these methods, you lead your student to take what he knows and discovers in applying logical reasoning to form general principles.

5 Providing activities to instill interest in science
- Each lesson begins with an activity to stimulate your student's interest in science.
- As much as possible the activities are home-spun, using items found at home or in your local community.

6 Evaluating scientific knowledge and skills
- Each lesson includes an activity that will indicate whether your student has grasped the scientific knowledge and skills.

7 Furnishing you with a flexible schedule
- The units may be rearranged to accommodate your family schedule and/or your seasonal teaching schedule.
- The number of lessons taught each week may be varied according to your schedule and subject matter.
- The same lessons usually may be taught to more than one child in grades 2-5 depending upon each student's level of understanding.
- All the activities may be done with more than one student. Information may be obtained from additional sources for your younger or older children in order to meet their individual learning needs.

8 Including Family Times
- These lessons have appealing activities to excite your student about the next science lesson.
- These activities may involve the whole family or just you and your child.

Suggested Daily Schedule
for Home Education

Grade 1

First Grade English Skills. . . . . 60-70 min.
    Listening . . . . 5-10 min.
    Phonics and Structural Analysis . . . . 15-20 min.
    Handwriting. . . . . 5-10 min.
    Word Work. . . . . 10-15 min.
    Grammar and Composition . . . . 10-15 min.
Spelling . . . . 15-20 min.
Bible . . . . 20-30 min.
Reading . . . . 20-30 min.
Heritage/Science . . . . 20-30 min.
Math . . . . 15-25 min.
Music/Art. . . . . 15-25 min.

Grades 2-6

Bible . . . . 20-25 min.
Writing and Grammar . . . . 15-30 min.
Reading . . . . 20-30 min.
Math . . . . 20-30 min.
Spelling . . . . 15-25 min.
Handwriting. . . . . 5-10 min.
Heritage/Science . . . . 20-30 min.
Music/Art. . . . . 15-25 min.

Summary of Correlated Skills and Instructional Materials

	Chapter and Lessons	Lesson numbers	Lesson pages	Text pages
1	**HOW LONG DO PLANTS LIVE?**			
	How Long Do Plants Live?	1	2-5	2-5
	Favorite Gardens	FT* 2	6	
	Planning a Garden	2	7-10	6-7
	Planting a Garden	3	11-13	8-9
	Caring for a Garden	4	14-17	10-12
2	**THE HISTORY OF EARTH**			
	Fossil Find	FT 5	21	
	Theories About the Earth	5	22-24	14-15
	What Is a Fossil?	6	25-28	16-19
	Play Dough	FT 7	29	
	Kinds of Fossils	7	30-32	20-21
	Fossil Walk	FT 8	33	24-25
	Where Are Fossils Found?	8	34-37	22-23, 26-28
3	**FORCES**			
	Finding Out About Bones	FT 9	40	46
	Gravity	9	41-43	30-33
	Hunt for Magnets	FT 10	44	
	Magnetic Force	10	45-47	34-36
	Mechanical Force	11	48-50	37-38
	Friction	12	51-53	39-42
4	**YOUR BONES**			
	Bones and Cartilage	13	56-59	44-46
	Names and Shapes of Bones	14	60-62	47-49
	Where Bones Meet	15	63-65	50-51
	Jobs of the Skeleton	16	66-69	52-54

* Family Time

Notebook pages	Bible Action Truths, Bible Promises/ Reflections of God	Process Skills
1-2	BAT: 8b Faith in the power of the Word of God/God is unchanging	observing, classifying
3-4	BATs: 2d Goal setting, 2e Work, 4a Sowing and reaping/God sustains	observing, classifying, using space-time relationships
5	/God is unchanging, God sustains	observing
6-9	BAT: 8a Faith in God's promises	observing, classifying
10-11	/God creates, God sustains	observing
	Bible Promise: I. God as Master/ God sustains	observing, classifying
12	/God creates, God sustains	observing
	BAT: 8b Faith in the power of the Word of God; Bible Promise: I. God as Master/God creates, God judges	observing, predicting
13	/God creates	observing, measuring
	Bible Promise: I. God as Master/ God creates	observing, classifying, inferring
14	BAT: 2a Authority; Bible Promise: I. God as Master	observing
	/God creates	observing
15	/God creates	observing, inferring
	Bible Promise: H. God as Father	observing, classifying
	BAT: 3d Body as a temple	observing, inferring
16-18	BATs: 3c Emotional control, 7c Praise; Bible Promise: I. God as Master/ God creates	classifying

	Chapter and Lessons	Lesson numbers	Lesson pages	Text pages
5	**A ROUND EARTH**			
	Round Like a Ball	17	72-74	56-58
	Where Do People Live?	18	75-77	59-61
	A Ball in Space	19	78-80	62-63
	What Is Down?	20	81-83	64-66
6	**LIGHT AND SHADOWS**			
	The Source of Light	21	86-88	68-71
	How Light Travels	22	89-91	72-73
	Shadow Silhouettes	FT 23	92	
	Shadows	23	93-95	74-75
	Shadows Growing and Changing	24	96-99	76-78
7	**LIVING AND NOT LIVING**			
	Living Things Move	25	102-5	80-83
	Living Things Have Needs	26	106-9	84-85
	Trapped	FT 27	110	
	Living Things Respond	27	111-14	86-88
	Living Things Make New Living Things	28	115-18	89-90
	Living Things Grow	29	119-22	91-92
8	**HOW LONG IS IT?**			
	How Long Is It?	30	124-26	94-95
	What Do You Measure?	31	127-30	96-99
	Why Do You Measure?	32	131-34	100-103
	Why Do You Measure?	33	135-36	104
9	**HOW EARTH MOVES**			
	Day and Night	34	138-41	106-8
	Time Zones	35	142-44	109-10
	A Revolving Earth	36	145-47	111-13
	A Year	37	148-49	114

Notebook pages	Bible Action Truths, Bible Promises/ Reflections of God	Process Skills
19 20	BAT: 8a Faith in God's promises/ God is all-powerful BAT: 5c Evangelism and missions /God is all-powerful, God sustains /God creates, God sustains	using space-time relationships observing, inferring observing observing
21 22	BATs: 5c Evangelism and missions, 7b Exaltation of Christ/God is love BAT: 1a Understanding Jesus Christ /God is unchanging, God is love	observing observing observing, classifying observing
23 24-26 27 28-30	Bible Promise: I. God as Master BATs: 1a Understanding Jesus Christ, 1b Repentance and faith; Bible Promise: H. God as Father/God is love BAT: 5e Friendliness /God creates BATs: 5c Evangelism and missions, 5e Friendliness	observing, classifying, using space-time relationships classifying classifying classifying, inferring observing, measuring, using space-time relationships
31-32 33 34 35	/God is unchanging /God is all-knowing /God is all-knowing	observing, measuring, inferring, interpreting measuring, using numbers observing, classifying, measuring observing, classifying
36 37 38	/God creates, God sustains Bible Promise: I. God as Master/ God is all-powerful /God is unchanging	observing, using space-time relationships using numbers, predicting observing, using space-time relationships observing

	Chapter and Lessons	Lesson numbers	Lesson pages	Text pages
10	**YOUR MUSCLES**			
	Names and Structure of Muscles	38	152-55	116-19
	Muscles Move Bones	39	156-58	120-21
	Muscles Move Food	40	159-61	122
	The Heart	FT 41	162	
	Muscles Move Blood	41	163-66	123-24
11	**LAYERS OF THE EARTH**			
	A Volcano Model	42	168	
	Volcanoes and Earthquakes	43	169-71	126-29
	The Layers of the Earth	44	172-74	130-32
	The Materials of the Earth	44	175-77	133-34
12	**WHERE THINGS LIVE**			
	Spin an Animal Home	FT 46	180	
	Homes for Living Things	46	181-83	136-38
	Nonliving Parts of the Environment	47	184-86	139-40
	Wind and Water	48	187-90	141-44
	Communities and Populations	49	191-94	145-48
13	**MOTION**			
	Move with Haste	FT 50	196	
	What Causes Movement	50	197-99	150-53
	The First Law of Motion	51	200-202	154-55
	The Second Law of Motion	52	203-5	156-57
	The Third Law of Motion	53	206-8	158-60
14	**OCEAN SHORELINES**			
	The Hurricane Game	FT 54	210	
	Types of Shorelines and Beaches	54	211-14	162-65
	What Is in Sand?	55	215-18	166-70

Notebook pages	Bible Action Truths, Bible Promises/ Reflections of God	Process Skills
39	/God creates, God sustains	observing, classifying observing observing, using space-time relationships
40	BATs: 1b Repentance and faith/ God is love	observing
41 42	/God is all-knowing /God is all-knowing /God creates /God creates	observing observing, inferring observing, classifying observing, inferring
43 44	Bible Promise: I. God as Master/ God creates, God is all-knowing /God creates, God sustains	observing, classifying observing, classifying observing observing, classifying
45 46	BAT: 8a Faith in God's promises /God is all-powerful /God is all-powerful /God is all-powerful	observing, predicting, using space-time relationships, measuring observing, inferring, using space-time relationships observing, predicting, inferring observing, predicting
47-48 49	BAT: 4a Sowing and reaping Bible Promises: G. Christ as Friend, I. God as Master/God creates, God is all-knowing, God is all-powerful	observing, inferring observing

General Lesson Plan Format

SCIENCE 2 for Christian Schools is a developmental science program. In the hands of a skillful teacher, these materials can be used to teach not only scientific literacy but also a knowledge of God and Christian character. The lessons are designed to fit your scheduling needs and should be arranged to accommodate your student's and your family's schedules. The recommended time for teaching science is twenty to thirty minutes per lesson. Many of the lessons may be taught over a period of several days. One day could be devoted to the preparation and the setup. Another day could be given to the activities of the lesson, and a third day might be used for reading, discussing, and evaluating the lesson. If you desire to shorten the actual teaching, you could prepare the materials ahead of time and teach the lesson in one day. These are suggested paces for accomplishing the lessons.

There is a uniform format for the lesson plans. Each lesson contains three major divisions: Preview, Lesson, and For Your Information. The following is an overview of each division.

Preview

The Preview contains the main lesson objectives and the materials needed for each lesson. The *Objectives* are statements describing the outcome of instruction in terms of student behavior. It is important that you read the objectives and keep them in mind as you plan and teach the lesson.

Materials is a list of items to be obtained or prepared. They are listed for your convenience and should be taken into consideration before the day of the lesson. You will find some materials marked with an *. These items need to be obtained or prepared before the presentation of the lesson. The materials marked with a † may be purchased from BJU Press.

Occasionally this section will also contain *Notes,* which will give you helpful hints for teaching the lesson.

Lesson

The section *Introducing the Lesson* suggests an activity to begin the lesson. The activity will stimulate your student's interest in science and in the lesson that follows.

The section *Teaching the Lesson* contains a text activity. Questions are given to stimulate your student's interest in what he is going to read silently. There are questions and statements to help you guide a discussion with your student about what he read.

Evaluating the Lesson is a section that gives activities to evaluate, not test, the student's grasp of the material presented.

Enrichment

This is an optional section found in some lessons. It contains experiments or games that your student can do independently.

For Your Information

This section provides you, the teacher, with extra information to help you expand your scientific knowledge. It is not necessary to understand, or even to read, the information in this section in order to teach the lesson. Your student does not need to become acquainted with the information in this section unless he shows special interest in the topic.

Instructional Materials

Teacher Materials

SCIENCE 2 for Christian Schools Home Teacher's Edition This edition includes all of the lesson plans for teaching second-grade science. It includes a section on *General Lesson Plan Format,* which gives an overview of each segment of the lesson plan. In the *Supplement* there is a list of concepts, which are given by lesson number. The concepts are short statements of scientific knowledge which your student will learn about in that lesson. The *Appendix* contains prepared visuals, charts, and games to aid in teaching the lessons.

Write It Flip Chart This flip chart is a tablet of blank paper that you can use instead of a chalkboard or chart paper.

Science supplies Refer to the materials section in the *Supplement* of this book for a complete list of items needed to teach each lesson.

Student Materials

Text *SCIENCE 2 for Christian Schools* is a hardcover four-color text containing a variety of developmental subtopics built around seven major topics: *Living Things, Human Body, Earth, Space, Matter, Energy,* and *Motion.*

Notebook *SCIENCE 2 Notebook Packet* is a consumable companion tool for the text. It contains sixty-one pages that are used primarily for recording scientific data. These recording activities will help your student understand the importance of keeping scientific records. The notebook will also save time for the teacher. The pages are designed to be used in a three-ring notebook binder.

Miscellaneous supplies Your student will need standard supplies: crayons or felt-tip pens, pencils, scissors, glue, etc.

Lesson Plans

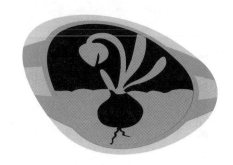

How Long Do Plants Live?

In this chapter your student will learn about grouping plants as annuals, biennials, and perennials. He will also discuss planning, planting, and caring for a garden. Your student will practice what he has studied as he plants seeds and records what happens in his miniature garden.

Materials

The following items must be obtained or prepared before the presentation of the lesson. These items are identified with an * in the materials list in each lesson and in the Supplement. For further information see the individual lessons.

- *SCIENCE 2 Notebook Packet*† (Lesson 1)
- A Write It flip chart † (Lesson 1)
- A three-ring binder (Lesson 1)
- 1 garden magazine for each family member (Family Time 2)
- 1 piece of construction paper for each family member (Family Time 2)
- 1 package of flower seeds (Lesson 3)

 The impatiens seeds used in this lesson may need to be ordered from a seed catalog. Impatiens seeds are rarely found locally. Because of the emphasis on flowering plants in this chapter, the impatiens plant was chosen with the goal that it would eventually bloom *indoors*.

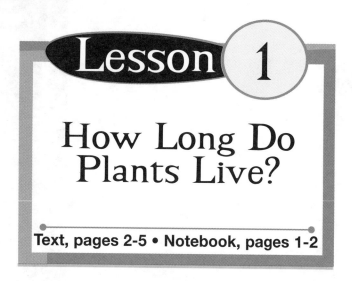

Lesson 1

How Long Do Plants Live?

Text, pages 2-5 • Notebook, pages 1-2

Preview

Objectives

Given proper instruction, your student will be able to

- Demonstrate that plants can be divided into three groups according to their life spans.
- Plan a site by designing a park.

Materials

Have available

- A Write It flip chart*†
- A SCIENCE 2 Notebook Packet *†
- A three-ring binder*

Lesson

Introducing the Lesson

Each lesson begins with an activity to stimulate your child's interest in science.

Introduce the activity. Take your student to a plant nursery to examine the different varieties of flowering plants. Since annuals are generally grouped together, biennials together, and perennials together, your student will readily be able to examine these types of plants.

It will not be necessary for your child to learn the terms for these three types of flowering plants; however, since the term *annual* is simple and heard frequently, you may want to encourage your child to learn and use this one term.

Direct the activity. When examining the annuals, ask your student whether these flowers are of various colors, sizes, and heights. *(yes)* Tell him that these are flowers that live only one year. Allow your student to read the names of some of the annual plants. Which annual is his favorite? Why?

Next, find the biennials. Are there more biennials than annuals? *(The answer to this question will vary depending upon the type of flowers that the nursery orders and sells.)* Give time for your student to read some of the names of biennials. Tell him that this group of flowering plants lives for two years. Ask him where he has seen any of these types of plants growing. Which is his favorite flower in this group? Why?

Now find the perennials. Tell your student that these plants live for many years. Allow him to read some names of perennials. Are any of these names familiar to him? Which ones? Where has he seen some of these types of plants growing?

Continue the activity. If necessary, go back to each section where annuals, biennials, and perennials are displayed. Ask your student which type of flowering plant costs the least. *(annuals)* Why? *(because they live for only one year)* Which type of flowering plant is most expensive? *(perennials)* Why? *(because they live for many years)* Point out that biennials are medium-priced because they live longer than one year but not as long as perennials.

Conclude the activity. Allow your student to select and purchase a package of flower seeds appropriate for planting in your yard at this season. Save these seeds for the activity in Lesson 3. Explain to your student that he will learn more in his science textbook about plants that live for one year, two years, or for many years.

"And the Lord God planted a garden eastward in Eden; and there he put the man whom he had formed."

Genesis 2:8

Gardeners are people who plan, plant, and care for flower beds and gardens. To do those jobs, gardeners have to know many things. One thing they have to know is that plants can be sorted into groups by how long the plants live.

"The grass withereth, the flower fadeth: but the word of our God shall stand for ever." Isaiah 40:8

2

When plants are sorted into groups by how long they live, there are three groups. One group has plants that live only one year. Another group has plants that live two years. The third group has plants that live many years.

Think about the plants in your yard. Can you think of any plants that live year after year? Did you think of trees? Maybe you didn't know that trees are plants. They are, and they live a long time. Some live for a hundred years or more. Many bushes and shrubs live for years too. Do you have any plants that live only one year? If you have a vegetable garden, you have many plants that live only one year. You may even have a few plants that live two years. Carrots, beets, and turnips can live two years if you don't pick and eat them the first year.

3

Teaching the Lesson

Direct a text activity on pages 2-5. Use the following questions to initiate your student's interest in what he is going to read.

1. What does a gardener do?
2. When plants are sorted into groups by how long they live, how many groups are there?
3. What is a site?

> Asking your child questions will encourage him to develop his own ideas.

Continue with discussion questions. After your student completes his silent reading, use the following questions and statements as a guide to discuss the pages he read.

1. How long do most vegetable plants live? *(one year)*
2. How long do carrots, beets, and turnips live? *(two years if you do not pick and eat them the first year)*
3. How long do most trees and shrubs live? *(many years)*

4. Explain what Isaiah 40:8 means. *(The grass will eventually dry up and the flower's beauty will fade away. In time, everything on this earth will fade away—plants will wither, people will die, buildings will crumble. God promises in this verse that His Word will not fade away but will stand forever. [BAT: 8b Faith in the power of the Word of God])*

Conclude the discussion. Direct your student's attention to pages 4 and 5 and ask him to name the person who works on a site. *(the planner)* Then ask him to name the person who works on a garden. *(the gardener)*

Take turns with your student reading aloud the parts of the planner and the gardener with you, the teacher, being the planner and your student being the gardener.

When you reach the end of page 4, instruct your student to listen while you read the items on the planner's list. Write the planner's list on the Write It flip chart and describe or draw those items (for example, gazebo) that may be unfamiliar to your child. After some discussion, direct your student's attention to page 5, containing the planner's instructions for the site plan of the White House. As your student identifies the various items on the site plan, circle the corresponding item on the Write It flip chart.

Planning a Garden

A garden is a plot of land for growing plants, and a flower bed is a special plot just for flowers. A site is the whole area around a building. It is the front yard, the back yard, and the side yards. Before a gardener starts planting anything, he should know how his whole site is to look in the end. Read this talk between a gardener and the person planning the site.

Planner: Why don't you look at other sites to get ideas?

Gardener: What do I look for?

Planner: Well, first you might look for how the earth, rocks, water, and plants are used. Then you could look for things people have added. Here's a list of some of those things.

1. greenhouses, toolsheds, and playhouses

2. seats, tables, barbecues, and umbrellas

3. statues, fountains, birdbaths, and wells

4. gazebos and pavilions

5. walks, roads, and decks

6. walls and fences

7. steps and bridges

4

Planner: Now, here is a site plan of the White House in our nation's capital. Notice how many things from the list were used on the site plan of the White House.

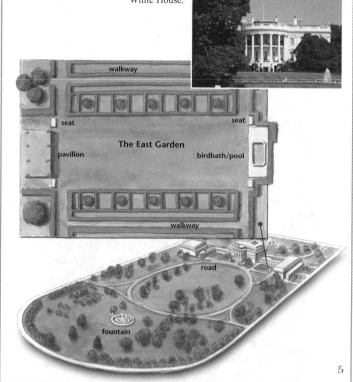

5

name _____

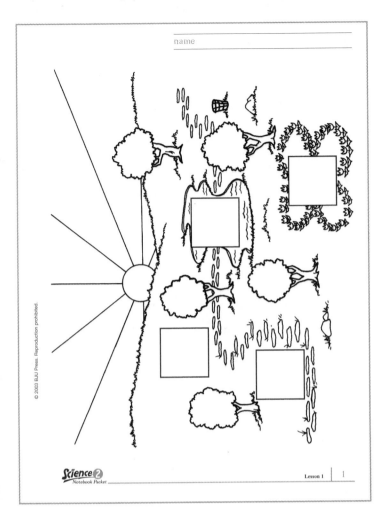

name _____

Evaluating the Lesson

Direct a notebook activity on pages 1-2. Tell your student that he will practice planning a site by designing his own park. Direct his attention to page 1 and the scene of the park. Point out the various boxes on the page. Explain that those boxes represent areas where park furniture or equipment may be placed. Direct his attention to page 2, which includes park furniture and other items. Instruct your student to cut out the sections and to place them in front of him. Inform him that although all of these items are commonly found in parks, only five are part of the planner's list on page 4 in his book. The boxed areas on the park drawing (page 1) should include *only* items from the planner's list. After the items from the list have been glued in place, your student may glue the remaining park items on the notebook page. Encourage him to make his park look attractive by coloring his finished notebook page.

 You might want your child to display his finished park on the refrigerator, on a family bulletin board, or in his science notebook binder.

For Your Information

Most herbaceous plants are *annual plants*. Annuals sprout, grow, flower, and produce seeds in one growing season. Many showy flower beds contain herbaceous annuals like zinnias, pansies, and marigolds. *Biennial plants,* like the foxglove and the sweet William, sprout and develop in one growing season but do not flower and produce seeds until the following growing season. After the second year most biennials die. *Perennial plants* grow year after year. Woody plants are usually perennials. Some herbaceous plants have thick, underground stems that live many years, even though the above-ground leaves and stems die each year. Tulips, irises, peonies, cattails, and gladioli are common examples of herbaceous perennials.

Family Time 2

Favorite Gardens

 Family Time has appealing activities to excite your child about the next science lesson. These activities do not need to be handled during your teaching time. They can involve the whole family or just you and your child.

Materials

Have available

- 1 garden magazine for each family member*
- Scissors
- 1 piece of construction paper for each family member*
- Glue

Instructions

Give each family member an old garden magazine and time to look through it. Instruct him to cut a picture of his favorite garden from the magazine and to glue the picture onto a piece of construction paper. Label each picture with the name of the person and the words *Favorite Garden* (for example, *Mom's Favorite Garden*).

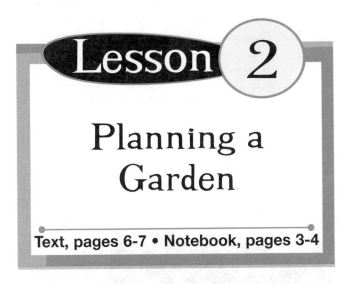

Lesson 2

Planning a Garden

Text, pages 6-7 • Notebook, pages 3-4

Preview

Objective

Given the proper instruction, your student will be able to

- Plan a flower bed by arranging the flowers by height and choosing pleasing color combinations.

Materials

- A Write It flip chart

Lesson

Introducing the Lesson

 Many large corporations or office parks have well-kept, beautiful garden sites on their premises.

Introduce the activity. Tell your student that today you are going to visit a site to see which plants are used and how they are arranged to make the site attractive.

Direct the activity. Take your student to an actual park or garden. Once there, use some of the following questions to generate discussion between you and your student. Are the flowers there of different heights or of the same height? What colors are used in this site? Notice which colors are next to each other. Are there any colors of flowers that would not be attractive next to each other? Name the colors. Do you know any of the names of the flowers in this site? Name the ones you know. What do you like best about this particular site?

Continue the activity. After returning home, give your student the pictures of the favorite gardens that he and the other family members selected from the garden magazines. Encourage him to compare the gardens, noting the similarities and differences. Which garden is the most colorful? Which garden uses the largest variety of flowers? Ask your student to identify some of the types of flowers pictured. Which ones will continue to live for many years? Which ones are annuals, flowers that live for only one year?

Conclude the activity. Display the favorite garden pictures on the refrigerator, on a family bulletin board, or in the science notebook binder. Encourage your student to share with the family his findings about what makes an attractive site.

Gardener: OK, I've got some ideas from the list. What do I do next?

Planner: Just answer some questions. Do you need a children's play area or an outdoor cooking area?

Gardener: Yes, I'd like both.

Planner: Do you want a flower bed?

Gardener: Oh, yes. I want at least two flower beds by the front door.

Planner: I'll add those to the site plan and get back to you in a week or so. For now, here is an example of a site plan. It will give you an idea of how your plan will look.

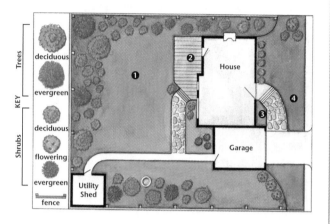

Gardener: Is there anything else we need to do?

Planner: After I add the flower beds to the site plan, we can decide what building materials we need. Then while I go to work putting this plan into action, you can choose what flowers you will use.

After the site is planned, a gardener chooses plants to use. To make good choices, he needs to know how long the plants live. In some gardens he puts plants that live many years next to plants that live just one year. In other gardens he puts only plants that live one year. Study the pictures of different kinds of flower gardens.

Teaching the Lesson

Direct a text activity on pages 6-7. Use the following questions to initiate your student's interest in what he is going to read.

1. Which buildings are identified in the site plan?

2. What does the gardener need to know in order to make good choices for plants in his site?

Continue with discussion questions. After your student completes his silent reading, use the following questions and statements as a guide to discuss the pages he read.

1. Which types of trees are included in the site plan? *(deciduous and evergreen)*

2. Which types of shrubs are included in the site plan? *(deciduous, flowering, and evergreen)*

3. Why does the gardener use a variety of trees and shrubs in his site plan? *(The variety of heights and shapes of trees and shrubs, as well as the variety of colors of their leaves and flowers, makes the garden site very attractive.)*

4. Which numbered area would make the best play area? *(area number 1, because it has the largest amount of yard)*

5. Which numbered area would make the best place for outdoor cooking? *(area number 2, because it is close to the kitchen)*

6. In which numbered area will the gardener place the two flower beds? *(area number 3, because it is by the door)*

Conclude the discussion. Direct your student's attention to the pictures on page 7. Ask your student to name the colors of flowers used in these flower beds. Are they pleasing arrangements? Ask your student why flowers of differing heights are planted in the same flower bed. *(The variety of heights, as well as the variety of colors, adds to the attractiveness of the garden site.)* Your student will need to keep these factors, variety of color and height, in mind when assembling his "garden" in his science notebook.

Evaluating the Lesson

Introduce the notebook activity on pages 3-4. Ask your student to tell you some of the things the gardener had to remember while planning and planting his garden. *(Your student should mention the colors of the flowers, the heights of the flowers, and when the flowers bloomed.)* Direct your student's attention to the two assigned notebook pages. Explain that he will be planning and "growing" his own garden on paper. Since his garden is made up of annual plants, he does not need to be concerned about when the flowers bloom, but he does need to decide the colors of his flowers and the best arrangement of these flowers in his garden.

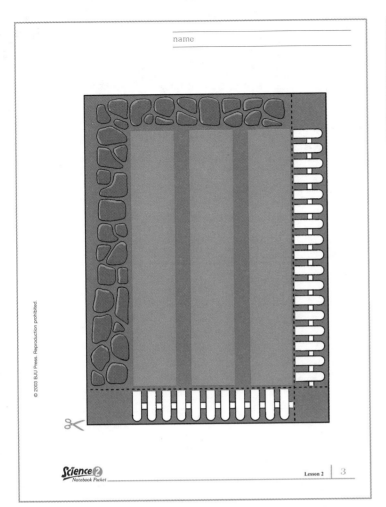

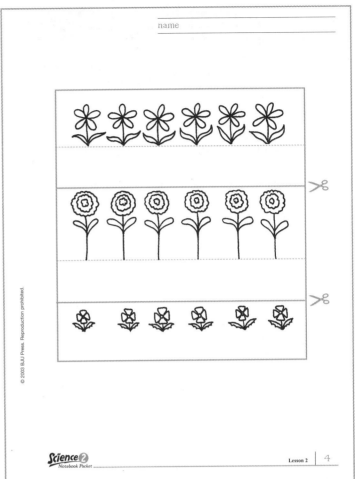

Introduce the notebook activity. Prepare the garden plot on page 3. Show your student how to prepare the edging along the garden plot by folding along dotted lines A and B. Demonstrate how to fold the corner of the paper between the two fences enabling the paper to sit up.

 To correctly fold the corner between the two fences, draw a dotted line from the outside point of the corner box to the opposite point inside the box. Fold on the dotted line, forming two triangles that extend outward. Press the two triangles together and fold back along the edge.

Direct the activity. Secure the corner of the paper with tape. If time permits, wood chips or small pebbles could be glued along the front edge of the garden to form an attractive border. Flat toothpicks could be glued along the picket fence pieces.

Prepare the flowers by instructing your student to color the flowering plants and then to cut out the flower strips.

Warn your child not to cut on the dotted line. This line is for folding only.

Continue the activity. Tell your student to place the strips flower-side-up in front of him. Instruct him to first form a guideline by pinching along the dotted line and folding in the strip. Then he should tuck the bottom section of the strip underneath the flowery top section and press firmly along the dotted fold line. The flowers now have a base for standing up. Your student should arrange the rows of flowers by their proper height and then glue them in place on the garden page.

Conclude the notebook activity. Display your student's completed garden on the table during mealtime and encourage him to tell the rest of the family about his experience at the park or garden site.

When planning a garden, one of the most important things to consider is the texture of the soil in the area. Soil contains *humus,* or dead organic matter; minerals in forms such as sand or clay; water; air; and living organisms. Both clay and sand can be important for good soil. Clay holds water; sand allows more air to penetrate the soil. The humus is one of the most important parts of soil; it is extremely absorbent and helps keep the soil loose. It acts as a filter for water and air also.

Lesson 3

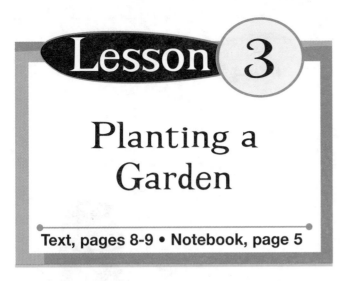

Planting a Garden

Text, pages 8-9 • Notebook, page 5

Preview

Objective

Given proper instruction, your student will be able to

- Identify important information on a seed packet.

Materials

Have available

- 1 package of flower seeds*
- A Write It flip chart

Lesson

Introducing the Lesson

 As you teach this lesson, you will direct attention to a *Finding Out* activity for the first time this year. One of your purposes in using these sections of the text will be to teach your student to follow the directions for gathering materials, doing the activity, and considering the results of the activity.

Introduce the *Finding Out* activity. Tell your student that today he will be planting the seeds that he purchased earlier in the week.

Direct the activity. Refer your student to page 9 of his textbook. Guide him as he follows the steps given for this activity.

 Direct sunlight is too strong for these seedlings and will cause them to wither.

Conclude the activity. Direct a review of the steps to the Finding Out activity. On the Write It flip chart make two columns. In the left column write the following list of phrases: *Time of year, Place for growth, Light for growth, Soil for growth.* Ask your student if he has to consider the time of year for planting his seeds. *(yes)* Write yes in the right column next to *Time of year*. Continue by asking your student whether he provided the right place, light, and soil for the seeds to grow. *(yes)* Write yes in the right column next to each phrase. Tell your student that he will learn more about information on a seed package in today's lesson.

Planting a Garden

Gardeners have several ways to find out how long plants live. They can get this information from a seed package or from a nursery. Did you know that there is more than one kind of nursery? You probably know the kind where babies are cared for. Another kind grows and sells small plants. Have you ever visited a plant nursery? What did you see? Look at the picture of the front of a seed package and the picture of the back of a seed package. What can you find out?

Purple Coneflower $1.19
NET WT 2 g

Purple Coneflower
Sow early spring—blooms midsummer to fall

Purple Coneflower. Perennial. Long-lived plants produce beautiful, long lasting, 4-inch purple flowers, each with a striking, bronze, cone-shaped center that attracts butterflies and bees. Ht. 2 to 3 ft.

PREPARATION
Select a sunny location. Loosen well-drained soil with rake or hoe.

PLANT
For easier planting, mix seeds with a cup of sand or vermiculite and spread over the garden area. Lightly rake seed into soil and cover with 1/8 in. of soil, peat moss, or fine sand. Keep moist until seeds germinate in 15-20 days.

TIPS
Drought-resistant plants prefer dry soil and need little watering. For additional plants, divide established clumps in spring or fall.

8

Finding Out... About Planting Seeds

1. Get

a package of flower seeds

2. Read the steps for planting the seeds.

3. Find out what time of year the seeds should be planted.

4. Choose a place to plant the seeds. Do they need a special place? How much light will the plant need when it grows? What soil is best?

5. Make the soil ready the way the seed package says.

6. Plant the seeds.

9

Teaching the Lesson

Direct a text activity on pages 8-9. Use the following questions to initiate your student's interest in what he is going to read.

1. Which season is recommended for planting purple coneflowers outdoors?

2. What kind of lighting do these seeds require?

3. How far apart should the plants be placed?

Continue with discussion questions. After your student completes his silent reading, use the following question as a guide to discuss the pages he read.

What special tools will you need to plant the seeds?
(A trowel or hoe might be useful in chopping the ground to make it soft and workable.)

Conclude the discussion. Ask your student what he will need to do each day to care for his seeds. *(water them with a light mist)* What will he need to do after he has finished planting his seeds before going on to another activity? *(put away the tools and wash his hands)*

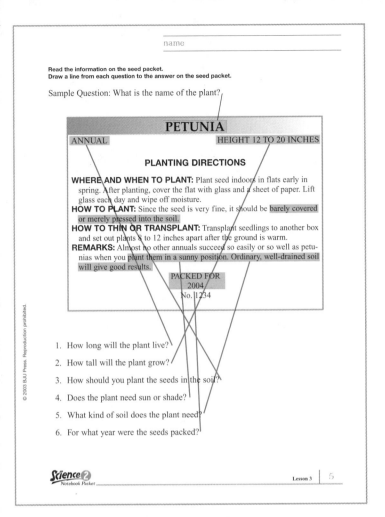

name _____

Read the information on the seed packet.
Draw a line from each question to the answer on the seed packet.

Sample Question: What is the name of the plant?

PETUNIA

ANNUAL   HEIGHT 12 TO 20 INCHES

PLANTING DIRECTIONS

WHERE AND WHEN TO PLANT: Plant seed indoors in flats early in spring. After planting, cover the flat with glass and a sheet of paper. Lift glass each day and wipe off moisture.
HOW TO PLANT: Since the seed is very fine, it should be barely covered or merely pressed into the soil.
HOW TO THIN OR TRANSPLANT: Transplant seedlings to another box and set out plants 8 to 12 inches apart after the ground is warm.
REMARKS: Almost no other annuals succeed so easily or so well as petunias when you plant them in a sunny position. Ordinary, well-drained soil will give good results.

PACKED FOR
2004
No. 1234

1. How long will the plant live?
2. How tall will the plant grow?
3. How should you plant the seeds in the soil?
4. Does the plant need sun or shade?
5. What kind of soil does the plant need?
6. For what year were the seeds packed?

© 2003 BJU Press. Reproduction prohibited.

Science 2
Notebook Packet

Lesson 3   5

If your child has difficulty reading the seed packet by himself, you may need to read the answers in the shaded boxes after each question.

For Your Information

Germination, the beginning of the growth of a plant within a seed, happens only when three conditions are met: *proper moisture, proper temperature,* and *proper oxygen.*

The exact amounts of moisture, heat, and oxygen necessary for germination vary considerably among species. Most seeds do not require light for germination. A seed contains enough stored energy for the plant to get its roots established to absorb water and to force its first leaves above the soil. At this time the stored food in the seed is usually used up, and if the plant is not producing its own food by photosynthesis, it soon dies.

Evaluating the Lesson

Introduce the notebook activity on page 5. Read the instructions to your student. Point out the seed packet in the center of the page. Read *all* of the information given on the seed packet.

Direct the activity. Read the information found only in the shaded boxes. Help your student follow along by pointing to each box as you read. Explain that the shaded boxes contain the answers to the questions listed on the notebook page. Read the sample question at the top of the page. Ask your student to find the answer to the question by tracing the line to the correct answer.

Continue with the activity. Begin the unanswered portion of the page by reading the first question. Remind your student about Lesson 1—How Long Do Plants Live? Review the following: How long do annuals live? *(one year)* How long do each of the other two groups of plants live? *(two years for one group and many years for the other group)* Continue to guide your student through the remainder of the notebook page.

Lesson 4

Caring for a Garden

Text, pages 10-12 • Notebook, pages 6-9

Preview

Objective

Given proper instruction, your student will be able to
- Identify various ways a gardener cares for his plants.

Materials

Have available
- 1 spray mist bottle
- Crayons
- Scissors
- 1 stapler
- A Write It flip chart

Lesson

Introducing the Lesson

Introduce the activity. Tell your student that a good gardener takes notes on the progress of the plants in his garden. In today's lesson he will learn about a gardener's notes.

Direct the activity. Take your student outside to the place where he planted his seeds in the previous lesson. Give time for your student to carefully examine the soil, checking for any sign of growth of his seeds. Tell your student to water his plants with a light mist, making sure to completely saturate the soil. Every day, this will be your student's job as "gardener" to make his plants grow.

Continue the activity. Direct your student's attention to page 6 of his notebook packet. Tell him that you will help him begin taking notes about his "garden." Since each entry should be dated in some way, instruct your student to write in his garden notes the date that he put his seeds in

name

My Garden Notes

Science 2
Notebook Packet

Lesson 4 | 6

the ground. Next to the date, help him to formulate a few sentences about how he planted the seeds. (For example: *I read the seed package to find out how to plant my seeds. I dug up the soil with a trowel, pushed my finger into the soft soil, and placed my seed in the little hole. I then covered up the seeds with some soil and patted it smooth. I planted more seeds in little holes about 15 inches apart. I watered the soil using a spray mist.*)

 Rather than dictating sentences to your child, you may want to work together forming the sentences orally; then write the complete sentences agreed upon on the Write It flip chart for your child to copy.

Conclude the activity. For the second day's entry, instruct your student to write the date and a sentence stating that he examined the soil but saw no little plants yet. He should also say that he watered the soil again.

Caring for a Garden

To care for his garden, a gardener needs to know how long plants live. Here is a monthly plan for taking care of plants that live year after year.

JANUARY ———————————

Read the gardening notes from last year. Order any new plants or seeds that you want. Check your winter mulch.

Mulch comes from a word that means "soft." It is any material that gardeners put on the ground around plants to keep the roots safe and to keep weeds from growing up too near. Gardeners sometimes use straw or sawdust as mulch. Can you think of anything else gardeners might use?

FEBRUARY ———————————

Trim leafless shrubs. Look for roots that have come out of the soil. Carefully press them back into the soil. Add more mulch to those plants. Sharpen your tools. Take notes.

What are some tools gardeners use? Rakes, spades, hoes, and clippers? Which would get dull? How would they get dull? Why is it important to take care of tools?

10

The gardener writes down which plants grew best in each bed. He might also record how fast they grew and how much water they needed. What notes do you think this gardener made about the roots that came out of the soil?

MARCH ———————————

As the weather warms up, remove the mulch from plants that are beginning to grow. After the ground thaws, fertilize the plants. Transplant any plants that need transplanting. Soon the seeds and plants that you ordered will start to arrive. Mark each seed package with the date that the seeds are to be planted. Check the plants for damage and disease. Store the plants in a damp and cool place until you plant them. Take notes.

APRIL ———————————

Remove all leftover mulch. Begin to stake plants. Watch for insects and disease. Take notes.

A stake is a stick or a pole that stands beside a plant. The plant is tied to it with soft strips of cloth. Why would some plants need to be tied up this way?

MAY ———————————

Plant your seeds. Stake plants as needed. Take notes.

11

➤ **Which [tools] would get dull? How would they get dull?**
(Spades, hoes, and clippers could get dull if left out in the rain, used on material they were not meant to be used on, or stored improperly.)

Although this is the final lesson about plants for Grade 2, you will want your child to continue to watch his plants grow. Allow time each day for your child to check the growth of his plants and to make an entry for that day in his gardener's notes. Add additional paper for notes if necessary. Encourage your child to keep his gardener's notes in his three-ring notebook binder.

Teaching the Lesson

Direct a text activity on pages 10-12. Use the following questions to initiate your student's interest in what he is going to read.

1. What is mulch?
2. When does the gardener first transplant the plants?

Continue with discussion questions. After your student completes his silent reading, use the following questions and statements as a guide to discuss the pages he read.

1. What materials do gardeners use as mulch? *(straw or sawdust)*
2. Do you know of anything else that can be used as mulch? Name the items you know. *(Mulch may also be of manmade material such as dark plastic or aluminum foil, or of plant material such as bark or hay.)*
3. What does mulch do for the plant and the soil? *(It keeps the roots of the plant safe and keeps weeds from growing up too close to the plant. Mulch also helps keep the soil moist, protects the soil from heavy rain, provides a good place for earthworms to live, and in time enriches the soil.)*
4. What months does the gardener work with mulch? Direct your student to write these months on the Write It flip chart. *(January, February, March, April, July, and November)*
5. What is the first job for the gardener in February? *(trimming shrubs)*

Enjoy your garden! Remove dead flowers. Transplant the plants that you ordered. Take notes.

JULY

Water and weed your plants. Use mulch to help keep in moisture and cut down on weeds. Take notes.

AUGUST

Cut back the plants that have finished blooming, but keep some leaves. Order the fall and spring flowering bulbs, such as tulips. Take notes.

SEPTEMBER

Prepare flower garden for fall planting. Take notes.

OCTOBER

Clean up garden. Remove stakes. Tie them in a bundle. Take notes.

NOVEMBER

Gather materials for winter mulching. Mulch the plants when the ground has frozen. Clean and store tools. Take notes.

DECEMBER

Rest! Most of the work is finished. Think about next year. Get your notes together.

12

| August | September | October | November |

Science 2
Notebook Packet

Lesson 4 | 7

Write *trimming* on your Write It flip chart; then tell your child that the special name for trimming is *pruning*. Write *pruning* on the Write It flip chart and explain that pruning is cutting away sections of a plant. By thinning out some of the branches and removing any dead parts, the gardener makes more food, water, and sunlight available to the rest of the plant. Although pruning is helpful to the general growth of a plant, the gardener may prune a plant for a special reason. For example, he prunes a boxwood shrub to keep it a certain shape and to provide a hedge around his yard; he prunes a rosebush so that it will produce more flowers.

6. Why do you think a gardener would prune a grapevine or fruit tree? *(so that the vine or tree will produce more fruit)*

7. What do you think makes the roots come out of the ground as mentioned in the entry for February? *(This action, called heaving, usually occurs when the soil freezes, then thaws, freezes, then thaws, and so on.)*

8. In what kind of areas will heaving not occur? *(cold areas where the ground remains frozen and warm areas where the ground does not freeze)*

9. What do you think the term *transplant* means? *(to move the plant to another place)*

10. How does a gardener transplant a plant? *(by carefully digging up the whole plant, complete with roots, and moving it to another place)*

11. What does fertilizer do for the soil and plants? *(It contains special ingredients that enrich the soil and allow the plants to grow better.)*

Conclude the discussion. Direct your student's attention to the December entry on page 12 of the text. Instruct him to read the entry orally. Ask him what he thinks the gardener might do differently next year. Will he plant some different plants? Will he get someone to help him with the garden? Ask your student whether he would like to help a gardener with his garden. Would your student enjoy having a garden of his own next year? If so, make some plans together about where to plant the garden and what plants to grow.

name _____

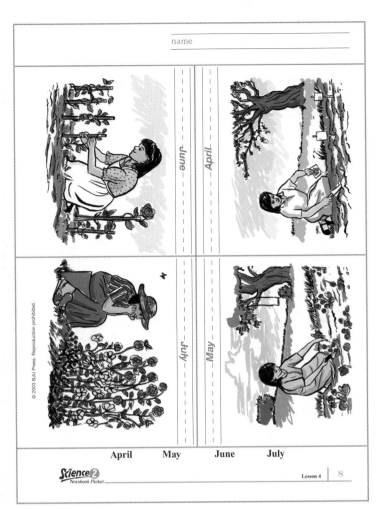

June   April

July   May

April   May   June   July

Science 2
Notebook Packet   Lesson 4 | 8

name _____

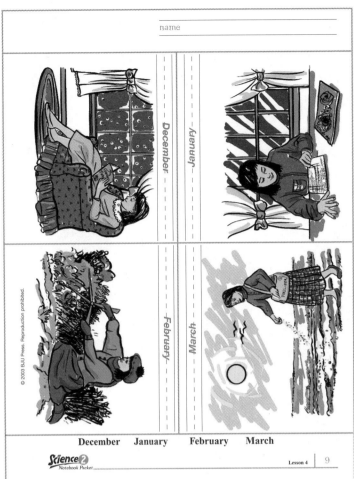

December   January

February   March

December   January   February   March

Science 2
Notebook Packet   Lesson 4 | 9

Evaluating the Lesson

Introduce the activity. Direct your student's attention to pages 7-9 of the science notebook packet. Tell him that each picture represents a different month of the year.

 If your child needs help labeling the pictures, he may refer to the monthly information given in the gardener's notes on pages 10-12 of his textbook.

Direct the activity. Instruct your student to study the pictures on page 7 and correctly label each picture with *August, September, October,* or *November.* Label each of the pictures on page 8 correctly with *April, May, June,* or *July.* Continue on to page 9, labeling each picture with *December, January, February,* or *March.*

 If your child has difficulty sequencing the months, offer him assistance or allow him to refer to a calendar.

Conclude the activity. After your student labels all twelve pictures, instruct him to cut out each gardening scene and sequence the pictures into one pile with January on top and December on the bottom. Staple these pages together to form a complete calendar as a review of today's lesson.

For Your Information

Seeds produced in the fall usually must go through a period of dormancy before they can germinate. For some seeds this dormancy may be broken by a period of cold weather; other seeds require scraping of the seed coat while some seeds require water to wash away inhibiting chemicals from the seed coat. If kept cool and dry, seeds may remain *viable,* or able to germinate, for many years. The embryonic plants in seeds use stored food to maintain life during dormancy. If they do not get oxygen, the stored food cannot be used, the embryo will die, and the seeds will become inviable. Some seeds, especially those produced in the spring, germinate without periods of dormancy.

CHAPTER TWO

Lessons 5-8

The History
of the Earth

This chapter presents the two main beliefs about the earth's beginnings: Creation and evolution. It also describes fossils, lists the clues that they provide about the earth's history, and explains the differences between the Creationist's and the evolutionist's interpretations of the clues. The chapter ends with II Peter 3:3-6, the clear scriptural explanation of why unregenerate man rejects true science and sound biblical interpretation and tries to explain the earth's history apart from God.

The contents of this chapter are somewhat technical and do not lend themselves easily to observable demonstrations. However, this is an important chapter to cover, because an understanding of evolution and Creation is basic to a true understanding of science. If your student can develop a foundation of truth now, even in the second grade, his Christian beliefs will be much stronger and will enable him to refute the false philosophies he will be exposed to later on.

Materials

The following items must be obtained or prepared before the presentation of the lesson. These items are identified with an * in the materials list in each lesson and in the Supplement. For further information see the individual lessons.

- Home Teacher's Edition, pp. A1-A3† (Family Time 5)
- 1 manila file folder (Family Time 5)
- Clear Con-Tact paper (Family Time 5)
- 1 metal brad (Family Time 5)
- 1 box of instant pudding (Lesson 5)
- Fossil collection (Lessons 6 and 7)
- Small plastic animals (Lesson 7)
- Stiff leaves, such as holly leaves (Lesson 7)

- A few dead insects (Lesson 7)
- Rubber cement (Lesson 7)
- Small pebbles, fine-grained sand, and coarse sand (Lesson 8)
- Magazines and brochures showing various land forms, rocks, and fossils (Lesson 8)
- Poster board (optional) (Lesson 8)
- An encyclopedia or reference book written from an evolutionist viewpoint (Lesson 8)

Family Time 5

Fossil Find

Appendix, pages A1–A3

This Family Time needs to be completed if you plan to use the game "Fossil Find" found in the Enrichment section of Lesson 8.

Materials

Have available
- Home Teacher's Edition, pp. A1–A3*†
- Glue
- 1 manila file folder*
- Clear Con-Tact paper*
- Scissors
- 1 metal brad*
- Tape
- 1 resealable plastic bag or envelope
- Small colored rocks or buttons

Instructions

To assemble the **game board,** remove pages A1 and A2 from the Home Teacher's Edition and glue them side-by-side to the inside of a manila file folder. To ensure durability, either laminate the game board or cover it with clear Con-Tact paper.

Next, cut out the **spinner** from page A3 of the Home Teacher's Edition. Glue the spinner to a stiff backing and cover with clear Con-Tact paper. Cut out the numbered square and the dial. Assemble the spinner by pushing a metal brad through the X on the dial and then through the center of the numbered square. To let the dial spin freely, bend the prongs of the brad $\frac{1}{8}$" from the head. Tape the prongs to the back of the square to keep the brad from spinning with the dial. For additional spinning ease, bend the square slightly away from the dial. The square will curve slightly downward, and the dial will spin freely.

Put the spinner into a resealable plastic bag or an envelope and attach the bag or envelope to the back of the game board folder. You will also need a bucket of rocks, because the purpose of the game is for the participants to "collect" rocks as they answer the review questions. The game players will need colored rocks or buttons to serve as game markers.

Lesson 5

Theories About the Earth

Text, pages 14-15

Preview

Objectives

Given proper instruction, your student will be able to

- Discriminate between things that can and cannot be observed.
- List the differences between evolution and Creation.

Materials

Have available

- 1 box of instant pudding*
- Enough milk to prepare the pudding
- 1 large bowl
- A mixer (optional)
- 1 large spoon
- Individual spoons (optional)
- A Write It flip chart

Notes

In this lesson you will have the opportunity to explain that science is limited. Since science is learned only through the senses, science must be limited. That is, science can be wrong, or it can change. In fact, there are many things that science cannot do. For example, since science is based on what can be observed, it cannot deal with beginnings (for example, the beginning of the earth, the moon, the solar system, the universe, or life). What someone believes about those origins is by faith, not science.

Lesson

Introducing the Lesson

Introduce the activity. Place in front of you the pudding mix and milk. Ask your student how long he thinks it would take for the pudding mix and the milk to change into

It is easy to understand how scientists study things that they can see or watch. They call watching "observing." But scientists did not observe the earth's history. So how do they study it? Scientists study the rocks for clues to what happened to the earth in the past.

14

pudding if you just left the two items there for a while. Would they change into pudding in an hour? Overnight? A week? A year? *(No, the mix and the milk need someone to stir them together.)*

Direct the activity. Make the pudding according to the directions. If desired, give your child a spoonful of pudding to taste. Emphasize that the mix and the milk became pudding only because you stirred them together. They would never have become pudding on their own.

Conclude the activity. You may want to expand the lesson by discussing more complicated things that will never be able to go together by themselves. Ask your student the following questions: Would a watch be able to put itself together? How about a car? A house? A skyscraper? How about the world? Direct each response to the conclusion that everything made in the world must have somebody put it together. Things do not go together on their own. Tell your student that this is an important principle in today's lesson. Remind him that just as man put together the watch and built the skyscraper, it is God who made the world and everything in it. God as Master rules and controls everything about the world—its form, its life, its growth, and even its destruction. In John 1:3 we read "All things were made by him; and without him was not any thing made that was made." (Bible Promise: I. God as Master)

Ideas About the Beginning

There are two main ideas, or beliefs, about how the earth was made. One idea is called *creation*. The other is called *evolution*.

People who believe the creation theory believe that God made the earth. They also believe that God changed the earth at least two times in the past. The Bible says that the earth changed when God cursed it and when God destroyed it with a flood. People who believe the evolution theory believe that the earth made itself. They also believe that the earth changed many times in the past. Each theory has a different way to explain the clues scientists find in the rocks.

Teaching the Lesson

Direct a text activity on pages 14-15. Use the following questions to initiate your student's interest in what he is going to read.

1. What do scientists call "watching?"
2. What are the names of the two main beliefs about how the earth was made?

Continue with discussion questions. After your student completes his silent reading, use the following questions and statements as a guide to discuss the pages he read.

1. How do scientists study the earth? *(by studying the earth's rocks)*
2. What information do you think the rocks give the scientists? *(By examining the rocks, the scientists could possibly see the outlines of plants and animals, indicating the age of the earth and the effects of elements on that particular location of the earth.)*
3. If people believe the Creation theory, how do they think the earth was formed? *(God made it.)*
4. If people believe the evolution theory, how do they think the earth was made? *(It made itself.)*

5. What do people who believe the Creation theory think about how the earth has changed? *(God changed the earth at the curse in the Garden of Eden and at the Flood.)*
6. What do people who believe the evolution theory think about how the earth has changed? *(The earth has changed many times over a long, long time.)*
7. Are these beliefs much alike? *(No, they are different.)*

 Your child may know the difference between a fact and a theory. If he does not, you may find the following definitions helpful. A fact is something that a person knows from his observations; it can be proved. A theory is an idea that a person comes up with by studying the facts; it is an opinion. (*NOTE:* A theory not only includes assumptions but also accepts principles and rules.) If a theory is tested and retested and produces the same results, that theory may become a fact.

Conclude the discussion. To readily see how the beliefs of evolution and Creation are different, direct your student's attention to page 15 of the textbook. On the Write It flip chart, make two columns, one entitled *Evolution* and the other entitled *Creation*. Instruct your student to reread page 15 to complete the following chart on the Write It flip chart.

Creation

Earth made by ___God___ .

Earth changed ___two times___ .

Evolution

Earth made by ___itself___ .

Earth changed ___many times___ .

Ask your student to tell you about the two times that God changed the earth. *(at the curse in the Garden of Eden and at the Flood)*

Tell your student that during the next few lessons he will learn more about the differences between the beliefs of Creation and evolution as he studies more about the history of the earth.

Evaluating the Lesson

Introduce the review activity. Tell your student that you are going to read a list of items to him. Some can be observed and some cannot be observed.

 This exercise will limit "observing" to "seeing." It will not include the other senses in the observation process.

Tell your student that if the item can be observed, he should stand up. If it cannot be observed, he should sit down.

Direct the review activity. Read the following phrases aloud one at a time, waiting between each item for your student's response.

1. a horse *(can observe)*
2. the earth 100 years ago *(cannot observe)*
3. a pencil in a closed drawer *(cannot observe)*
4. a living person's skin *(can observe)*
5. a living person's bones *(cannot observe with unaided eyes)*
6. the center of the earth *(cannot observe)*
7. water running from a faucet *(can observe)*
8. the threads in a dress or shirt *(can observe)*
9. a person in another town *(cannot observe with unaided eyes)*
10. the floor underneath the carpet *(cannot observe)*
11. a fish at the top of a pond *(can observe)*
12. a fish at the bottom of a pond *(cannot observe)*

For Your Information

Although the Bible is scientifically accurate, it is not meant to be a scientific textbook and so does not reveal everything there is to know about creation. God gave men intelligence to learn how to use His creation, and this is why science is important to the Christian. For example, it is easy to observe that God designed water to run downhill. But man uses this observation to design systems to use the running water for turning the turbines that produce electricity. Evolutionists fail when they try to develop a system of science that does not acknowledge the presence of original creation before the development of scientific thought.

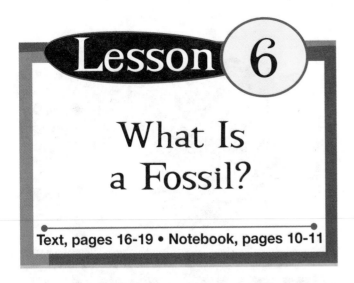

Lesson 6

What Is a Fossil?

Text, pages 16-19 • Notebook, pages 10-11

Preview

Objectives

Given proper instruction, your student will be able to

- Define *fossil*.
- Discriminate between a fossil and a nonfossil.

Materials

Have available

- A fossil collection*†
- 1 can of food

Notes

The fossil collection listed under materials is used several times during this chapter to help your student to visualize the concepts of fossilization. If you cannot obtain a fossil set of your own, check with local junior high or high school science teachers, a cooperative extension agent, or your public library to see if they have this set, or a comparable set, for you to use for several days.

Lesson

Introducing the Lesson

Introduce the activity. Using the fossil collection that you have obtained, show your student various fossils.

Direct the activity. Ask your student to tell you the names of any of the fossils that he recognizes. Check his answers by using the information sheet. Show your student some of the other fossil specimens, tell him the names of these, and give him a little information about each fossil as given on the information sheet.

 The names of the fossils and information about them are given to help you in the discussion with your child. It will not be necessary for him to memorize these facts.

Allow your student to touch some of the fossils. Ask him to describe how they feel. *(hard)* Ask your student whether he thinks a fossil could be soft. *(no)* Why not? *(If the plant or animal were still soft, it would be more likely to decay.)* Point out that most of the fossils in the collection are probably petrified—things that have turned to rock. Ask your student whether he thinks scientists have found fossils of animals only, since most of the fossils in the box are of animals. *(No, they have found fossils of both plants and animals.)*

Continue the activity. Show your student the can of food. Ask him why the food is in a sealed can. *(so that it will not spoil)* If you freeze strawberries or can beans, show a sample of your work. Ask your student to explain why you do this. *(so that you can preserve the food—save its nutritional value and taste to enjoy later on)* Ask what preserving the strawberries and beans does. *(It keeps the food from spoiling.)*

Conclude the activity. Ask your student to tell you how scientists learn. *(by observing)* Can scientists observe things that lived long ago? Why? *(No, because things that lived long ago are dead.)* Point out to your student that scientists can observe things that have been preserved from long ago. Tell your student that this lesson is about how things that used to be living are preserved.

Fossil Clues

There are many clues to help scientists guess what happened in the earth's history. Perhaps the most important clues come from fossils.

Fossils are parts of living things and marks made by living things that are preserved by nature. Study the pictures. Which things are fossils? Why do you say so?

16

17

Teaching the Lesson

Direct a text activity on pages 16-19. Use the following questions to initiate your student's interest in what he is going to read.

1. What is a fossil?
2. What name is given to a living thing that turns to rock?

Continue with discussion questions. After your student completes his silent reading, use the following questions and statements as a guide to discuss the pages he read.

1. Look at pages 16 and 17. Which things are fossils? *(The only fossil pictured on page 16 is the leaf. The top and bottom left pictures on page 17 are fossils preserved in stone. The fish are not preserved.)*

2. What can cause things to be buried quickly, forming fossils? *(a flood)*

3. Explain how a mold forms. *(Mud hardens around a living thing; then the living thing rots and leaves a hole in the rock. This is a mold.)*

4. What are imprints? *(molds of very thin things like leaves)*

5. Explain how a mold becomes a cast. *(A cast forms when a mold fills with mud that hardens.)*

6. Sometimes only a black outline of a plant or animal is left on the rock. What is this kind of fossil called? *(a carbon copy)*

Conclude the discussion. Ask your student what preserved these fossils. Was it man? *(Your child may give several answers, but direct him to the correct answer that it was not man, but God's use of nature that preserved the fossils.)* (Bible Promise: I. God as Master)

How Do Fossils Form?

Clue 1: **Things buried quickly can become fossils.**

Clue 2: **Fossils are found nearly everywhere.**

Clue 3: **Many fossils are found in groups.**

Fossils can form when parts of living things or marks made by living things get trapped quickly by mud or sand. Most often a flood moves enough mud fast enough to bury living things. Many kinds of fossils are formed that way.

Clue 1: Things buried quickly can become fossils.

Things that have turned to rock are petrified things. These petrified things are kinds of fossils. Tracks preserved in rocks are also kinds of fossils. Find the pictures of petrified things.

18

Sometimes mud hardens around a living thing. Then the living thing rots and leaves a hole in the rock. This hole is called a mold.

Molds of very thin things like leaves are called imprints.

If a mold later fills with mud that hardens, a cast of the living thing forms. Molds, imprints, and casts are kinds of fossils.

> *Sometimes all that is preserved of a plant or animal is a black outline on the rock. This black copy is left by carbon, an important material found in all living things. A carbon copy is a kind of fossil.*

19

Color the pictures below. Cut on the lines.

name

Is It a Fossil?

Glue the pictures of fossils in this column.   Glue the pictures of nonfossils in this column.

Yes	No
coral	fish
imprint	paw print
shell	duck
clam	leaf

Evaluating the Lesson

Guide the use of notebook pages 10-11. Point out that the first page contains several pictures, some of which are fossils and some of which are not. Tell your student to color the page of fossils and nonfossils and then to cut out the pictures. Point out on the second page the two columns underneath the question *Is it a fossil?* Instruct your student to glue each picture in the correct column. Be available to answer questions or to assist him if he needs help.

For Your Information

The word *fossil* comes from the Latin word *fodere,* meaning "to dig up." A fossil is any trace or remains of a living organism that has been preserved by natural means. If plants and animals are left exposed to the elements after they die, they will decay and completely disappear; however, if through some method they can be preserved in rock (usually sandstone), the remains will survive to give scientists evidence about that organism. Fossils give us samples of what living things on the earth used to be like. However, they do not show gradual changes from one organism to another. Some fossils represent plants and animals that are still surviving, while others are examples of organisms that have become extinct—direct evidence of the degeneration (Creation) rather than the improvement (evolution) of the earth.

Family Time 7

Play Dough

Materials

Have available

- 2 cups flour
- 1 cup salt
- 2 cups water
- 4 teaspoons cream of tartar
- 2 tablespoons cooking oil
- Food coloring (optional)

Instructions

Combine all the ingredients in a saucepan and cook over low heat for about three minutes, stirring frequently. When the mixture forms a ball, remove from heat. Add food coloring if desired. After the mixture has cooled, store in an airtight container. Do not refrigerate. This mixture will keep a month or more.

An alternate recipe is simply to mix together 1 cup salt, $2\frac{1}{2}$ cups flour, 1 tablespoon cooking oil, and 1 cup water. Add food coloring as desired.

 For the *Finding Out* activity, plaster of Paris may work more effectively for you. Also, you could possibly purchase commercial clays that can be baked. Either method would be a workable alternative to the play dough described above.

Lesson 7

Kinds of Fossils

Text, pages 20-21 • Notebook, page 12

Preview

Objective

Given proper instruction, your student will be able to
- Identify five kinds of fossils and how they are preserved.

Materials

Have available
- The play dough made during Family Time 7
- The fossil collection*†
- Small plastic animals*
- Stiff leaves, such as holly leaves*
- Some dead insects*
- Rubber cement*
- 2 paper cups

Prepare
- An example of a frozen fossil by putting some insects into water in a paper cup and freezing them ahead of time.
- An example of amber by putting several insects into a paper cup and covering them with rubber cement. It should dry overnight. The dried rubber cement may cling to the sides of the cup but is still a workable example of "amber" when peeled off the cup.

Lesson

Introducing the Lesson

Introduce the *Finding Out* activity. Give your student a lump of the play dough that you prepared during Family Time 7. Also give him a plastic animal, a leaf, or some other object that represents a living thing.

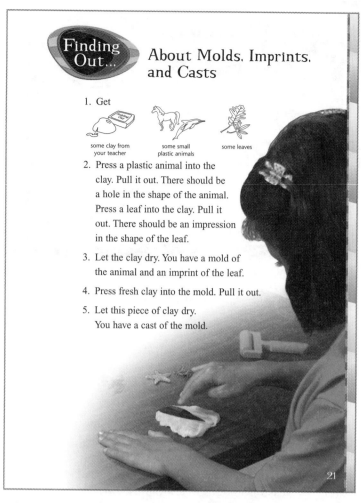

Finding Out... About Molds, Imprints, and Casts

1. Get

some clay from your teacher   some small plastic animals   some leaves

2. Press a plastic animal into the clay. Pull it out. There should be a hole in the shape of the animal. Press a leaf into the clay. Pull it out. There should be an impression in the shape of the leaf.

3. Let the clay dry. You have a mold of the animal and an imprint of the leaf.

4. Press fresh clay into the mold. Pull it out.

5. Let this piece of clay dry. You have a cast of the mold.

21

Direct the activity. Instruct your student to read the instructions on page 21 of his textbook. Then give him time to shape his lump of play dough into a flattened circle about three-fourths of an inch to an inch high. He should lay the lump of play dough onto a piece of paper on a table in front of him and then press the object into the play dough disc.

 If your child's object is a very thin item, like a leaf, he will make an imprint. A mold is made by using a larger object. Of course, what is made will not be a true imprint or mold; it will only represent a fossil since true fossils are made of hardened rock or mud.

Conclude the activity. Put the molds or imprints in a safe place since the play dough will take several days to dry. If time permits, you may want to make casts from the prints and molds after they have dried. Tell your student that today's lesson gives him more information about scientific activities similar to what he just did.

Do you see something on this page that looks like a hairy elephant? It is an animal from long ago called a "woolly mammoth." Is that a good name for it? What would you have named it? Scientists have found woolly mammoths frozen in the ground and stuck in tar pits. These kinds of fossils look much like the living things that they once were.

Amber is also a kind of fossil. Amber is tree sap that is preserved. Sometimes insects and leaves were trapped in the tree sap before it was preserved.

Look at the picture of the amber. Do you see the insect?

20

Teaching the Lesson

Direct a text activity on page 20. Use the following questions to initiate your student's interest in what he is going to read.

1. What is the name of the animal pictured on page 20?
2. What kind of fossil does the bottom picture represent?

Continue with discussion questions. After your student completes his silent reading, use the following questions and statements as a guide to discuss the page he read.

1. Why is *woolly mammoth* a good name for the hairy elephant pictured on page 20? *(It has long hair, somewhat like wool, and it is very large.)*
2. What would you have named this animal? *(Your student may have a variety of appropriate names.)*
3. How was this hairy mammoth preserved? *(It was frozen.)*
4. Where have scientists found woolly mammoths? *(in the ground and in tar pits)*
5. Do you think people have ever eaten mammoth meat? *(probably not many)* Could people buy mammoth meat at the grocery store? *(no)*

Tell your child that mammoth meat is unusual because it is a fossil, but a few people who live near the North Pole (Siberia) have eaten it.

6. What is amber? *(tree sap that is preserved)*
7. What insect do you think is trapped in the amber pictured on page 20? *(a wasp)*

Conclude the discussion. Ask your student to tell you once again the definition of a fossil. *(a living thing or a mark of a living thing from the past that has been preserved by nature)* Tell him that for something to become a fossil it must be in the right place at just the right time. Most or all of it must have been preserved rather than allowed to decay.

Evaluating the Lesson

Display homemade "fossils." Show your student the frozen insects and remind him of the woolly mammoth that was frozen and thereby preserved. Show your student the example of "amber." Allow him to hold the amber specimen. Tell him that real amber is often used to make pretty jewelry. If a person puts a candle to a piece of amber, it will slowly burn. Why would this kind of fossil burn? *(It is made of tree sap.)* Since tree sap burns, the fossilized sap would burn also. Tell your student that many kinds of fossilized animals and plants are found in amber.

If possible, visit a local jewelry store or museum where amber or other fossils could be seen and possibly handled by your student.

name _____

Fossils

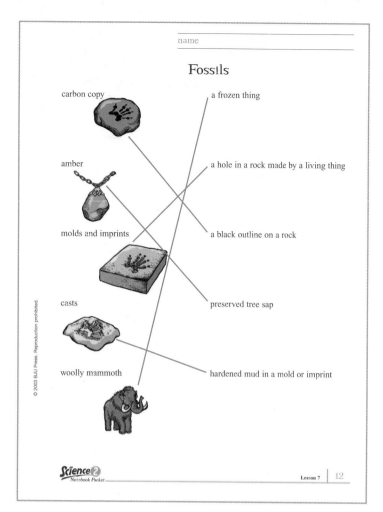

carbon copy

amber

molds and imprints

casts

woolly mammoth

a frozen thing

a hole in a rock made by a living thing

a black outline on a rock

preserved tree sap

hardened mud in a mold or imprint

Science 2
Notebook Packet

Lesson 7 | 12

Direct the use of notebook page 12. This page involves matching the types of fossils with drawings and sentences. Be available to help your student if necessary.

Molds, imprints, and casts are formed when the organism lasts long enough to leave an impression of its body but then decays. This may occur in tar pits, but it is unusual. Tracks of animals can easily be found, although most animal tracks today are washed away before they are preserved. The key to their preservation is that the sediment must quickly change to rock in some way. Some organisms are frozen whole. The mammoths in Siberia were preserved so well that the meat was still edible in recent years. There must have been some kind of disaster that caused them to be preserved without decaying. Amber is primarily found in the Baltic Sea off Northern Europe, and supplies of the clear, hard resin are often washed ashore. The substance has been used as a gem for many years and was used as a currency by early man. Many species of plants and animals have been found trapped in amber.

Enrichment

With some thin leaves and old pieces of carbon paper, your student could make carbon-copy rubbings. Place the carbon paper over the leaf and rub it to transfer some of the carbon onto the leaf. Then place the leaf, carbon side down, on a piece of white paper. Rub it with the flat edge of a pencil to transfer the carbon image to the paper.

Family Time 8

Fossil Walk

Text, pages 24-25

You may want to use the *Fossil Walk* to introduce Lesson 8 or as a follow-up activity to review the whole chapter about fossils.

Instructions

Direct a *Finding Out* activity on pages 24-25. If your home is in a rural area or near an area of exposed rock where your family could be taken safely (a creek bed, a little-used road or railroad track, a construction area), go for a walk. Look for rocks, such as sandstone or conglomerate, to demonstrate examples of rocks made of sand and rocks that have been fused together. If possible, collect samples of rocks in small buckets or bags to take back to your house. Look for fossil examples, though these may be difficult to find.

If a fossil walk is not practical, allow your child to look through magazines and brochures to find examples of rocks and fossils. If you do not want to save the magazines, permit your child to cut out the pictures of rocks and fossils and glue them to poster board to make a display.

Finding Out... About Fossils

1. If you live in a place where there are rocks formed from water, take a walk with your teacher or parents. Look for some rocks that seem to be made of layers of hard mud or sand. If you live in a place where there are no rocks formed from water, get some magazines to find some pictures of such rocks.

2. Look for places on your walk, or in your pictures, where the ground has been worn down or dug into. Look for places where workmen have blasted the ground to build roads or railroad beds. Look for places where water has made gullies. Look along streambeds.

3. On your walk, you may want to look for fossils when you find rocks formed from water. If you find any fossils, call a nearby museum or college to report your find.

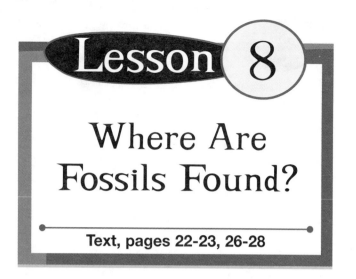

Lesson 8

Where Are Fossils Found?

Text, pages 22-23, 26-28

1. *Many oceans, lakes, and little floods buried fossils.*
1. *The Genesis Flood buried fossils.*
2. *Fossils show us how living things changed to other living things on their own.*
2. *Fossils show us animals and plants that lived in the past.*
3. *The earth has changed many, many times over the years.*
3. *The earth changed when God cursed it and when God sent the Genesis Flood.*
4. *Each group of fossils lived in a different time.*
4. *Each group of fossils lived in a different area.*

Figure 8-1

The Genesis Flood buried fossils.

Preview

Objectives

Given proper instruction, your student will be able to

- Describe how fossils and fossil groups formed.
- Choose which theory—evolution or Creation—is right for a person who believes the Bible.

Materials

Have available

- 1 quart or half-gallon jar (A large mayonnaise jar would work well.)
- Several small containers with different kinds of sediment in each—small pebbles, fine-grained sand, coarse sand*
- Magazines and brochures showing various land forms, rocks, and fossils*
- Poster board (optional)*
- 8 sentence strips
- Home Teacher's Edition, p. A4
- Some construction paper
- A Bible
- An encyclopedia or reference book that is written from an evolutionist viewpoint*

Prepare

- The sentence strips by writing the following sentences, one sentence on each strip. (*NOTE:* See Figure 8-1.) Write the corresponding number on the back of each sentence strip.

 There are two of each number because the first sentence is an evolutionist statement and the second is a Creationist statement.

Lesson

Introducing the Lesson

Introduce the activity. Show your student the small containers with stones and sand. Allow your student to empty the containers into the quart jar. (*NOTE:* You need about one and a half inches of sedimentary material in the bottom of the jar.) Fill the jar with water and put the lid on tightly.

Direct the activity. Instruct your student to shake the jar. Ask him what he thinks will happen when he stops shaking the jar. *(The sand and stones will stop moving around in the jar.)* Direct your student to set the jar on a table and watch how all the sand, pebbles, and dirt settle out. *(The sand and dirt will swirl for a while; then they will slowly settle to the bottom.)*

Conclude the activity. Instruct your student to shake the jar vigorously once again. When he stops, quickly set the jar upright. The sediment will fall quickly. Tell your student to inspect the jar but to be careful not to disturb it, because the lightweight sediments are easily stirred up again. (*NOTE:* The lightest sediment will take several hours to clear and settle out.) Ask your student to tell you what he notices about how the dirt and sand settled to the bottom. *(The particles are in layers.)* The bigger pieces are at the bottom, and the smaller pieces are nearer the top. Tell your student that this is how water causes dirt to settle on the earth also.

Where Are Fossils Found?

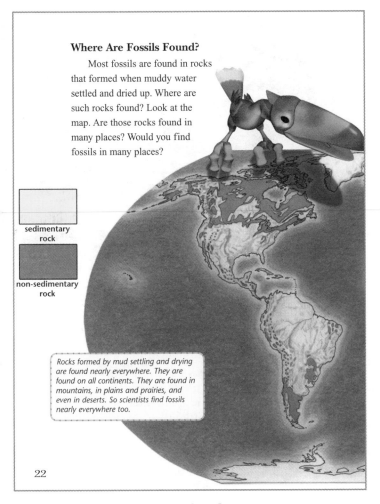

Most fossils are found in rocks that formed when muddy water settled and dried up. Where are such rocks found? Look at the map. Are those rocks found in many places? Would you find fossils in many places?

sedimentary rock

non-sedimentary rock

Rocks formed by mud settling and drying are found nearly everywhere. They are found on all continents. They are found in mountains, in plains and prairies, and even in deserts. So scientists find fossils nearly everywhere too.

22

Clue 2: **Fossils are found nearly everywhere.**

Many Creationists believe that the worldwide Flood in Noah's time made most of the water-formed rocks in about a year.

Many evolutionists believe that many oceans, lakes, and small floods made most of the water-formed rocks over millions and millions of years.

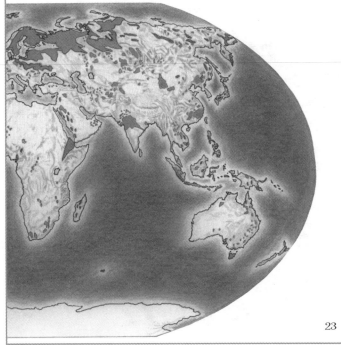

23

Teaching the Lesson

Direct a text activity on pages 22-23 and pages 26-28. Use the following questions to initiate your student's interest in what he is going to read.

1. Where are fossils found?

2. About how many main groups of fossils are there?

Continue with discussion questions. After your student completes his silent reading, use the following questions and statements as a guide to discuss the pages he read.

1. In what kind of rocks are most fossils found? *(in rocks formed from muddy water that dried up)*

2. Can these kinds of rocks be found in many places or in a few places? *(many places)*

3. How do Creationists believe these rocks were formed? *(by the Genesis Flood)*

4. How do evolutionists believe these rocks were formed? *(by oceans, lakes, and little floods)*

5. Are most fossils found by themselves or in groups? *(in groups)*

6. Do Creationists and evolutionists explain this in the same way? *(no)*

7. Do Creationists and evolutionists both think they explain the clues the best? *(yes)*

Conclude the discussion. Ask your student whether he believes the Bible. *(yes)* Ask him why he must accept Creation as the best explanation for the origin of the earth. *(In the Bible God told us He created the world.)* Explain to your student that if he believes the Bible, then he must believe in Creation because it is God's explanation for how the earth was formed. Evolution tries to explain where the earth came from by leaving out God; a person who accepts God's Word cannot accept evolution. (BAT: 8b Faith in the power of the Word of God; Bible Promise: I. God as Master)

Look at the artist's depiction of the Genesis Flood on page 28. Ask your student to point out the different animals and types of vegetation that are caught up in the water. *(Some animals pictured are turtle, alligator, squid, mammoth, and pterodactyl. Vegetation includes plants and tree bark.)*

 Although II Peter 3:3-6 is included in the student text, we suggest that you read this section aloud from the Bible to your student. Throughout the year, take every opportunity to reinforce the fact that the Bible is vital to a Christian's study of science.

Fossils in Groups

Many fossils are found in groups. There are about a dozen main groups in all. One group of fossils has sponges, snails, jellyfish, and crablike creatures called trilobites. Another group has sharks, lungfish, frogs, and land plants. A third fossil group has ducks, pelicans, and dinosaurs.

Clue 3: **Many fossils are found in groups.**

Many Creationists believe that each group once lived in a different area. Many evolutionists believe that each group once lived in a different time.

Creationists say that their theory explains the clues the best. Evolutionists say that their theory explains the clues the best.

The main question should be, Do you believe the Bible to be God's Word? If you do, then the Creation theory is the only theory to explain the clues. If you do not believe the Bible to be God's Word, see what the Bible says about people who are *willingly ignorant* about such things as the history of the earth.

Evaluating the Lesson

Introduce a role-playing activity. Display the *Fossil Clues* chart from page A4 of the Home Teacher's Edition. Reveal only one clue at a time as indicated in the text below by covering the remaining clues with a sheet of construction paper. Give your student the sentence strips face down so that the numbers show on the back. Tell him that he will read two statements for each clue and decide which statement is being made by a "Creationist professor" and which statement is being made by an "evolutionist professor." After making his decision, he should place each statement in its corresponding "professor's guidebook."

The Bible, of course, represents the guidebook for the "Creationist professor" while the encyclopedia or reference book represents the guidebook for the "evolutionist professor."

Direct the activity. Reveal the first clue on the *Fossil Clues* chart and read it aloud. Then instruct your student to read the sentence strips labeled #1. Tell your student to be prepared to identify which "professor" is which and place the corresponding statement in that professor's "guidebook."

Continue with the activity. Read and reveal one clue at a time. Instruct your student to read the corresponding pair of numbered statements, decide which "professor" made that statement, and place each statement in the correct "guidebook."

"There shall come in the last days scoffers, . . . saying, Where is the promise of his coming? for since the fathers fell asleep, all things continue as they were from the beginning of the creation.

"For this they willingly are ignorant of, that by the word of God the heavens were of old, and the earth standing out of the water and in the water:

"Whereby the world that then was, being overflowed with water, perished." II Peter 3:3-6

Enrichment

 Instructions for preparing the "Fossil Find" game are given in Family Time 5. The game is appropriate for two to four players and would be enjoyable for the whole family.

Introduce the "Fossil Find" game. First, explain each game piece and show your student the **game board.** Explain that the squares on the board form a winding path from the *Start* square at the top to the *Finish* square at the bottom. Point out that each of the squares has something about fossils or the theories studied in this unit. Discuss the question squares on the board to make sure your student understands what the questions are asking. Your student will collect rocks by answering questions correctly when he lands on some squares (one rock per question answered correctly). He will also collect rocks and lose rocks sometimes by landing on "free" spaces.

Second, demonstrate how to use the **spinner.** Place the spinner on the top of a flat surface and hold the edge of the numbered square with one hand. Then place the middle finger of your other hand against one of the dial points and flick your finger toward you, spinning the dial.

Third, show the colored rocks or buttons to be used as game markers. Show your student the bucket of plain rocks that he will be collecting to win the game.

Give the directions. Explain that the object of the game is to try to be the player with the most rocks when all the players have reached the end of the game trail. All players start with their game markers on the *Start* square. Each player spins once, the highest number going first. Then after spinning, each player moves his marker ahead as many spaces as the spinner indicates. If he lands on a free or directional space, he follows the instructions regarding taking or losing rocks, and his turn is over. If he lands on a question space, he is to answer the question. You will act as a "monitor" to check correct answers. If he answers correctly, he may take a rock. If he misses, his turn is over. Play continues until all players reach the *Finish* square. (*NOTE:* The exact number on the spinner is NOT required to finish.) When all players have completed the game, they will total the number of rocks they have collected. The player with the most rocks is the winner.

For Your Information

Many Creationists believe that the waters of the Genesis Flood laid down a large amount of sedimentary rock, especially those layers that contain fossils. Such formations give evidence of a rapid process that is no longer in operation today. Because the purpose of the Flood was to destroy the inhabitants of the world, the Flood currents would have been strong enough to carry any loose material on the face of the earth that could be moved. As the currents slowed down or changed course, they would have deposited the materials they carried. This sedimentation accounts for the layers of fossils and sedimentary rock on the earth now. Several conclusions support the theory of Flood formation of fossils. Since abundant fossilization is not taking place today, sometime in the past fossilization rates must have been very different. The huge numbers and arrangements of fossils indicate a major catastrophe, as does the fact that the organisms actually fossilized instead of decaying. Furthermore, most of the types of fossils we find today apparently required water movements to be deposited as they were.

CHAPTER THREE

3

Lessons 9-12

Forces

This chapter makes the student aware of the different kinds of forces around him: gravity, magnetic force, mechanical force, and friction. The student will be able to recognize how forces are applied. He will understand, through the use of Scripture, that God created the forces and He controls them.

Materials

The following items must be obtained or prepared before the presentation of the lesson. These items are designated with an * in the materials list in each lesson and in the Supplement. For further information see the individual lessons.

- 1 large baby food jar (Family Time 9)
- A rubber glove (Family Time 9)
- Postage scales or food scales (Lesson 9)
- Poster board (Family Time 10)
- 1 large bar magnet with poles marked † (Lesson 10)
- 1 small bar magnet † (Lesson 10)
- 1 empty cardboard half-gallon milk carton (Lesson 11)
- Corn syrup (Lesson 12)
- 2 marbles (Lesson 12)

Family Time 9

Finding Out About Bones

Text, page 46

The completion of this Family Time is important to your teaching of Lesson 13. It will take approximately two weeks for the bone to demineralize and become usable for that upcoming lesson.

Materials

Have available

- 1 large baby food jar*
- A rubber glove*
- 1 long chicken bone (thigh or leg)
- $\frac{3}{4}$ cup of white vinegar
- 3 tablespoons of salt
- Masking tape

Instructions

Prepare the chicken bone by washing it and scrubbing off any leftover meat. Do not boil the chicken bone.

Prepare the vinegar and salt solution by following Steps 1-4 on textbook page 46. On a piece of masking tape, write the date and time the experiment began and place the tape on the jar. Allow the bone to soak at least two weeks (longer is better). If time is limited, you may speed up the process by replacing the old vinegar solution with new solution every two to three days.

Tell your child that he will use this bone in Lesson 13 when discussing bones and cartilage.

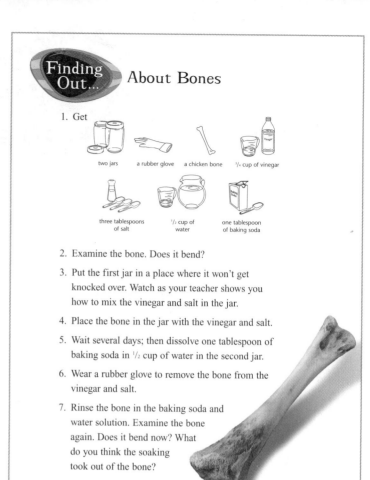

Finding Out... About Bones

1. Get

two jars   a rubber glove   a chicken bone   ¼ cup of vinegar

three tablespoons of salt   ½ cup of water   one tablespoon of baking soda

2. Examine the bone. Does it bend?

3. Put the first jar in a place where it won't get knocked over. Watch as your teacher shows you how to mix the vinegar and salt in the jar.

4. Place the bone in the jar with the vinegar and salt.

5. Wait several days; then dissolve one tablespoon of baking soda in ½ cup of water in the second jar.

6. Wear a rubber glove to remove the bone from the vinegar and salt.

7. Rinse the bone in the baking soda and water solution. Examine the bone again. Does it bend now? What do you think the soaking took out of the bone?

46

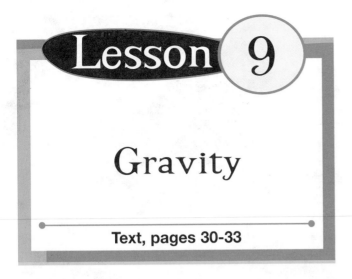

Lesson 9

Gravity

Text, pages 30–33

Preview

Objectives

Given proper instruction, your student will be able to

- Identify gravity as the force that pulls things down to the earth.
- Measure the amount of gravity on objects by weighing them.

Materials

Have available

- Scales (postage scales or food scales)*

Notes

As you read the student text pages in this chapter, please notice that the statement about the effects of gravity is qualified to say "many things" and not "all things," because there are limits to the effects of gravity's pull. For example, the moon, though subject to earth's gravity, is at such a distance from the earth that the force does not pull the moon "down" to the earth as it does other objects.

To be prepared for the first lesson in Chapter 4, you must refer now to *Materials* and *Notes* in Lesson 13.

Lesson

Introducing the Lesson

Direct an activity. Instruct your student to stand up with his arm extended, holding his science textbook in his hand. After about thirty seconds, ask your student what he feels. *(The book is getting heavy; his arm is getting tired.)*

Continue the activity. Instruct your student to sit down and put his book on the table in front of him. Ask him why he thinks the book got heavy. Was something pulling down on the book? *(Yes, something was pulling on his arm and the book.)* Ask your student what was doing the pulling. *(gravity)*

Conclude the activity. Instruct your student to drop a book and some other object. Ask him what happens to these objects. *(They fall down.)* Ask him why he thinks that the objects fall down. *(Answers may vary. Gravity causes objects to fall.)* Once gravity has been identified as the force that was pulling, ask your student in what direction gravity pulls things. *(down)*

Ask your student what he thinks would happen if everything did not get pulled down to the earth by gravity. *(We would not be able to walk, catch a ball, roll down a hill, or go sledding; we would be able to fly or jump over a house.)* Tell your student that he will learn more about gravity in today's lesson.

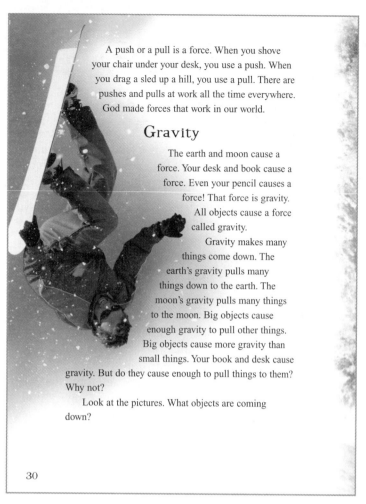

A push or a pull is a force. When you shove your chair under your desk, you use a push. When you drag a sled up a hill, you use a pull. There are pushes and pulls at work all the time everywhere. God made forces that work in our world.

Gravity

The earth and moon cause a force. Your desk and book cause a force. Even your pencil causes a force! That force is gravity. All objects cause a force called gravity.

Gravity makes many things come down. The earth's gravity pulls many things down to the earth. The moon's gravity pulls many things to the moon. Big objects cause enough gravity to pull other things. Big objects cause more gravity than small things. Your book and desk cause gravity. But do they cause enough to pull things to them? Why not?

Look at the pictures. What objects are coming down?

30

31

Teaching the Lesson

Direct a text activity on pages 30-33. Use the following questions to initiate your student's interest in what he is going to read.

1. What is a force?
2. What two things does gravity do to objects?

Continue with discussion questions. After your student completes his silent reading, use the following questions and statements as a guide to discuss the pages he read.

1. What force do all objects cause? *(gravity)*
2. Which cause more gravity, big objects or small objects? Why? *(Big objects cause more gravity because they have more mass.)*

 To avoid confusion between *mass* and *weight*, see *For Your Information* at the end of this lesson.

3. Why does a book or a desk not cause enough gravity to pull things to it? *(It does not have enough mass.)*
4. Name the objects that are coming down in the pictures on pages 30-31. *(the snowboarder, the parachutist, the kayak, and the astronaut)*

5. What is weight? *(how much pull gravity has on something)*
6. Look at the pictures on pages 32-33 and tell how much pull gravity has on each thing. *(candy—less than 1 pound, pumpkin—about 7 pounds, man—about 190 pounds)*

Conclude the discussion. Take a brief walk around the house with your student, discussing which items are heavy and which items are light. Then ask your student to name the object in the house on which he thinks gravity has the biggest pull. *(Answers will vary, but your student may mention the refrigerator, freezer, piano, or items of similar weight.)* Next ask your student to name the object in the house on which he thinks gravity has the least amount of pull. *(Answers will vary, but your student may mention a grain of rice or cereal, a straight pin, or items of similar weight.)*

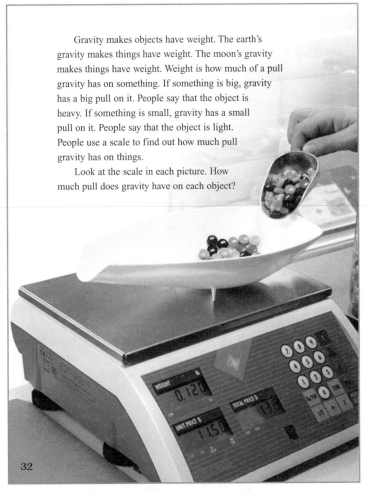

Gravity makes objects have weight. The earth's gravity makes things have weight. The moon's gravity makes things have weight. Weight is how much of a pull gravity has on something. If something is big, gravity has a big pull on it. People say that the object is heavy. If something is small, gravity has a small pull on it. People say that the object is light. People use a scale to find out how much pull gravity has on things.

Look at the scale in each picture. How much pull does gravity have on each object?

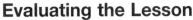

Evaluating the Lesson

Direct a weighing activity. Allow your student to select three objects from his room and arrange them, left to right on top of a table, from the object that he thinks gravity has the least pull on to the object that he thinks gravity has the most pull on. Then instruct him to list on a piece of paper the names of those objects in that order, with number 1 being the lightest and number 3 the heaviest. If possible, assist your student with the weighing of each object to check his estimates of the pull of gravity.

For Your Information

Mass should not be confused with weight. Mass is the measure of how much matter an object has. Any given object will have the same mass in any gravitational field. For example, a gold brick would have the same mass on Mars or the moon as it would have on Earth. Weight, the measure of how much gravity pulls on an object, varies from place to place. A six-pound gold brick would weigh only one pound on the moon. Even on Earth the weight of the brick might vary: it would weigh slightly less on a mountaintop than it would in a deep valley. The closer an object is to the center of the earth, the more gravity pulls on it.

Hunt for Magnets

This Family Time needs to be completed if you plan to use the activity *Hunt for Magnets* found in the Enrichment section of Lesson 10.

Materials

Have available
- Poster board*
- Felt-tip pens or crayons in a variety of colors

Instructions

Work together as a family to draw a simple diagram (not necessarily to scale) of each room of your house, including the attic, basement, and garage or carport. Allow each member of the family to fill in details—furniture, windows, and doors—about his own bedroom plus one or two more rooms. Your child will use this diagram of the house in the Enrichment section of Lesson 10 if you choose to do this extra activity.

Lesson 10

Magnetic Force

Text, pages 34-36 • Notebook, page 13

Preview

Objectives

Given proper instruction, your student will be able to

- Identify magnetic force as the force that magnets exert.
- Differentiate among objects by how they react to magnetic force.

Materials

Have available

- 1 large bar magnet with poles marked*†
- 1 small bar magnet*†
- 1 small paper bag
- Small items to test: eraser, plastic button, penny, staples, nail

Notes

This lesson requires hands-on experience for your student. It is important to have adequate materials available so that your student may actually participate.

Lesson

Introducing the Lesson

Introduce the activity. Place a large bar magnet on a table in front of your student and instruct him to gather four to six objects that he can test from around the house. Explain that he should place each object near the magnet, and then gently nudge it toward the magnet and watch what happens.

Direct the activity. Observe as your student tests his objects. Ask him to describe what happened to each object as it got close to the magnet. *(Some were pulled to the magnet; others showed no reaction.)* Ask your student to tell you why he thinks the objects acted that way. *(Some are made of metal, so they are attracted to a magnet. Others have no metal in them, so they are not attracted to a magnet.)*

Continue the activity. Now give your student a small bar magnet to test. Ask him to explain what happens to the small magnet when it gets close to the large magnet. Pose questions like "If you hold the small magnet tightly with your fingers, can you make the magnet attract each end of the large magnet?" *(The small magnet will be attracted to one end of the large magnet but not to the other end.)* Encourage your student to hold both magnets and feel the pushing and pulling that is taking place. Ask your student to explain why he thinks the magnets act that way. *(Like poles repel, and unlike poles attract.)*

Conclude the activity. Tell your student that he will learn more about magnets in today's lesson.

Science 2
Home Teacher's Edition

Magnetic Force

Magnets cause a force called magnetic force. Magnetic force makes certain objects come toward the magnet. Magnetic force *attracts* objects made of the metals iron, nickel, and cobalt. Magnets also attract things made partly of those metals.

Magnetic force is stronger in some areas of a magnet than in other areas. Magnetic force is stronger in the ends of a bar magnet than in the middle. Magnetic force is stronger in the ends of a horseshoe magnet than in the middle. The areas of stronger magnetic force are called the poles of the magnet. Look at the picture of a bar magnet. The poles are marked with the letters *N* and *S* because magnet poles are called north and south poles.

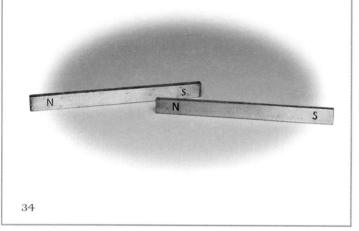

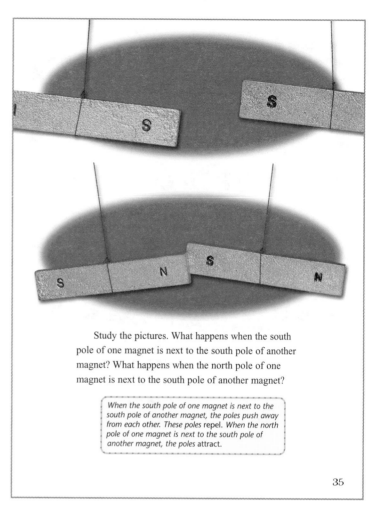

Study the pictures. What happens when the south pole of one magnet is next to the south pole of another magnet? What happens when the north pole of one magnet is next to the south pole of another magnet?

> When the south pole of one magnet is next to the south pole of another magnet, the poles push away from each other. These poles repel. When the north pole of one magnet is next to the south pole of another magnet, the poles attract.

Teaching the Lesson

Direct a text activity on pages 34-35. Use the following questions to initiate your student's interest in what he is going to read.

1. What kind of objects does magnetic force attract?

2. Where is magnetic force the strongest in magnets?

3. What is the name of the areas where the magnetic force is strongest on a magnet?

Continue with discussion questions. After your student completes his silent reading, use the following questions and statements as a guide to discuss the pages he read.

1. What do the "N" and "S" represent on magnets? *(north and south poles)*

2. What happens when the north pole of one magnet is next to the north pole of another magnet? *(The magnets push away; they repel each other.)*

3. What happens when the north pole of one magnet is next to the south pole of another magnet? *(They pull together; they attract each other.)*

Evaluating the Lesson

Introduce the *Finding Out* activity on page 36. Tell your student that he will record on his notebook page 13 what he observes when he does the *Finding Out* activity with the magnets. Take turns reading aloud the steps involved in the activity, *Finding Out About Magnets,* as given on page 36.

Direct the activity. Gather the materials, keeping the magnet away from the other objects. Hold the paper bag as your student drops each item into the bag. Instruct your student to place the magnet in the bag and to shake the bag. Allow time for your student to mark his notebook page in the Guesses column. Now direct your student to take from the bag the magnet with everything sticking to it. Tell your student to put a check in the *Observations* column beside the name of everything that he sees sticking to the magnet.

Conclude the activity. Tell your student to compare his checks in the *Guesses* column with those in the *Observations* column. Ask him how many correct guesses he made. Then briefly discuss his reasons for making any inaccurate guesses. You may need to explain that the penny did not stick to the magnet because the metal (copper) is not attracted to magnets.

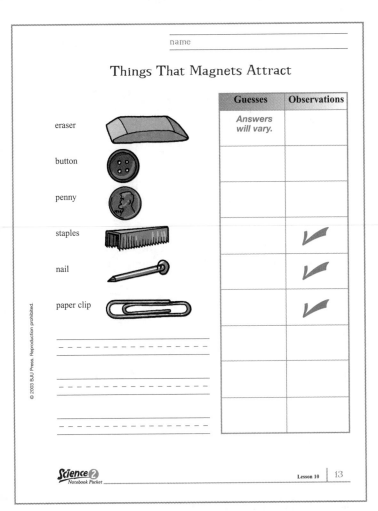

name _____

Things That Magnets Attract

	Guesses	Observations
eraser	Answers will vary.	
button		
penny		
staples		✔
nail		✔
paper clip		✔

- - - - - - - - - - - - - - -

- - - - - - - - - - - - - - -

- - - - - - - - - - - - - - -

Science 2
Notebook Packet

Lesson 10 | 13

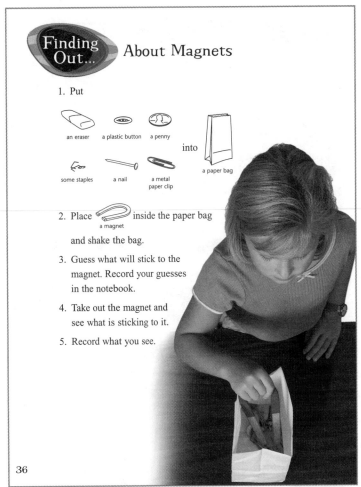

Finding Out... About Magnets

1. Put

an eraser   a plastic button   a penny

into   a paper bag

some staples   a nail   a metal paper clip

2. Place a magnet inside the paper bag and shake the bag.

3. Guess what will stick to the magnet. Record your guesses in the notebook.

4. Take out the magnet and see what is sticking to it.

5. Record what you see.

36

Enrichment

Make available the diagram of your house that you prepared during Family Time. Challenge your student to "Hunt for Magnets." Write the following directions on the diagram.

1. Find every magnet in your house.
2. Check the kitchen first.
3. Then hunt in the other rooms.
4. Put a star on this house diagram for every place where you found a magnet in your house.

 Some metal objects can become magnetized for a short time. Some examples of true magnets that are present in many homes are decorative note holders or pot holder hooks, parts of latches for cabinets, weights in the bottom of shower curtain liners, part of a flashlight handle, paper-clip holders, etc.

For Your Information

In Magnesia, an old city in Asia Minor, ancient Greeks found black stones with an unusual property. If a stone was suspended in air on a string, one end of the stone would always point north. The ancients called their find *lodestones,* meaning "way-finding stones." A crude form of the compass was actually a lodestone with an iron bar as the needle. In the 1200s, a French courtier discovered and labeled the two poles of the lodestone. His discovery showed that the earth's own magnetic poles attract the poles of the compass and indicate direction. The study of magnetism grew rapidly from its simple beginnings with the lodestone. Such scientists as Michael Faraday and James Maxwell developed theories about magnetic fields and electromagnetic waves.

Lesson 11

Mechanical Force

Text, pages 37-38 • Notebook, page 14

Preview

Objectives

Given proper instruction, your student will be able to

- Name things being moved by mechanical force.
- Name things being stopped by mechanical force.

Materials

Have available

- 1 empty cardboard half-gallon milk carton*
- Scissors

Prepare

- The cardboard milk carton by cutting it into four-inch squares.

Lesson

Introducing the Lesson

Introduce an observing activity. Give your student a four-inch square of cardboard, scissors, and a pencil. Tell him that by referring to Figures 11-1 and 11-2 and by following directions, he will make a pinwheel that really works.

Direct the activity. Tell your student to follow along as you demonstrate how to make a pinwheel. Then do each of the following steps, pausing to allow time for your student to follow the same steps to assemble his own pinwheel.

1. Push the pencil through the middle of the square.
2. Wiggle the pencil back and forth so that the square will turn loosely around the pencil.
3. At each corner of the square, cut in toward the pencil, ending the cut about $\frac{1}{2}$ inch from the pencil. (*NOTE:* See Figure 11-1.)

Figure 11-1

4. Fold the cardboard back from the left of each slit to make a triangle. (*NOTE:* See Figure 11-2.)

Figure 11-2

Continue with the activity. Ask your student how he thinks he could make his pinwheel turn. *(spin the wheel with his finger; blow on the wheel; wave the wheel back and forth; run water on the wheel)* Allow your student to try each of these ways to make the pinwheel spin.

 To run water over the pinwheel, use the running water from the faucet of the bathtub or the sink.

Conclude the activity. After your student tests all of the ways for making his pinwheel turn, ask him to tell you what he thinks started the pinwheel turning each time. *(his finger, his breath, motion of the air and running water)* Tell your student that he will learn more about this force in today's lesson.

Mechanical Force

Sometimes force changes how things move. That force is called mechanical force.

Mechanical force starts movement. It also stops movement. It can make moving things slow down or speed up. It can make them go in another direction. Name the things that are being moved by mechanical force.

"And Moses stretched out his hand over the sea; and the Lord caused the sea to go back by a strong east wind all that night, and made the sea dry land, and the waters were divided."
Exodus 14:21

37

How is mechanical force important here?

38

➤ **Name the things that are being moved by mechanical force.** *(A sailboat and a windmill are being moved by mechanical force.)*

Teaching the Lesson

Direct a text activity on pages 37-38. Use the following questions to initiate your student's interest in what he is going to read.

1. What is mechanical force?
2. What is being moved by mechanical force in the pictures on page 37?

Continue with discussion questions. After your student completes his silent reading, use the following questions and statements as a guide to discuss the pages he read.

1. How does mechanical force influence movement? *(It starts movement, stops it, and makes moving things slow down, speed up, or go in another direction.)*
2. Identify the items pictured on page 38 that are being stopped by mechanical force. *(the machine, cooler, and soccer ball)*

Conclude the discussion. Read Exodus 14:21 aloud and ask your student what changed the movement of the water and caused it to divide. *(the wind)* Does the wind usually blow a dry path through the middle of a sea? *(no)* Remind your student that God not only made the forces but also controls them. Although Moses stretched out his hand over the sea, it was God who told him what to do, and it was God who directed the wind. (BAT: 2a Authority; Bible Promise: I. God as Master)

Evaluating the Lesson

Guide the use of notebook page 14. First, instruct your student to circle the things that are being moved by mechanical force. Second, instruct him to put an *X* on the things that are being stopped by mechanical force.

Newton's first law of motion is sometimes called *inertia*. The word *inertia* means an "unwillingness to change." The tendency to stay at rest is called *inertia of rest*. The tendency to stay in motion is *inertia of motion*. *Speed* and *velocity* are two important quantities connected with Newton's second law of motion. *Speed* is how fast something is moving. *Velocity* is the same thing, but also implies direction. Sixty-five miles per hour is a speed; sixty-five miles per hour due east is a velocity.

Lesson 12

Friction

Text, pages 39-42

Preview

Objectives

Given proper instruction, your student will be able to

- Identify negative effects of friction.
- Tell ways to decrease friction.
- Identify positive effects of friction.
- Tell ways to increase friction.
- Identify the three kinds of friction.

Materials

Have available

- 1 metal cookie sheet
- 2 tall, clear glasses
- Water
- Corn syrup*
- 2 marbles*
- A stopwatch or watch with a second hand
- Round objects: a marble, a smooth round pencil
- Flat objects: a wooden block, a spoon, a coin, an eraser
- A Write It flip chart

Lesson

Introducing the Lesson

Introduce an observing activity. To introduce the difference between sliding and rolling friction, place the following objects at one end of a metal cookie sheet: a marble, a round pencil, some flat plastic or glass objects, a small wooden block, and a spoon.

Direct the activity. Ask your student to predict which objects will start moving first when you lift the end of the tray. If you wish, you could conduct the activity with two

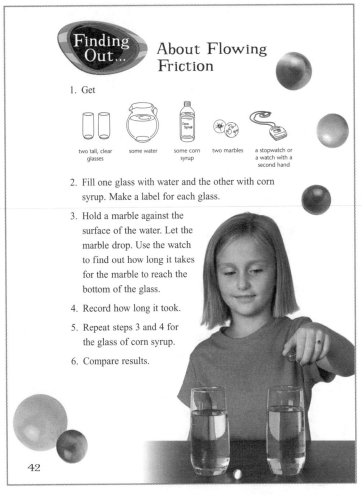

Finding Out... About Flowing Friction

1. Get

two tall, clear glasses · some water · some corn syrup · two marbles · a stopwatch or a watch with a second hand

2. Fill one glass with water and the other with corn syrup. Make a label for each glass.

3. Hold a marble against the surface of the water. Let the marble drop. Use the watch to find out how long it takes for the marble to reach the bottom of the glass.

4. Record how long it took.

5. Repeat steps 3 and 4 for the glass of corn syrup.

6. Compare results.

42

objects at a time, slowly lifting the tray as your student observes which objects roll and which objects slide.

To test the difference between sliding and rolling friction, instruct your student to rub his hands together. Place a pencil between his palms and instruct him to rub his hands together again. Ask him which rubbing method was easier and why. *(Rubbing with the pencil is easier because there is less friction when something rolls across a surface than when two surfaces slide across each other.)*

Continue the activity. Direct your student's attention to the *Finding Out* activity on page 42 of his textbook. As your student follows in his text, read the steps in the *Finding Out* box. Ask your student whether the marble flows through the water and the corn syrup at the same rate. Why? *(No; it flows through the corn syrup slower because there is more friction involved.)*

Write *water* and *corn syrup* on the Write It flip chart. As you keep time, allow your student to follow the steps listed in the *Finding Out* box. As you give the elapsed time, instruct your student to write the time on the Write It flip chart under the appropriate heading.

Conclude the activity. Ask your student to look at the times that have been written on the flip chart; then ask whether there was more friction between the marble and the water or between the marble and the corn syrup. *(between the marble and the corn syrup)*

Tell your student that he will learn more about these three types of friction in today's lesson.

Teaching the Lesson

Direct a text activity on pages 39-41. Use the following questions to initiate your student's interest in what he is going to read.

1. Which kind of surfaces, rough or smooth, cause more friction?

2. What are the three kinds of friction?

Continue with discussion questions. After your student completes his silent reading, use the following questions and statements as a guide to discuss the pages he read.

1. What can you do to increase friction? *(make the surfaces rougher)*

2. Identify the type of friction illustrated by each picture on page 41. *(sliding friction—drawing, rolling friction—bowling, and flowing friction—the submarine moving in the water)*

3. Tell how you think people could increase friction in the following situations:

 Read the following situations one at a time, allowing your child the opportunity to tell how he could increase friction in each situation.

   a. A boy's hands keep slipping on the grip of a baseball bat. *(He puts friction tape around the grip. He dusts his hands with rosin or dirt.)*

   b. A girl's hands slip off the shiny metal handlebars of her bike. *(She puts handle grips on the handlebars.)*

   c. A baby's dish slips and slides all over the tray of his highchair. *(His mother puts some kind of mat on the tray, or she gets a dish with a suction cup on the bottom.)*

Friction

Surfaces that touch cause a force. That force is called friction. Rough surfaces cause more friction than smooth ones. Friction tries to stop movement.

Friction Is Useful

Sometimes friction is helpful. Friction keeps your feet from sliding on the ground. It helps you walk and run. It helps you stop too.

If there isn't enough friction, you can increase it. To make more friction, you make surfaces rougher. What made the surfaces in each picture rougher?

39

Evaluating the Lesson

Introduce an identifying game. Tell your student that you are going to see how much he has learned about the different kinds of friction—sliding, rolling, and flowing. Point to each word on the Write It flip chart as you say it. Explain that you are going to name an activity that he might like to do. If sliding friction is involved in the activity, he should rub his hands together. If rolling friction is involved, he should rotate his hands around each other. If flowing friction is involved, he should move his hands back and forth like flowing water.

Friction Can Be a Problem

Sometimes friction is not helpful. Friction makes things like socks or shoelaces wear out. It makes windows or drawers get stuck. It makes wheels squeak and hinges creak. If there is too much friction, sometimes you can make less. To make less friction, you make surfaces smoother. What surface is the boy in the picture making smoother? How is he making it smoother?

There are three kinds of friction. Sliding friction results when two surfaces slide across each other. Rolling friction happens when something rolls across a surface.

Flowing friction happens between two moving liquids or gases. Or, flowing friction happens between a moving liquid or gas and a solid. Find pictures of each kind of friction.

➤ **What surface is the boy in the picture making smoother?** *(a snowboard)*

➤ **How is he making it smoother?** *(He is using wax to make the surface of the snowboard smoother.)*

Direct the game. Practice the motions a few times; then make the following statements and allow time for your student to respond. Stop to clarify or discuss an activity when your student seems unsure of the correct response or when he responds incorrectly.

1. Kevin likes to roller-skate. *(rolling)*
2. Troy likes to ice-skate. *(sliding)*
3. Melissa likes to swim. *(flowing)*
4. Stacy likes to hike. *(sliding)*
5. Steve likes to bowl. *(rolling)*
6. Alan likes to fly kites. *(flowing)*
7. Carol likes to ride her bike. *(rolling—wheels on pavement; sliding—hands on handlebars, feet on pedals)*
8. Melody likes to play the violin. *(sliding)*
9. Tim likes to draw. *(sliding)*

For Your Information

Friction is always a problem in machinery. Although lubrication can decrease friction, friction can never be completely removed. Therefore the *mechanical advantage* (the number of times a simple machine can multiply force), determined by dividing the *resistance* by the *effort,* is always a bit optimistic. For example, if a lever has a mechanical advantage of 8, you should be able to lift a load (resistance) of 200 pounds with an effort (a push) of 25 pounds. That is, you should be able to multiply your force eight times. But friction will take a small toll, and in reality you will have to use a little more than 25 pounds of force.

CHAPTER FOUR

Lessons 13-16

Your Bones

This chapter will familiarize your student with the framework of the human body. He will learn about the structure and function of the skeleton, as well as the important role that joints play in the movement of the body. In addition, this hands-on approach to science will allow your student to discover for himself that certain minerals make bones hard and that bones can be classified by shape. Each of these lessons provides opportunity for your student to relate what he learns to the way his body works.

Materials

The following items must be obtained or prepared before the presentation of the lesson. These items are designated with an * in the materials list in each lesson and in the Supplement. For further information see the individual lessons.

- 1 large baby food jar (Lesson 13)
- 1 rubber glove (Lesson 13)
- 1 chicken skeleton (Lesson 14)

Lesson 13

Bones and Cartilage

Text, pages 44-46 • Notebook, page 15

Preview

Objectives

Given proper instruction, your student will be able to

- Locate areas of bone or cartilage in the body.
- Conclude that certain minerals in bone make it hard.

Materials

Have available

- The chicken bone in the vinegar-salt solution prepared in Family Time 9
- 1 long chicken bone (thigh or leg)
- 1 large baby food jar*
- $\frac{1}{2}$ cup of water
- 1 tablespoon of baking soda
- 1 rubber glove*
- 1 measuring cup
- 1 tablespoon

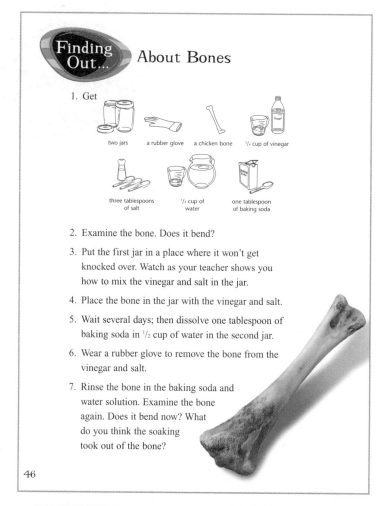

Finding Out... About Bones

1. Get

two jars   a rubber glove   a chicken bone $\frac{1}{4}$ cup of vinegar

three tablespoons of salt $\frac{1}{2}$ cup of water   one tablespoon of baking soda

2. Examine the bone. Does it bend?

3. Put the first jar in a place where it won't get knocked over. Watch as your teacher shows you how to mix the vinegar and salt in the jar.

4. Place the bone in the jar with the vinegar and salt.

5. Wait several days; then dissolve one tablespoon of baking soda in $\frac{1}{2}$ cup of water in the second jar.

6. Wear a rubber glove to remove the bone from the vinegar and salt.

7. Rinse the bone in the baking soda and water solution. Examine the bone again. Does it bend now? What do you think the soaking took out of the bone?

46

Lesson

Introducing the Lesson

Introduce the *Finding Out* activity on page 46. Review with your student Steps 1-4 that you completed previously in Family Time 9. Show the jar containing the chicken bone in the vinegar-salt solution. Ask your student to name the ingredients that were placed in the jar. *(vinegar, salt, and a chicken bone)* Direct his attention to the date on the masking tape. Remind your student that this is the date on which you began the experiment. Assist your student in figuring out how long the chicken bone has been soaking in the vinegar-salt solution.

Instruct your student to hold the chicken bone, examine it, and tell you what changes occurred in the bone after it soaked in the vinegar-salt solution for a long time. *(The only change that occurred was in the hardness of the bone. The vinegar dissolved the calcium in the bone, making the chicken bone very pliable in contrast to its original stiff form.)* To demonstrate this characteristic, allow your student to try to bend it.

	Changed	**Did Not Change**
The color of the bone	Answers will vary.	Answers will vary.
The size of the bone		✓
The shape of the bone		✓
The stiffness of the bone	✓	

Science 2
Notebook Packet

Lesson 13 | 15

Conclude the activity. Ask your student what makes bones hard and stiff. *(minerals)* Hold up the bone that did not go into the vinegar and demonstrate that it will not bend. Ask your student if this bone is hard and stiff. *(yes)* Now hold up the bone from the experiment, demonstrating how this bone bends. Comment that this bone is no longer hard and stiff. Ask your student what the vinegar took out of the bone to make it rubbery. *(minerals)* Ask whether he thinks minerals are an important part of bones. *(yes)*

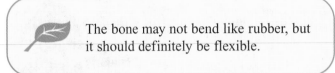

The bone may not bend like rubber, but it should definitely be flexible.

Ask your student why he thinks you sometimes say, "Drink your milk." Why is drinking milk so important? *(Milk contains the minerals necessary for building good, strong bones. When he drinks milk, his body takes in these minerals and uses them for building bones. Making sure that his bones get the minerals that they need is especially important while he is still growing.)*

Direct the activity. Direct your student's attention to notebook page 15. Point out the three columns. Explain that the first column includes some ways in which vinegar and salt might change a bone. Instruct your student to write in the column any additional predictions that he has. In the next two columns, your student will mark whether the change actually occurred.

Assist your student as he follows Steps 5-7 of the *Finding Out* activity on page 46 of his textbook. Instruct your student to hold *both* bones (the bone that soaked in vinegar and the bone that did not) while you read the list of predictions from the notebook page. Ask your student to compare the bones and tell you which changes took place. *(The bone soaked in vinegar is no longer stiff and will now bend. Your student may also think that the color of the bone has changed.)* Ask your student which changes did not take place. *(The bones did not change size or shape.)*

A form as big as your body needs support. God could have given you a shell on the outside. Lobsters have shells. Instead, God gave you a skeleton on the inside.

Parts of the Skeleton

Your skeleton is made of bones and cartilage. Cartilage is a strong, white material. Cartilage bends. Wiggle the end of your nose with a finger and thumb. That part of your nose is cartilage. Feel the top of your ear with a finger and thumb. That part of your ear is cartilage. Cartilage is also found where two or more bones meet.

44

Much of bone is made of minerals, a special kind of matter. Minerals make bones hard. Do you think cartilage has these minerals? Use your finger and thumb and try to wiggle your nose where it meets your forehead. It won't bend because that part of your nose is bone.

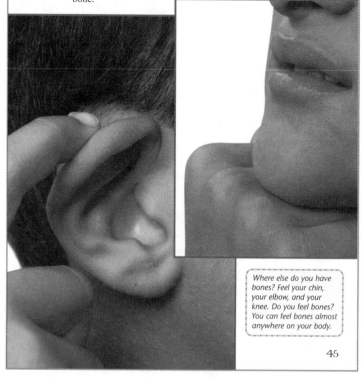

Where else do you have bones? Feel your chin, your elbow, and your knee. Do you feel bones? You can feel bones almost anywhere on your body.

45

Teaching the Lesson

Direct a text activity on pages 44-45. Use the following questions to initiate your student's interest in what he is going to read.

1. What is your skeleton made of?
2. What is cartilage?

Continue with discussion questions. After your student completes his silent reading, use the following questions and statements as a guide to discuss the pages he read.

1. Why does our body need a skeleton? *(for support)*
2. Name some parts of your body where cartilage is found. *(at the end of your nose, at the top of your ear, and where two or more bones meet)*
3. What do minerals do for bones? *(They make bones hard.)*
4. Do you think that cartilage contains minerals? *(no)*

Evaluating the Lesson

Introduce a guessing game. Ask your student to once again name the parts of the body where cartilage is found. *(at the end of the nose, the ear, and where two or more bones meet)* Clarify this last point by instructing your student to place his hand on his elbow. Ask him whether he thinks that there is bone in the elbow. *(yes)* Ask him whether he thinks that there is cartilage in the elbow. *(yes)* If your student looks unsure, review the three areas of the body where cartilage is found. Then ask him if two or more bones meet at the elbow. *(yes)* Now repeat your earlier question about cartilage in the elbow. *(Yes, there definitely is cartilage in the elbow since two bones meet there.)* Choose another joint to discuss if your student still has difficulty.

Tell your student that he will have the opportunity to do some guessing about bones and cartilage. As you point to several different parts of the body, your student should decide whether the skeleton in that area is made up of bone, cartilage, or both. Instruct him to use sign language for his answer. Explain that he should sign B if the area is bone, C if the area is cartilage, or sign both B and C (using two hands) if the area includes both bone and cartilage. (*NOTE:* See Figure 13-1.)

Figure 13-1

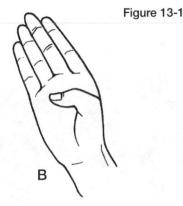

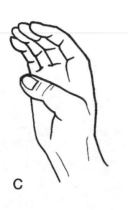

B   C

List for Guessing Game:
1. End of nose *(cartilage)*
2. Upper arm *(bone)*
3. Shin *(bone)*
4. Elbow *(bone and cartilage)*
5. Skull *(bone)*
6. Ear *(cartilage)*
7. Shoulder joint *(bone and cartilage)*

For Your Information

Bones are made of two different kinds of materials—inorganic minerals and organic proteinlike matrix. Placing the bone in a weak acid (vinegar) helps demonstrate this fact. The acid dissolves the minerals (i.e., calcium phosphate) in the bone. Only the protein matrix of the bone is left. Although this matrix will retain the size and shape of the bone, it has lost its rigidity with the removal of the minerals. As a result, one can bend the bone without breaking it.

For calcium to be absorbed from the intestines and used by the bone, vitamin D must be present. This vitamin can be readily obtained through cod-liver oil or vitamin D milk, both of which are usually available in the United States. Sunshine, another valuable source of vitamin D, produces this vitamin by acting on the skin.

Lesson 14

Names and Shapes of Bones

Text, pages 47-49

Preview

Objectives

Given proper instruction, your student will be able to

- Identify the four shapes of bones.
- Sort bones into groups by shape.

Materials

Have available

- 1 chicken skeleton*
- 1 shoebox
- Home Teacher's Edition, pp. A5-A9

Prepare

- 1 chicken skeleton by cooking a medium-sized roasting hen. (*NOTE:* Cooking the hen in a slow-cooker is a good way to get the meat to separate from the bone easily.) Remove the bones and allow them to soak in sudsy dishwater to remove the animal fat. Scrub the bones, and then place them in a large pan of boiling water. Cover the pan and boil the bones for at least forty-five minutes. Thoroughly scrub the bones to remove any remaining cartilage, meat, or animal fat. Once prepared, the bones should last for several years, although they will become increasingly brittle. (*NOTE:* One alternative for preserving the bones is to spray them with polyurethane, preferably with a matte finish. Such a coating should allow the bones to remain intact for many years.)
- 4 labels describing the shapes of bones: *Long bones, Flat bones, Irregular bones, Short bones.*

1. Get

a chicken skeleton

2. Sort the bones into groups by shape. How many long bones did you find? How many flat bones? Can you name any of the bones?

Here is how a chicken skeleton looks. What bones do you see here that are not among the bones you are sorting?

49

➤ **What bones do you see here that are not among the bones you are sorting?** *(Answers will vary: head, neck, feet, etc.)*

Lesson

Introducing the Lesson

Introduce a *Finding Out* activity. Direct your student's attention to page 49 of the text. Place the box of chicken bones in front of your student. Instruct him to read Step 2 on page 49. Give him time to sort through the bones, placing all of the short bones together, all of the long bones together, and all of the flat bones together. Instruct him to place the correct name description next to the corresponding set of bones. Tell him that any bones not fitting in these categories should be left in the box.

Direct the activity. After your student finishes sorting the bones, ask him how he identified the long bones with so many bones to choose from. *(Long bones look like skinny tubes with swollen ends.)* Display the visual for a long bone next to your student's collection of long bones. Encourage him to check for any errors in identification in this group. Continue checking his work by asking him to describe the short

Names of Bones

Study the drawing of the skeleton. How many bone names do you know?

Shapes of Bones

Your bones can be put into groups by shape. You have long bones that are skinny tubes with swollen ends. You have short bones that are wide and chunky. You have flat bones. And you have irregular bones. They are bones that do not fit into any other group. Find pictures of each bone shape.

Your leg, arm, finger, and toe bones are long bones. Your wrist and foot bones are short bones. Your ribs, shoulder, and skull bones are flat bones. And your spine and ear bones are irregular bones.

47

48

bones. *(The short bones are wide and chunky.)* Display the visual illustrating a short bone next to your student's assortment of short bones. Ask your student to look at the flat bones and describe them. *(Flat bones look thin.)* Display the visual for flat bones next to his collection of flat bones and give him time to correct any errors in identification.

Conclude the activity. Finally ask your student to look at the remaining bones in the box and to describe them. *(They are wide and have unusual shapes.)* Display the visual illustrating this type of bone and tell your student that these bones are called irregular. Tell your student that he will learn more about bones in the remainder of today's lesson as well as in the lessons that follow.

Some bones, such as the sternum, have flat sides but are unusually shaped. Allow your child to sort these as he sees fit. A chicken has only a few short bones in its entire skeleton. These bones are tiny and are often lost when the chicken is cooked. In the crook of the chicken wing are two small bones smaller than a pea.

Teaching the Lesson

Direct a text activity on pages 47-48. Use the following questions to initiate your student's interest in what he is going to read.

1. How are bones grouped?
2. What are the four groups of bones?

Conclude the discussion. After your student completes his silent reading, use the following questions and statements as a guide to discuss the pages he read.

1. What is the name of the large bone that protects your brain? *(the skull)*
2. Do you think that a baby has more bones or fewer bones than an adult? Explain. *(A baby has more bones than an adult. An adult has 206 bones, and a baby has 64 more bones. As a baby grows, some of its bones "fuse," or join.)*

The backbone is an example of bones fusing together. It is a group of odd-shaped bones called vertebrae. A child has 33 vertebrae, whereas an adult has only 26. The last 9 vertebrae in a child will eventually grow together to form 2 bones.

3. Which names of bones do you know? *(Answers will vary depending upon your student's prior knowledge of bones.)*

 A few names of bones are skull (cranium), shoulder bone (clavicle), shoulder blade (scapula), backbone (vertebrae), and thighbone (femur). Use your own judgment in having your child learn these names.

Evaluating the Lesson

Direct a review. Place the five bone visuals in front of your student. Give him the opportunity to name each type of bone (flat, irregular, long, or short), describe it, and give an example of this type of bone in the body. He could use the illustration on page 47 to help him locate specific types of bones in the body. The answers are listed below. The common names of the bones pictured are included for your information.

    page A5 long (arm bones)
    page A6 short (finger bones)
    page A7 flat (ribs)
    page A8 irregular (ear bones)
    page A9 irregular (vertebra or back bone)

For Your Information

Adults have approximately 206 bones in their skeletons. There are 8 bones in the cranium, 14 bones in the face, 6 bones in the ear, 26 bones in the backbone, 25 bones in the chest, 64 bones in the shoulders, arms, hands, and fingers, and 62 bones in the pelvis, legs, feet, and toes. Over twenty-five percent of the bones in the human body are in the hands and feet.

Bone names sometimes indicate their positions, such as carpal (from Greek *karpos* meaning "wrist"). Others indicate a function: *vertebra* comes from the Latin *vertere* meaning "to turn." Still others reflect the shape of the bone. *Pelvis,* for example, means "basin" in Latin.

Lesson 15

Where Bones Meet

Text, pages 50-51

Objectives

Given proper instruction, your student will be able to

- Match a particular group of joints to the type of movement it allows.
- Indicate which groups of joints the elbow, neck, and shoulder belong to.

Lesson

Introducing the Lesson

Direct the game "Simon Says." Instruct your student to stand while you direct him in the game. Use the following commands:

Simon says touch your nose with your right hand.
Simon says touch your nose with your left hand.
Simon says shake your head.
Simon says make big arm circles.
Simon says make little arm circles.
Sit down.
Simon says squat down and touch the floor.
Simon says stand up and reach for the ceiling.
Simon says touch your right elbow with your left hand.
Touch your left elbow with your right hand.
Simon says touch your left knee with your right foot.
Simon says touch your left knee with your left foot.
(Repeat) Simon says touch your left knee with your left foot.

Conclude the activity. After repeating the last "Simon Says" command, tell your student to sit down. Ask him why he cannot touch his left knee with his left foot. *(Answers may vary—foot will not reach, toes are too short, etc.)* Ask him which parts of his leg bend. *(the knee and the ankle)* Does his leg bend at the shin? *(no)* Ask your student what is different about the structure of the knee and the ankle compared to the shin bone. *(The knee and the ankle are places in the skeleton where two or more bones meet. The shin bone is one long bone.)* Ask your student what the name of these bone "meeting places" is. *(joints)* Tell your student that in today's lesson he will learn more about where bones meet.

Teaching the Lesson

Direct a text activity on pages 50-51. Use the following questions to initiate your student's interest in what he is going to read.

1. What is a joint in the body?
2. What are the three types of joints?

Continue with discussion questions. After your student completes his silent reading, use the following questions and statements as a guide to discuss the pages he read.

1. Do all joints allow movement? *(No, but most of them do.)*
2. Do the joints in your fingers and toes allow movement? Show me. *(Yes, I can wiggle my fingers and toes.)*
3. Can you wiggle the joints in your skull? *(no)*

 There is *one* set of joints in the skull that allows movement. These joints are on either side of the jawbone.

Where Bones Meet

The place where two or more bones meet is called a joint. Most joints allow movement. Look at the drawings of some movements. Look at the drawings of some joints. Which allows movement back and forth? Which allows movement up and down?

Your elbow is a hinge joint. It allows up and down movement. Your neck is a pivot joint. It lets your head move back and forth. And your shoulder is a ball-and-socket joint. Hold your arm straight out from your shoulder. Make a big circle with your arm. How do you think a ball-and-socket joint lets bones move?

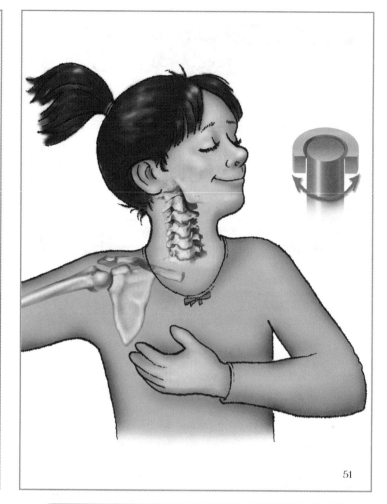

4. What joints are pictured on pages 50-51? Do these joints allow movement? *(Elbow, neck, and shoulder joints are pictured. Yes, they all allow movement.)*

5. Which joint pictured on page 50 allows up-and-down movement? What type of joint is it? *(The elbow is a hinge joint.)*

6. What kind of movement does the pivot joint allow? *(back-and-forth movement)*

7. What kind of joint allows bones to move in all directions? *(ball-and-socket joint)*

 Your child may question whether the neck joint also allows up-and-down movement. The neck area consists of several different joints. These joints work together to allow the neck wider range of motion and greater flexibility. For this lesson a particular joint was singled out (joint of the first and second cervical vertebrae). This joint is the chief joint involved when the head is turned from side to side.

Evaluating the Lesson

Introduce a review activity. Tell your student that you will be reading several descriptions of joints. After hearing each statement, he should decide whether it best describes the neck, shoulder, or elbow and then place his hand on the corresponding joint. Allow your student to practice his answers by placing his right hand on his neck, then his shoulder, and finally on his elbow. Provide a practice question so that your student can get accustomed to the activity.

Practice: I am a ball-and-socket joint. *(shoulder)*
Activity:

You use me when you shake your head. *(neck)*

You use me when you make arm circles. *(shoulder)*

You use me when you bend your arm to put food into your mouth. *(elbow)*

I allow movement back and forth. *(neck)*

I am a hinge joint. *(elbow)*

I allow movement in all directions. *(shoulder)*

I allow movement up and down. *(elbow)*

I am a pivot joint. *(neck)*

I am a ball-and-socket joint. *(shoulder)*

Enrichment

Write the following clues and the puzzle form on the Write It flip chart. Challenge your student to complete the puzzle on his own as a review of today's lesson.

Clues:

1. The _ _ _ contains the only joints found in the skull.

2. The _ _ _ _ _ is a hinge joint.

3. The joints in the _ _ _ _ _ group allow movement up and down.

4. The _ _ _ _ is a pivot joint.

5. The joints in the _ _ _ _ & _ _ _ _ _ _ group allow movement in all directions.

6. The _ _ _ _ _ _ _ _ is a ball-and-socket joint.

For Your Information

Joints can be classified as *diarthroses* or *synarthroses*. Joints with a small space between the two bones are diarthroses. These joints allow free movement. Most of our joints are in this class. Synarthroses are joints that have no spaces between bones. Instead they have fiber or cartilage or bone between the bones. These joints allow little or no movement.

The bones of a baby's head have spaces between them called *fontanels*. When the child is about eighteen months old, all the bones of the skull will have grown together and will fit tightly. These immovable joints are called *sutures*.

Figure 15-1

```
                         1.  J | A   W
                   2.  E  L  B | O   W
                       3.  H | I   N   G   E
                           4.  N | E   C   K
5.  B  A  L  L  &  S  O  C  K  E | T
                           6.  S | H   O   U   L   D   E   R
```

Lesson 16

Jobs of the Skeleton

Text, pages 52-54 • Notebook, pages 16-18

Preview

Objectives

Given proper instruction, your student will be able to

- Identify pictures illustrating the jobs of the skeleton.
- Match the brain, heart, lungs, and spinal cord to the parts of the skeleton that protect them.

Materials

Have available
- 1 metal brad
- 1 glue stick
- Scissors

Lesson

Introducing the Lesson

Introduce an activity. Take your student for a short drive through the city or countryside. Ask him to observe the various types of fences in these areas.

Direct the activity. As each fence is sighted, ask your student what kind of material the fence is made of. *(He may see fences of stone, wood, barbed wire, shrubbery, brick, split logs, etc.)* What is the purpose of each fence? *(Some possible answers are to give privacy, to keep animals within a certain area, to keep unwanted animals out, to protect plants or crops, and to add decoration to the yard.)*

Continue the activity. After your drive, ask your student to tell you the different kinds of fences that he saw. Though all of the fences are in different locations, made of different materials, and have different designs, what one thing do they all have in common? *(They all provide protection. Some provide protection for people, some for plants, and some for animals.)*

Conclude the activity. Read Job 10:11 and explain to your student that God designed bones to form a fence of protection around certain parts of the body—the brain, the heart and lungs, and the spinal cord. (Bible Promise: I. God as Master) Ask your student how he is using his brain right now. *(thinking)* Explain that each person's brain is what makes him unique, or one of a kind. (BAT: 3 Uniqueness-Unity Principle) There he registers happiness, sadness, anger, pride, and fear. The brain is also responsible for putting together all the information that a person receives through his eyes, ears, and other sense organs. It helps control the organs and their functions.

Ask your student what he thinks the function of the heart is. *(to keep blood pumping throughout the body)* What is the job of the lungs? *(to take in the air that the body needs)* What does the spinal cord do? *(passes on the messages from the brain to the arms and legs)* Tell your student that he will learn more about the jobs of the skeleton in today's lesson.

Jobs of the Skeleton

"Thou hast clothed me with skin and flesh, and hast fenced me with bones and sinews."
Job 10:11

The skeleton has many jobs. Here are some pictures of the jobs that the skeleton does. Which picture shows the skeleton giving the body shape and support? Which picture shows the skeleton helping the body move? Which picture shows the skeleton protecting the body?

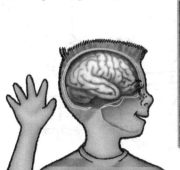

Your leg bones give shape to your legs and support your body.

Your arm and hand bones let you move to play instruments and sports. Your skull protects your brain. Your ribs protect your heart and lungs.

52

53

Teaching the Lesson

Direct a text activity on pages 52-54. Use the following question to initiate your student's interest in what he is going to read: What are some jobs of the skeleton?

Conclude the discussion. After your student completes his silent reading, use the following questions and statements as a guide to discuss the pages he read.

1. Which pictures show the skeleton giving the body shape and support? *(Answers will vary. Technically, all the pictures show this. Some students may select the drawing of the girl.)*

2. Which pictures show the skeleton helping the body move? *(the baseball player, the skier, the gymnast, and the karate team members)*

3. Which pictures show the skeleton protecting the body? *(the drawing of the boy's head, the baseball player, and the karate team members)*

4. Which of these do the skull bones protect—brain, heart and lungs, or spinal cord? *(the brain)*

5. Which of the three body areas do the ribs and breastbone protect? *(heart and lungs)*

6. Which of the three body areas does the backbone or vertebrae protect? *(the spinal cord)*

7. What is one of the main jobs of the skeleton? *(to protect the body)*

8. What other three jobs does the skeleton have? *(gives the body shape, helps support the body, and helps the body move)*

9. What do you think people would look like without bones? *(piles of skin and muscles)*

10. Name some ways that you can move because of your skeleton. *(run, jump, skip, hop, etc.)*

11. What are some things that you should thank the Lord for regarding your body? *(Answers will vary, but your student may suggest the following: helps me stand, hear, see, smell, think, keep my balance, etc.)* (BAT: 7c Praise)

"I will praise thee; for I am fearfully and wonderfully made: marvellous are thy works; and that my soul knoweth right well."

Psalm 139:14

54

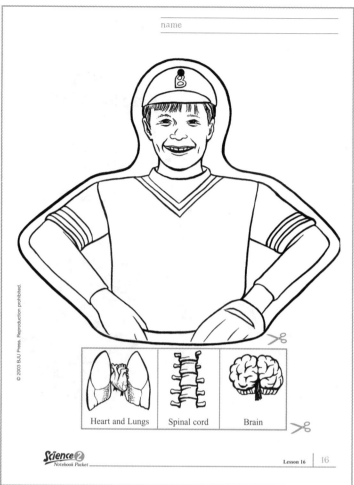

name

Heart and Lungs | Spinal cord | Brain

Science 2
Notebook Packet

Lesson 16 | 16

Evaluating the Lesson

Introduce a notebook activity on pages 16-18. Point out to your student that this lesson has three notebook pages. The figures on pages 16 and 17 will be cut out. The figure on page 18 will not be cut out. In addition to the baseball figure on page 16, there is a strip of boxes at the bottom. Explain that these are pictures of important body parts (heart and lungs, spinal cord, and brain) that need special protection. Your student should cut out each box and glue it in the correct square on page 18.

Direct the activity. After your student finishes gluing each picture of a body part in its correct location, give him opportunity to color all three illustrations. He may then complete the evaluation by placing the baseball player and skeleton cutouts on top of the body-part figure. Secure the figures together by carefully inserting a brad through the top of all three sections. Each flap can then be pulled up to see how the skeleton provides protection, shape, and support for the body.

name

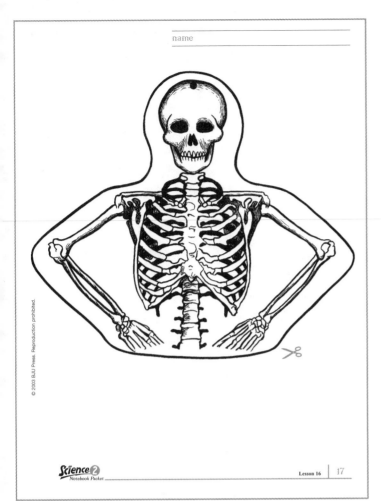

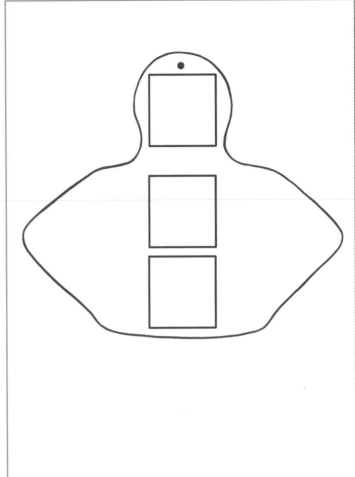

For Your Information

The bones that make up the skull are tightly fitted together. There is no space between them for even a thin knife to get in. Moreover, the very shape of the skull is one that makes for the greatest protection. It is a dome, just about the strongest shape possible. It will withstand heavy blows, especially blows from the top, which is the part most likely to be hit by falling objects.

CHAPTER FIVE

Lessons 17-20

A Round Earth

This chapter focuses on the shape of the earth and where people live on the earth. Along with a study of gravity, inductive activities help your student to visualize the concepts of up and down.

 Inductive teaching is a method of teaching whereby you, as the teacher, stimulate your student to learn through observations, experiments, questions, and discussion. Using any of these methods, you lead him to discover what he knows and to apply logical reasoning to form a general principle.

Materials

The following items must be obtained or prepared before the presentation of the lesson. These items are designated with an * in the materials list in each lesson and in the Supplement. For further information see the individual lessons.

- Models or pictures of model cars, airplanes, ships, furniture, or houses (Lesson 17)
- 1 globe† (Lessons 17 and 18)
- 1 Styrofoam ball, 2 inches or more in diameter (Lesson 20)

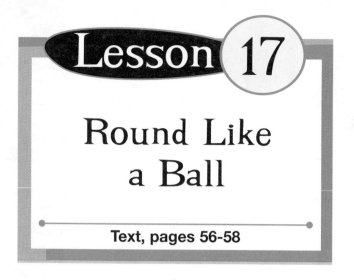

Lesson 17

Round Like a Ball

Text, pages 56-58

Preview

Objectives

Given proper instruction, your student will be able to

- Identify the partial, close-up view of the earth as flat.
- Identify the whole, distant view of the earth as round like a ball.

Materials

Have available

- Models or pictures of model cars, airplanes, ships, furniture, or houses
- Some disc-shaped objects (a record or CD, a Frisbee, a plate, a plastic lid)
- Some ball-shaped objects (a rubber ball, a grapefruit, an orange, a ball of yarn or string, a Ping-Pong ball)
- 1 globe*†
- Home Teacher's Edition, p. A10
- Cellophane tape

Prepare

- Page A10 of the Home Teacher's Edition by cutting out the rocket, folding back the flaps to form a base, and taping it upright on the globe.

Lesson

Introducing the Lesson

Introduce the activity. Show some models or pictures of model cars, airplanes, ships, furniture, or houses to your student. Ask your student to look at these examples and then to tell you what he thinks a model is. *(a small object that looks very much like a larger object)*

Direct the activity. Show your student the globe with the removable figure of a rocket taped to it. Ask your student to pretend that he is inside the rocket. Direct your student to count down from 10 to 1 and then to "fly" the rocket from the globe into "space." Ask what he "did" to see a round earth. *(He flew into space.)*

Conclude the activity. Now repeat the "liftoff." This time ask your student to describe what the ground would look like around the rocket's launching pad before "takeoff" *(flat)* and what the earth would look like from space after "takeoff." *(round, a ball)* Tell your student that he will learn more about our round earth in today's lesson.

What Is Earth's Shape?

Scientists say that the earth is round. Astronauts see a round earth when they travel in space. But most people see a flat earth. How can this be?

Most people see a flat earth because they see only a small part of it. But astronauts see a round earth because they see the whole thing.

56

What is round? A plate is round, and a ball is round. But is a plate round like a ball? How are a plate and a ball different? How are they alike?

The earth is round. But is it round like a plate or round like a ball? A model of the earth gives the answer.

57

Teaching the Lesson

Direct a text activity on pages 56-58. Use the following question to initiate your student's interest in what he is going to read: Is the earth round like a plate or round like a ball?

Continue with discussion questions. After your student completes his silent reading, use the following questions and statements as a guide to discuss the pages he read.

In an attempt to relate the flat ground and the ball-shaped earth, your student might give one of the following explanations.

- There are different earths—one that people live on and one where astronauts go.
- The earth is round like a plate or record, and so it seems round when you are over it and flat when you are on it.
- The earth is round like a ball, but people live on a flat part in the middle or a flat part on top.
- The earth is flat, but the shapes of mountains and hills make it look round.

1. Why do astronauts see the earth as round? *(because they see the whole thing)*
2. Why does the earth seem flat to us when we look at it? *(because we see only a small part of it)*
3. Name the objects on page 57. How are they alike? How are they different? *(The objects are cookies, coins, a beach ball, and marbles. All of these objects are round, but the cookies and coins are round and flat like a plate; the ball and marbles are round and "puffed out.")*
4. What does the globe tell you about the shape of the earth? *(The earth is round like a ball.)*

Evaluating the Lesson

Introduce the activity. Hold up one of the disc-shaped objects and one of the ball-shaped objects. Explain that the objects represent two different ideas about the round shape of the earth.

Direct the activity. Ask the following questions to determine whether the earth is round like a disc or round like a ball.

Questions for disc-shaped objects:
1. Where is the equator? *(Your student will probably indicate the rim of the disc.)*

A globe is a model of the earth. Is a globe round like a plate or round like a ball? Is the earth round like a plate or round like a ball?

A globe is round like a ball. The earth is round like a ball.

58

2. Where are the North and South Poles? *(Points at the center of the disc, top and bottom, will probably be indicated.)*

3. What is the path of a ship on a round-the-world ocean cruise? *(Ships would have to sail around on the top of the disc, close to the outer edge.)*

4. What is the path of a space shuttle in a round-the-earth orbit? *(Shuttles would probably follow a sharply elliptical, or oval, orbit that would allow them to see each flat, round side.)*

5. What would happen if you walked too close to the edge of the earth? *(You would fall off.)*

6. What would happen to the oceans near the edge? *(They would run off and disappear.)*

7. What would the Genesis Flood, which covered the highest mountain, have been like? *(It would have spilled off the edges as fast as the rain piled up in the center of the disk.)* (BAT: 8a Faith in God's promises)

Questions for ball-shaped objects:

1. Where is the equator?

2. Where are the North and South Poles?

3. What is the path of a ship on a round-the-world cruise? *(Although this will not be an accurate path, it should indicate that the ship actually sails over the curved ocean surfaces of the earth.)*

4. What is the path of a space shuttle in a round-the-earth orbit? *(This path, too, will not be accurate, but it should indicate that the shuttle orbits in a curved path above and around the earth.)*

Conclude the activity. Ask your student what this activity proves about the shape of the earth. *(The earth is round like a ball.)*

Enrichment

If you have access to a large ball (four feet or more in diameter) encourage your student to try the following activity.

Position the ball on the playground or floor and instruct your student to press his cheek against it. Then tell him to close the eye away from the ball and look with the other eye over the ball's surface. Invite him to describe what he sees. *(If the ball is large enough, its surface looks flat.)* Then tell the student to walk away from the ball and to describe what he sees now. *(The ball looks round.)*

For Your Information

The roundness of the earth has now been scientifically established by photographs taken from space. But Isaiah 40:22 shows that the Bible gave us this information long ago: "It is he that sitteth upon the circle of the earth." Magellan was the first to provide a scientific answer to this question when he and his men sailed completely around the earth in 1522.

However, other observations had been available for years before Magellan's trip that also lent credence to the idea that the earth is round. People could notice that the North Star always rose higher as they traveled northward but sank closer to the horizon as they traveled southward. Some stars of the Northern Hemisphere were obscured by the horizon once ships entered the Southern Hemisphere, and new constellations of stars then became visible.

Another evidence for the earth's roundness is that during lunar eclipses the earth's shadow against the moon has always been circular. If the earth were flat, it would have appeared as a straight line. However, as geometrical principles will support, only a sphere will cast a circular shadow on another sphere.

Where Do People Live?

Text, pages 59-61

Objective

Given proper instruction, your student will be able to

- Trace the route on a globe from the country where he lives to the country where another person lives.

Materials

Have available

- 1 globe*†
- Cellophane tape or masking tape
- Home Teacher's Edition, p. A11

Lesson

Introducing the Lesson

Introduce the activity. Direct your student's attention to the *Finding Out* activity on page 61. Instruct him to read the steps involved in this activity.

Direct the activity. Give your student page A11 from the Home Teacher's Edition. Instruct him to select four country or state markers in addition to the "I am here" marker. He needs to cut each marker and fold it on the center dotted line and on the tab lines to make a long, thin triangle. He should then tape the sides together. (*NOTE:* See Figure 18-1.) Explain that each of these markers represents a boy and a girl in the country or state named at the top.

Figure 18-1

Using tape, help your student stick the "I am here" marker to the place on the globe representing the state where you live. The student should then say, "This marker marks (the name of your state). It is (close to the North Pole or between the North Pole and the equator)."

Assist your student in locating on the globe the country or state named on each marker that he selected. After your student places each marker in the correct location, instruct him to point to the marker that indicates where he is now and then to finger-trace a path to each of the other markers on the globe.

Conclude the activity. Ask your student to name which areas he reached by crossing either the North Pole or South Pole. Which paths did he have to approach from the East? Which ones did he have to approach from the West? *(Answers to the questions above will vary depending upon the states or countries that your child selected. You may need to assist your child in determining directions on the globe.)*

Where Do People Live?

Before people could see pictures of how the earth looks from space, they tried to guess what shape it is. Most people thought that the earth is like a plate. Now people know that the earth is like a ball. They have different ideas about where they live on that ball.

Some people think that they live on flat land on the middle of the earth. Some people think that they live on a flat place at the top of the earth. Some people think that people live in different places all around the earth. Look at the drawings of those ideas. Where do you think people live on the round earth? Why do you say that?

People live in different places all around the earth. Look at the people from the Philippines, Serbia, Nigeria, and Turkey. Do they all speak the same language? Do they look the same? Do they need to know Jesus? How will they hear? Missionaries will take them the gospel.

"Go ye into all the world, and preach the gospel to every creature." Mark 16:15

Teaching the Lesson

Direct a text activity on pages 59-61. Use the following question to initiate your student's interest in what he is going to read: What are some ideas that people have about where they live on the earth?

Continue with discussion questions. After your student completes his silent reading, use the following questions and statements as a guide to discuss the pages he read.

1. Before we had pictures of the earth taken from space, what did most people think about the shape of the earth? *(that it was round like a plate)*

2. Identify the countries represented by the people in the pictures on page 60. Do they look alike and speak the same language? *(Philippines—top left, Serbia—top middle, Nigeria—top right, Turkey—bottom right; No, they look different and speak different languages.)*

3. Do you know any missionaries in these countries? Name them. *(Answers will vary. Use this opportunity to talk about some specific missionaries, where they serve the Lord, and what the land and people are like there. [BAT: 5c Evangelism and missions])*

Evaluating the Lesson

Conduct a direction activity. Position the globe so that the marker indicating the place where you live is on the student's right and the marker indicating a country on the other side of the globe—perhaps China—is on the student's left. Trace with your finger the obviously curved route from the right marker to the left marker, going first across the Pacific Ocean and then across the North Pole. Ask your student why he thinks that the routes are curved. *(because the earth is round like a ball)*

Ask your student to imagine that the world, represented by the globe, is made of glass and he can see through it. Ask your student to point to the direction he would look if he were standing on the marker marking his place right now on the globe and looking straight through the glass earth to China. *(He should point down to the floor.)*

Enrichment

Provide your student with a globe, stationery, pencils, a sample letter form, and prayer cards from several missionary families. Instruct your student to mark his location on the globe with the "I am here" marker. He should also place markers on the globe indicating the missionaries' locations on the globe. Encourage your student to write letters periodically to missionaries or to missionaries' children.

 When you receive letters from the missionaries, use the opportunity to pray for them. Also this letter-writing activity might help your child develop an interest in stamp-collecting as he collects and organizes the stamps from the missionaries' letters.

For Your Information

The fact that people can live anywhere on the earth and weigh approximately the same everywhere is another evidence for the roundness of the earth. Isaac Newton stated in 1666 that the weight of an object is a measure of the attraction between the object and the body in the universe upon which it rests. This attraction, known as gravity, depends on the mass of the object. For example, astronauts on the moon weighed about one-sixth of their weight on the earth. The reason for this difference is that the moon has one-sixth the mass of the earth.

Since people weigh almost the same anywhere on earth, the attraction between them and the earth must be approximately the same at all places. If the earth were not round, its mass would be uneven, the gravitational attraction would also be uneven, and people's weights would vary depending on their location.

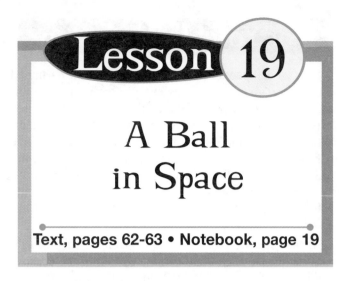

Lesson 19

A Ball in Space

Text, pages 62-63 • Notebook, page 19

name

Around the World

Draw lines to show where the balls would go.

Science 2
Notebook Packet

Lesson 19 | 19

Preview

Objectives

Given proper instruction, your student will be able to

- Identify the directions "up" and "down" as they apply above the earth.
- Define *above-the-ground down* as "toward the earth."
- Define *above-the-ground up* as "away from the earth."

Materials

Have available

- 1 ball
- A Write It flip chart
- 1 3" × 5" card

Lesson

Introducing the Lesson

Introduce the activity. Give your student a ball and ask him what he thinks will happen if he tosses it up into the air. *(It will go up; then it will fall to the floor.)* Instruct your student to toss the ball upward and let it fall to the floor.

Direct the activity. Direct your student's attention to notebook page 19. Explain that each child shown on the drawing of the earth is tossing a ball up into the air just as he did. Point to the child at the top of the earth and to the line that shows where the ball goes and where it lands. Ask your student whether he thinks that the drawing is correct. *(yes)* Then instruct your student to draw lines to show what happens to the other balls when they are tossed upward.

Conclude the activity. Discuss your student's answers with him. Point out that no matter where a person lives on this ball-shaped earth, objects fall "down" to the surface of the earth.

What Is Down?

A girl in Australia throws a ball up into the air. The ball comes back down to her, and she catches it. A girl in China throws a ball up into the air. The ball comes back down to her, and she catches it. A boy in Greenland throws a ball up into the air. The ball comes back down to him, but he does not catch it. It falls down to the earth.

> No matter where you are on the earth, when you throw things into the air, they come back down to you. All things come back down to the earth.

62

Look at the figures on the globe. Pretend that they are children from Canada, Mexico, and Poland. Pretend that the dotted lines are the paths their balls take up into the air. Trace the path of each ball with your finger. Did any of the balls fall off the earth? Do any balls ever fall off the earth?

Balls always fall back to the earth. Do you remember why? The earth's gravity pulls them back to the earth. When you throw things up into the air, they come back down to you, no matter where you are on the earth.

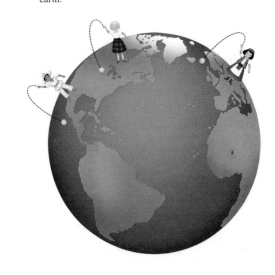

63

Teaching the Lesson

Direct a text activity on pages 62-63. Use the following question to initiate your student's interest in what he is going to read: What happens in different places in the world when people throw things into the air?

Continue with discussion questions. After your student completes his silent reading, use the following questions and statements as a guide to discuss the pages he read.

1. What happens when someone in Venezuela throws a ball into the air? *(The ball falls down to the earth.)*

2. What happens when someone in India throws a ball into the air? *(The ball falls down to the earth.)*

3. What causes the balls to fall down to the earth? *(the earth's gravity)*

Evaluating the Lesson

Introduce the activity. Give your student a 3" × 5" card and instruct him to draw an arrow on it. (*NOTE:* See Figure 19-1.) On the Write It flip chart, draw a large circle with stick figures at various places around the circle. (*NOTE:* See Figure 19-2.) Ask your student what he thinks the circle represents. *(the earth)* Tell him that the stick figures represent people who live in different countries on the earth. Tell your student that when you point to one of the stick figures, he should pretend that he is standing in that spot on the earth. Then, when you ask a question, he should answer by pointing his arrow in the correct direction.

Direct the activity. Point to the stick figure closest to the North Pole and ask your student which way is down. *(toward the floor)* On the Write It flip chart, draw an arrow pointing down toward the earth beside that stick figure. Continue around the circle, pointing to figures in random order, asking either "Which way is down?" or "Which way is up?" and drawing the arrow beside the figure.

Conclude the activity. When you complete questioning your student about most of the positions on the figure, ask him to help you write some sentences telling where "down" and "up" are all over the world. *("Down" is always toward the earth. "Up" is always away from the earth.)*

For Your Information

Most people realize that they are held to the surface of the earth because of gravity. What they do not consider, however, is that the earth is also attracted to them because of the same gravitational forces. As Newton stated, all bodies in the universe are attracted to all other bodies. The degree of attraction is dependent upon the mass of the objects involved. Since the mass of the earth is far greater than the mass of a person, people all over the world are held firmly to the surface of the earth.

Figure 19-1

Figure 19-2

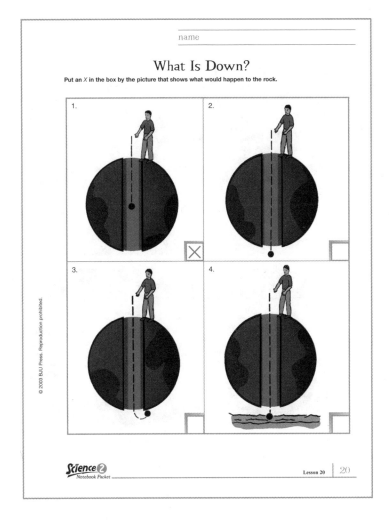

Preview

Objective

Given proper instruction, your student will be able to

- Identify *below-the-ground down* as "to the center of the ball-shaped earth."

Materials

Have available

- 1 Styrofoam ball, 2 inches or more in diameter*
- 1 pencil

Prepare

- The Styrofoam ball by boring a hole through its center with a pencil.

Lesson

Introducing the Lesson

Direct a notebook activity on page 20. Show your student the Styrofoam ball with the hole bored through the center. Ask him to imagine that the ball is the earth with a giant tunnel dug through it from the North Pole to the South Pole. At the North Pole end of the tunnel, he should picture a man dropping a rock into the hole. Then instruct your student to look at the diagrams on notebook page 20 and to put an *X* in the box beside the diagram that shows what would happen to the rock.

Tell your student that he will find out whether his answer is correct as he learns more about *What is down?* in today's lesson.

Look at the comic strip. What will happen to the shovels?

64

The shovels will fall down to the center of the earth. When things are dropped into the ground, they fall toward the center of the earth.

65

Teaching the Lesson

Direct a text activity on pages 64-66. Use the following questions to initiate your student's interest in what he is going to read.

1. When things are dropped into the ground, where do they fall?

2. Do things dropped from different parts of the world fall in different places?

Continue with discussion questions. After your student completes his silent reading, use the following questions and statements as a guide to discuss the pages he read.

1. What does the upside-down man on page 64 represent? *(the man at the "bottom" of the globe)*

2. What do you think will happen to the shovel of the man on the top of the globe? *(It will fall down to the center of the earth.)*

3. What do you think will happen to the shovel of the man on the bottom of the globe? *(It will also fall down to the center of the earth.)*

4. Why do the shovels not fall through to the other side of the earth? *(Things below the ground fall to the center of the earth.)*

 In theory the shovels would actually bob up and down at the center of the earth, somewhat as a telephone receiver would bob at the end of its coiled cord if it were dropped.

5. What clue does the word *screech* give you about what happens to the shovels? *(They seem to screech to a halt in the center of the earth; they "put on the brakes.")*

6. What do the arrows mean in the illustration on page 66? *(They are all pointing toward the center of the earth.)*

What do the arrows mean in this picture of the earth? What do things fall toward no matter where they drop from?

"Have ye not known? have ye not heard? hath it not been told you from the beginning? have ye not understood from the foundations of the earth?
"It is he that sitteth upon the circle of the earth, and the inhabitants thereof are as grasshoppers; that stretcheth out the heavens as a curtain, and spreadeth them out as a tent to dwell in."   *Isaiah 40:21-22*

66

For Your Information

Newton was able to calculate the force of attraction between objects by using a principle called the *center of gravity,* which theoretically concentrates all of the mass of the object at some central point. (This avoids the impossible problem of attempting to calculate the mass and force of every particle of an object against every particle in the object to which it is attracted.) In most simple geometric figures, the center of gravity is in the center. This is true of the earth also.

Though the earth is approximately a sphere, it is not a perfect one. Its spinning (rotation) on its axis makes it slightly flatter at the poles and slightly wider at the equator. Therefore, an object at the poles weighs slightly more than an object at the equator. This difference is a result of the object's being closer to the earth's center of gravity, where the gravitational pull is stronger.

Altitude makes a difference also. An object dropped from Mount Everest would not fall to the earth as quickly as an object dropped from sea level because the top of Mount Everest is farther from the center of the earth.

Evaluating the Lesson

Direct the evaluation. Refer to page 20 of the notebook. Ask your student to explain his answer. Ask him to name the force that makes things fall not only to the surface but also to the center of the ball-shaped earth. *(gravity)*

Then ask him which is the only diagram that shows the rock falling to the center of the earth. *(Diagram 1)* Ask him what would happen if a man dropped a rock into the hole at the South Pole. *(It, too, would fall to the center of the earth.)* Remind him that because gravity pulls things to the center of the ball-shaped earth, all people and things around the world stay on the earth rather than fall off.

Lessons 21-24

Light and Shadows

6

These lessons emphasize the importance of light to man. Your student will discover how light travels and what happens to light when it cannot pass through objects. He will observe light and objects in varying positions and notice the change in size and location of shadows. He will conclude this chapter by making a shadow silhouette.

Materials

The following items must be obtained or prepared before the presentation of the lesson. These items are designated with an * in the materials list in each lesson and in the Supplement. For further information see the individual lessons.

- 30 pieces of 9" × 11" construction paper (Lesson 21)
- 30 M&M candies or some other small items to use as rewards (Lesson 21)
- 1 marble (Lesson 22)
- 2 dusty chalkboard erasers (Lesson 22)
- Clay (Lessons 22 and 24)
- 1 sheet of black construction paper for each family member (Family Time 23)
- 1 sheet of white construction paper for each family member (Family Time 23)
- 1 large sheet of drawing paper for each family member (Family Time 23)
- Any type of film or filmstrip projector (Family Time 23)
- 1 strip of transparent acetate (Lesson 23)
- 6 empty baby food jars with lids (Lesson 23)
- Any two of the following transparent liquids: water, ginger ale, white vinegar, light corn syrup (Lesson 23)
- Any two of the following translucent liquids: apple juice, tea, strawberry pop, lemon juice (Lesson 23)
- Any two of the following opaque liquids: milk, strong coffee, soy sauce, grape juice (Lesson 23)

85

Lesson 21

The Source of Light

Text, pages 68-71

Preview

Objectives

Given proper instruction, your student will be able to

- Identify several sources of light.
- State that glowing objects are the source of light.
- Recognize that we see objects when they reflect light to our eyes.

Materials

Have available

- 1 shoebox
- 1 index card
- Cellophane or masking tape
- Small book or toy that will fit inside the shoebox
- 30 pieces of 9" × 11" construction paper*
- 30 M&M candies*

Prepare

- The shoebox by poking one hole in the lid and one hole in one end of the box. Tape the index card over the hole in the lid. Put the book or toy inside the box and put the lid on top.
- The construction paper by printing on each in large letters one of the following words: *sun, moon, stars, lightning, fireworks, candle, flashlight, desk lamp, bonfire, lightning bug, streetlight, night-light, car light, oil lantern, Christmas tree lights*. Then copy each word on another piece of construction paper. You will have a total of 15 words, each printed twice, for a total of 30 pieces of 9" × 11" paper. Number the sheets on the back from 1 to 30, in random order.

Lesson

Introducing the Lesson

Introduce the topic of the activity. Instruct your student to listen carefully to the following poem to discover what topic he will be learning about in today's lesson.

> I'm never late; I always come at dawn—
> (Before then you can call me with a switch);
> When nighttime comes, a lot of me is gone,
> And that's why you might fall into a ditch.
> You need me, for I'm useful as can be—
> With me the things you lost may soon be found;
> I have five letters in my name, you see—
> (But you *can't* see if I am not around!)
> I travel fast—much faster than you run;
> With me you tell if things are black or white;
> You add me to the end of *star* and *sun;*
> I don't weigh much; in fact, I'm very *light!*

After reading the poem, ask your student to guess what the topic of today's lesson is. *(light)* If your student has difficulty answering correctly, read the poem again, pointing out key phrases (the light switch mentioned in line 2, the number of letters referred to in line 7, the starlight and sunlight in line 11, and the play on the word *light* in line 12).

 This might be a good time to discuss with your child what Scripture teaches about light. In Genesis 1:3-5, we read that *light* was created *first*. Jesus presents Himself as "the light of the world" in John 8:12, meaning that He helps us see what is right. The "darkness" is the sin in our hearts before we accept Jesus as Savior. Christians are also to be "the light of the world" (Matthew 5:14) by telling others about Jesus. (BATs: 5c Evangelism and missions; 7b Exaltation of Christ)

Direct the activity. Instruct your student to look through the peephole in the end of the shoebox that you prepared. If the light hole in the lid is properly covered, he will not be able to see anything. Ask him why he cannot see anything. *(He will probably say that it is too dark inside the box.)*

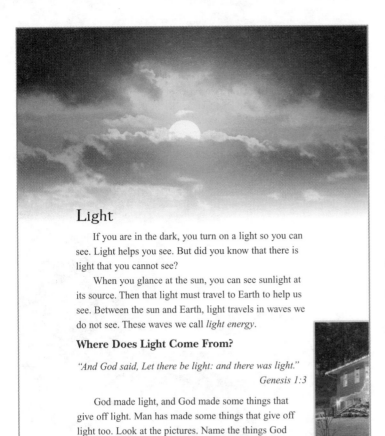

Light

If you are in the dark, you turn on a light so you can see. Light helps you see. But did you know that there is light that you cannot see?

When you glance at the sun, you can see sunlight at its source. Then that light must travel to Earth to help us see. Between the sun and Earth, light travels in waves we do not see. These waves we call *light energy*.

Where Does Light Come From?

"And God said, Let there be light: and there was light."
Genesis 1:3

God made light, and God made some things that give off light. Man has made some things that give off light too. Look at the pictures. Name the things God made. Name the things man has made.

How are all things that give off light alike?

68

69

Conclude the activity. Remove the index card from the light hole and ask your student to look through the peephole again and identify what is inside. Ask him why he can see the object inside the box now. *(We can see an object only when light is reflected from it, that is, when light bounces from the object to our eyes.)* Lead him to conclude that the light coming in through the light hole shines on the object and is reflected to his eye.

Teaching the Lesson

Direct a text activity on pages 68–71. Use the following questions to initiate your student's interest in what he is going to read.

1. Where does light come from?
2. What three things does light do?

Continue with discussion questions. After your student completes his silent reading, use the following questions and statements as a guide to discuss the pages he read.

1. What is light energy? *(waves that light travels in from the sun to the earth)*
2. Who made light? *(God)*

 Lights made by God are called *natural lights*. Other lights made by man out of forces that God has made available—such as electricity, friction, and chemical reactions—are *artificial lights*.

3. Look at the pictures on pages 68–69. What did God make? What did man make? *(God made the lightning. Man made streetlights, light from the candles, and Christmas lights by using substances that God created.)*

4. How are all things that give off light alike? *(They glow.)*

5. Why would you not be able to see if your room were completely dark? *(because there has to be light for you to see)*

6. What else does light do besides help you to see? *(keeps you warm and helps green plants make food)*

7. When you are in the sunshine with your eyes closed, how do you know that a cloud has passed in front of the sun? *(You do not feel as warm, and it seems darker.)*

All things that give off light glow. Can you think of other glowing objects that give off light?

What Does Light Do?

Could you see if your classroom were completely dark? Why? There has to be light for you to see. Light bounces from things to your eyes. Look at the drawing. What things does light let the boy see? What else does light do?

70

Light not only lets you see, but it also keeps you warm. Have you ever been in the sunshine with your eyes closed? When a cloud passed in front of the sun, did you know without looking that the light was not as strong? How did you know?

Light also helps green plants make food. The energy from the sun helps the plants make food from the water and other things they get from the soil.

71

Evaluating the Lesson

Introduce a matching game. Mix up the pairs of words and phrases printed on construction paper. Use small pieces of tape to fasten the papers to the wall in straight rows, numbered sides showing. (Use only one piece of tape at the top of each sheet so that you can easily turn the paper up to see what is written on the back.) Tell your student that on the wall there are fifteen pairs of hidden words that name a light source. His job is to find two papers with the same word printed on them.

Direct the matching game. Allow your student to select two numbers. Turn those two sheets so that he can see if the words match. If they do, remove them and give your student an M&M or some other small item as a reward. If he does not get a match, replace the papers and allow him to try again. When all the pairs have been found, Round 1 is over.

Continue with the game. Begin with Round 2 by telling your student that he must try to name from memory, one at a time, the fifteen sources of light that were on the wall in the previous round of the game. With each correct response, give a small reward to your student. When your student cannot think of a new source, give him a clue from one line in the riddle used in *Introducing the Lesson.* After your student names all fifteen sources of light, instruct him

to fill in the blank in the following sentence to end the game: *Light comes from _____ objects.* If your student misses the answer *(glowing)*, offer him some clues to reach that answer.

For Your Information

It is easy to describe the effects and properties of light, but what *is* light? For many centuries men have wondered about this. Since the 1600s, scientists have learned much about light. They now know that visible light is a form of electromagnetic radiation to which the eye responds. In other words, light is a type of energy that can be seen.

There are many forms of energy. Some examples are radio waves, infrared rays, X-rays, radar, gamma waves, and microwaves. Visible light is near the middle of what is called the *electromagnetic spectrum,* or line of energy forms that are arranged in order of how much energy each gives off. Visible light looks white or clear to us, but it is actually made up of various colors that also give off various amounts of energy. Red light has the longest wavelength (gives off the most energy), and violet light has the shortest.

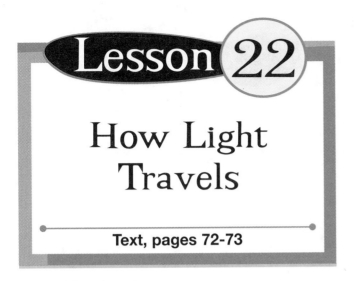

Lesson 22

How Light Travels

Text, pages 72-73

Preview

Objective

Given proper instruction, your student will be able to

- Demonstrate that light goes out from glowing objects in straight lines.

Materials

Have available

- 1 large bowl or cake pan
- 1 marble*
- Water
- 1 ball
- 1 candle
- Matches
- 2 dusty chalkboard erasers*
- Hole puncher
- Clay*
- 1 flashlight
- 3 4" × 6" cards

Notes

The next lesson, Lesson 23, requires small collections of transparent, translucent, and opaque materials—both solids and liquids—for your student to group. See the *Materials* section of Lesson 23 for suggestions of specific solids and liquids to have available.

Lesson

Introducing the Lesson

Introduce the activity. Ask your student whether he thinks light can travel. *(yes)* Ask him to give some examples of light traveling. *(It travels from the sun to the earth, from a car's headlights to the road, from a flashlight to wherever it is aimed, etc.)*

Fill the bowl with water about $\frac{1}{2}$ inch deep, and then allow your student to drop a marble into it. He will be able to see the ripples moving out from the center in all directions. Tell him to remember the movement of the water ripples since it will help him to understand something about the way light travels.

Now tell your student to roll a ball slowly across the table. Ask him to describe the path the ball took. *(straight)* This too helps to demonstrate something about the way light travels.

Direct the activity. Darken the room as much as possible and place a lighted candle on the table. If the room is dark enough, your student will see a soft glow radiating from the flame. Ask him in what direction the light from the candle is traveling. *(up, down, left, right)* Ask him whether light travels in a straight path similar to the marble rolling across the table. *(yes)* What else can you say about the path that light travels? *(in all directions, similar to the ripples made in the water by the marble)*

Continue the activity. Instruct your student to stand up and clap together two chalkboard erasers. Shine the flashlight beam into the chalk dust so that your student can see the beam of light traveling in a straight line.

 Your child may ask why the flashlight beam travels in only *one* direction if light is supposed to travel straight out from glowing objects in *all* directions. Point out that because the flashlight bulb is shielded by the case, the beam of light is *aimed* instead of radiating in all directions; the same is true of car headlights.

Conclude the activity. Ask your student whether he thinks light can bend around a corner. Open an interior door; then position your student behind the door as you stand in front of it. Aim the flashlight beam toward the edge of the door. Ask your student whether he thinks that the light will curve around the door to shine on him behind it. Why? *(No. Light travels in straight lines.)*

How Does Light Travel?

Can you tell what game the children in the picture are playing? Can the girl hear the boy as he looks for her? Why? Can she see him? Why?

The girl can hear the boy as he looks for her, but she cannot see him. Sound travels around corners, but light does not. Light travels only in straight lines.

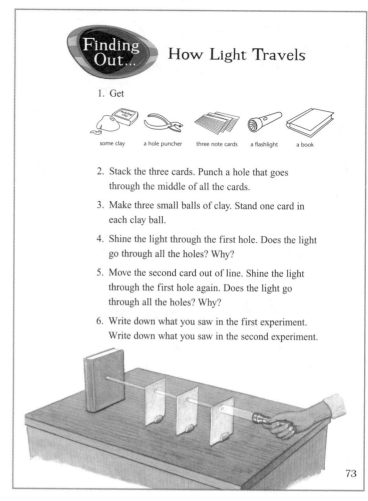

Finding Out... How Light Travels

1. Get

some clay   a hole puncher   three note cards   a flashlight   a book

2. Stack the three cards. Punch a hole that goes through the middle of all the cards.

3. Make three small balls of clay. Stand one card in each clay ball.

4. Shine the light through the first hole. Does the light go through all the holes? Why?

5. Move the second card out of line. Shine the light through the first hole again. Does the light go through all the holes? Why?

6. Write down what you saw in the first experiment. Write down what you saw in the second experiment.

Teaching the Lesson

Direct a text activity on pages 72-73. Use the following question to initiate your student's interest in what he is going to read: How does light travel?

Continue with discussion questions. After your student completes his silent reading, use the following questions and statements as a guide to discuss the pages he read.

1. What game are the children playing in the picture on page 72? *(Hide-and-Seek)*

2. Can the girl hear the boy as he looks for her? Why? *(Yes; she can hear him because sound travels around corners.)*

3. Can the girl see the boy as he looks for her? Why? *(No; she cannot see him because light does not travel around corners.)*

Evaluating the Lesson

Direct a *Finding Out* activity on page 73. Instruct your student to set up the three cards in balls of clay on the table. Read each step of the directions one at a time. Discuss the questions for each step after your student has followed the instructions. *(In the first experiment, the light traveled through all of the holes because the cards were lined up and light travels in a straight line. In the second experiment, when the cards were moved, the light did not go through all of the holes because light cannot bend around corners.)*

Enrichment

Tell your student that even though he cannot bend light around corners, he can use mirrors to make light *bounce* around corners.

 Although light can be reflected from surfaces such as mirrors to go around corners, it never bends or curves. It travels in straight lines between surfaces.

Instruct your student to sit under the table. Prop a mirror on another table or chair behind him and aim the mirror toward the top of the table under which he is sitting. (*NOTE:* See Figure 22-1.) Place an object on top of the table under which he is sitting, but do not tell your student what the object is. Now give him a hand mirror and ask him to experiment with it to see if he can use it, along with the mirror on the other table, to see what you placed on top of the table. (*NOTE:* You will need to test this activity in advance to determine the right distance and angle to use for the top mirror.) By looking into the hand-held mirror and aiming it toward the other mirror, your student should be able to see the top of the table under which he is sitting and identify the object above him.

Figure 22-1

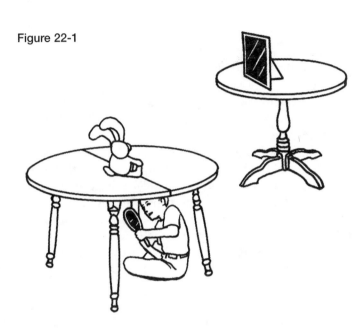

Light travels very fast—about 186,000 miles per second. That is more than 3,000 times faster than you drive on the highway! Light travels even faster than sound.

Light waves travel freely through space, but they always travel in a straight line. Each line of light is referred to as a *ray.* If a light ray hits an object through which it cannot pass, it bounces off. This is called *reflection.* When we say we "see" something, we are actually seeing reflected light rays that have bounced off the object and scattered. Mirrors allow us to see exact reflections because the mirrored surface is polished, and thus the rays leave the surface in a regular manner.

Whenever light travels through one substance to another, such as from air to water, it is *refracted,* or bent. You can see refraction by placing a pencil in a glass of water. The pencil is not bent, but it appears bent. The light rays are reflected in a different manner because the densities of the air and the water are different. Scientists and other people in industry have utilized the properties of refraction and reflection to design many kinds of lenses that help people see better. Some of these lenses are used to increase our knowledge of tiny or distant things.

Family Time 23

Shadow Silhouettes

Materials

Have available

- 1 large sheet of drawing paper for each family member*
- 1 pencil
- Any type of film or filmstrip projector*
- 1 sheet of black construction paper for each family member*
- 1 sheet of white construction paper for each family member*
- Glue
- Masking tape

Instructions

Make shadow silhouettes of each of your family members. Tape a large sheet of drawing paper to the wall, instructing each family member in turn to sit in front of the paper sideways so that the shadow of his profile appears on the paper when you shine the light from a film projector. Ask your child what he thinks causes the shadow. *(The person interrupts the passage of light and a shadow of that person projects on the paper that is on the wall.)* Trace each person's profile on a piece of drawing paper. Instruct each family member to use the drawing as a pattern to trace the shape onto black paper. Then mount the black silhouette onto white paper. Display your family's shadow silhouettes or send them as a gift to some special friends or relatives.

Lesson 23

Shadows

Text, pages 74-75 • Notebook, page 21

Preview

Objectives

Given proper instruction, your students will be able to

- Identify things that light goes through.
- Identify things that partially block light.
- Identify things that completely block light.
- Differentiate among faint, medium, and dark shadows.

Materials

Have available

- A Write It flip chart
- 1 strip of transparent acetate*
- 1 strip of waxed paper
- 1 strip of aluminum foil
- Opaque materials such as cardboard, a pie tin, a brick, and a book
- Translucent materials such as onionskin paper, toilet tissue, gauze, and frosted glass or plastic
- Transparent materials such as clear glass or plastic
- 6 baby food jars with lids*
- Any two of the following transparent liquids: water, ginger ale, white vinegar, light corn syrup*
- Any two of the following translucent liquids: apple juice, tea, strawberry pop, lemon juice*
- Any two of the following opaque liquids: milk, strong coffee, soy sauce, grape juice*

Prepare

- 2 baby food jars containing transparent liquids.
- 2 baby food jars containing translucent liquids.
- 2 baby food jars containing opaque liquids.
  (*NOTE:* Screw the lids on tightly so that the liquids will not seep out.)

Lesson

Introducing the Lesson

Introduce the activity. Place in front of your student an assortment of ten materials—some opaque (those that completely block light), some translucent (those that partially block light), and some transparent (those that allow light to pass through). Ask your student to help you think of a way to group the items. *(He may suggest grouping by color, size, or texture.)* Move the materials into different groups as your student offers his suggestions.

Direct the activity. Tell your student that he will now group the materials according to the amount of light that passes through them. On the Write It flip chart, write a *Yes* column and a *No* column. (*NOTE:* Leave space between these columns for another column to be added later during this activity.) Give your student a transparent material, and ask him to hold it up to the light. Can he see through it? Write the name of that material in the *Yes* column. Give him an opaque material to test, and then write its name in the *No* column. Give him a translucent material to test. Ask your student whether it belongs in the *Yes* column or *No* column.

Continue the activity. Lead your student to conclude that you need to add a third column between the other two columns—to keep the progression in order. Allow your student to suggest headings for the new column. *(Some, A little, Partly)* Explain that some things allow light to go through them, others allow only some of the light to go through, and others allow no light through.

Conclude the activity. Test all the materials on the table and write their names in the correct columns on your Write It flip chart. Tell your student that air is another material that lets light pass through. Point out that he does not have to brush the air aside as a curtain but that he can see clearly through it to the other side of the room or across the yard. Add *air* to the *Yes* column. Tell your student that he will learn more about light and these types of materials in today's lesson.

 If your child seems interested, you may want to tell him the real names for the three types of materials: *transparent, translucent,* and *opaque.*

Some materials, such as wood and brick, do not let any light pass through them. They stop light. Can you see through those things at all? Frosted glass and waxed paper let only part of the light pass through. You cannot see clearly through them. Air, water, and clear glass let almost all of the light pass through them. You can see clearly through those things.

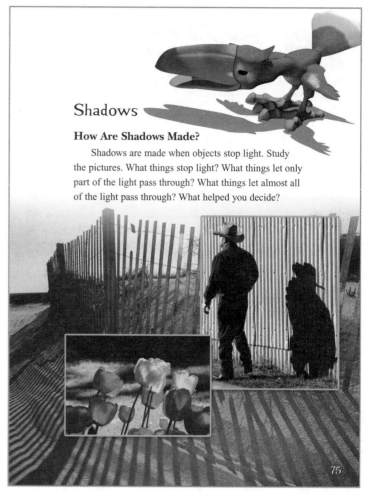

Shadows

How Are Shadows Made?

Shadows are made when objects stop light. Study the pictures. What things stop light? What things let only part of the light pass through? What things let almost all of the light pass through? What helped you decide?

Teaching the Lesson

Direct a text activity on pages 74-75. Use the following questions to initiate your student's interest in what he is going to read.

1. What kind of material allows light to pass through?
2. How are shadows made?

Continue with discussion questions. After your student completes his silent reading, use the following questions and statements as a guide to discuss the pages he read.

1. Can you see through wood or brick? Why? *(no, because they do not let light pass through them)*
2. Can you see clearly through frosted glass or waxed paper? Why? *(no, because they allow only a little light to pass through them)*
3. What materials allow almost all of the light to pass through them? *(air, water, and clear glass or plastic)*
4. How are shadows made? *(when objects stop light)*
5. Look at the pictures on pages 74-75. What things stop light? *(the brick wall, the fenceposts, and the man)* What things let only part of the light pass through? *(the balloons and the flowers)*
6. What allows almost all of the light to pass through? *(the glass windowpane)*

name _____

How Much Light Passes Through?

Look at the liquids. Write the number of each liquid in the correct column.   *Answers will vary.*

Almost All	Only Part	Not Any
These liquids are called **transparent.**	These liquids are called **translucent.**	These liquids are called **opaque.**

Science 2
Notebook Packet _____   Lesson 23 | 21

Evaluating the Lesson

Introduce an activity using notebook page 21. Ask your student to name once again the types of *solids* that he worked with in today's lesson. *(transparent, translucent, and opaque)* Tell him that now he will test and group different liquids to see how much light passes through them.

Direct the activity. Set up the six liquids—some of them transparent, some translucent, and some opaque—that you prepared in small numbered glass jars with lids. Direct your student's attention to notebook page 21 and instruct him to write the *number* of each liquid in the correct column. After your student records the numbers on his notebook page, hold up each jar in order, beginning with number 1, and ask your student to tell you which box each number should be in.

Conclude the activity. Take the jars outside on a sunny day and place them near your house so that their shadows appear on the wall. Ask what kind of shadow the transparent liquids cast *(faint)*, as well as what kind the translucent *(medium)* and opaque *(dark)* ones cast.

Because of the thickness of the glass jars, the shadows will appear darker than they would be if the liquids were not in a container.

Enrichment

Prepare a "shadow matching" game by shining a flashlight on several small objects and tracing the outline of the shadow onto a piece of paper. Display the drawings in random order on a table and challenge your student to match the shadow drawings to the correct object.

For Your Information

Different kinds of objects allow different amounts of light to pass through them. A windowpane allows light rays to go straight through it and so is said to be *transparent*. A piece of waxed paper, a frosted window, and a stained-glass window are called *translucent* because they allow some light rays to pass through but cause most of the rays to scatter. An *opaque* object is anything that will not allow light through. Most things are opaque, such as doors, buildings, walls, and statues. A *shadow* is the darkness caused because light has not passed through an opaque object. Shadows are always on the side opposite the light source. Many things cause shadows, including our own bodies. Even the earth casts a large shadow into space. That phenomenon causes eclipses of the moon—the shadow of the earth passes over the face of the moon when the earth and moon line up properly with the sun.

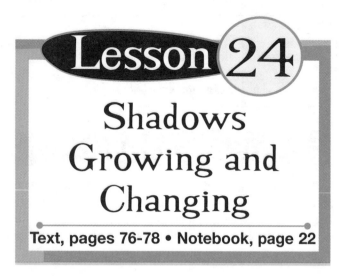

Lesson 24

Shadows Growing and Changing

Text, pages 76-78 • Notebook, page 22

Preview

Objectives

Given proper instruction, your student will be able to

- Demonstrate that the size of a shadow changes with the position of the light source.
- Demonstrate that the size of a shadow changes with the position of the object causing the shadow.
- Demonstrate how a shadow moves when the source of light moves.
- Demonstrate how a shadow moves when the object causing the shadow moves.

Materials

Have available

- 1 ruler
- Clay*
- 1 flashlight

Lesson

Introducing the Lesson

Introduce the activity. Ask your student what he thinks will happen to his shadow when he observes it in the morning, at noon, and again in the afternoon. *(The shadow will be at different positions each time.)* Ask him why he thinks that this will happen. *(The position of the sun changes.)*

If it is a sunny day, take your student outside in the morning (at 9:00 or 10:00), at noon, and in the afternoon (at 2:00 or 3:00). Direct him to stand facing west and observe his shadow at each of these times. *(NOTE: Remind*

Finding Out... How Shadows Move and Change

1. Get

    a ruler   some clay   a flashlight

2. Stand the ruler up in the clay.

3. Darken the room. Move the flashlight back and forth over the ruler. What happens to the shadow? Why?

4. Now hold the flashlight in one place and move the ruler back and forth under the light. What happens to the shadow of the ruler? Why?

5. Write down what you saw each time.

78

him never to stare directly at the sun.) Ask him to tell you how the shadows are different. *(In the morning his shadow will fall in front of him because the sun will be behind him. At noon, when the sun is directly overhead, his shadow will be beneath him, small and compact. In the afternoon his shadow will fall behind him since the sun is now in front of him.)*

Direct a *Finding Out* activity on page 78. Read the steps with your student. Assist him in setting up the demonstration with the clay, a ruler, and a flashlight, following the directions on page 78. Ask your student to explain what is happening to the shadow of the ruler as he moves the flashlight back and forth in an arc in front of the ruler. *(The shadow moves as the light moves; it is always on the other side of the ruler from where the light of the flashlight is. Shadows move when the light source moves.)*

Instruct your student to hold the flashlight steady as he moves the ruler back and forth in front of the beam. Ask him to explain what is happening now to the shadow. *(It is moving as the ruler moves; it is always on the opposite side of the ruler from the light of the flashlight.)*

Why Do Shadows Change Size and Move?

What happened to the shadows? Did they change size? Did they move? Why?

Shadows change size and move when the thing making the light moves.

76

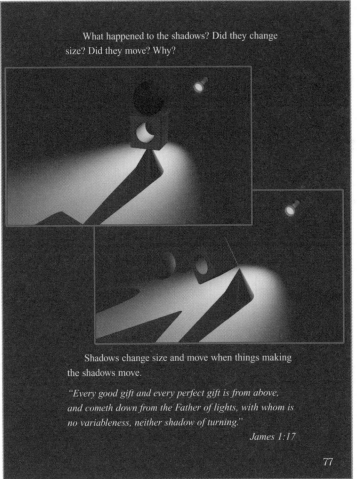

What happened to the shadows? Did they change size? Did they move? Why?

Shadows change size and move when things making the shadows move.

"Every good gift and every perfect gift is from above, and cometh down from the Father of lights, with whom is no variableness, neither shadow of turning."

James 1:17

77

Teaching the Lesson

Direct a text activity on pages 76-78. Use the following questions to initiate your student's interest in what he is going to read.

1. Why do shadows change size?
2. Why do shadows move?

Continue with discussion questions. After your student completes his silent reading, use the following questions and statements as a guide to discuss the pages he read.

1. What happened to the shadows in the pictures on page 76? *(The shadows moved to the other side of the objects and changed size.)*

 A shadow forms when light is blocked; therefore, the light source and the shadow are always on opposite sides of an object. As the earth rotates, the sun appears to change position; therefore, the shadows change position too.

2. Why did the shadows move and change size? *(The object making the light moved.)*
3. What happened to the shadows in the pictures on page 77? Why? *(The shadows moved because the objects moved.)*
4. Look around the room. Point to where you see shadows. Check these same areas again in thirty minutes. Are the shadows the same size and in the same place as they were before? Why? *(Locations of shadows will vary, but their size and location will probably be different after thirty minutes because either the light source will have moved or the object [person, animal, toy] will have moved.)*

 Most light sources change. They either burn out or shift position (or, in the case of the sun, *appear* to shift position). In James 1:17 we read that God, "the Father of lights," never changes. He does not turn away from us, and His love does not vary from day to day. (BAT: 8a Faith in God's promises, Bible Promise: G. Christ as Friend)

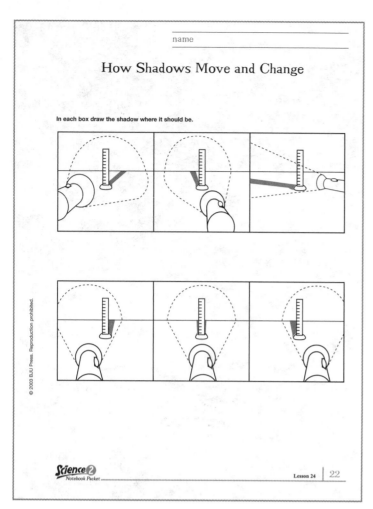

name

How Shadows Move and Change

In each box draw the shadow where it should be.

Science 2
Notebook Packet

Lesson 24 | 22

Evaluating the Lesson

Direct your student's attention to notebook page 22. Instruct him to read the directions and then draw and shade in the shadows. Check the page with him.

Enrichment

Give opportunity for your student to explore what causes a rainbow. Instruct him to place a small, flat mirror in a glass of water with the glass in the sunlight so that the mirror is facing the sun. Encourage him to hold a piece of white paper in front of the glass, experimenting with different angles until a spectrum appears on the paper. Ask your student to identify the colors. Tap the glass lightly and see what happens to the colored bands. *(They will move as the water moves.)* Ask your student what happens to light when it passes through water. *(A rainbow forms.)* Ask him how many colors he thinks light has. *(six or seven)*

 The bands of light together make up a *spectrum*. To our eyes, the spectrum seems to have only six or seven colors, but each band in the spectrum has a huge number of different wavelengths in it.

Ask your student what he thinks the colors of the rainbow's spectrum are. *(red, orange, yellow, green, blue, and violet)* Ask your student what he thinks makes the light separate into colors. *(When light passes through water, it bends and separates into colors.)*

Read the following poem, "My Shadow," by Robert Louis Stevenson, which discusses some concepts about shadows that were covered in this lesson. Ask your student to listen for the funny ways a shadow acts.

I have a little shadow that goes in and out with me,
And what can be the use of him is more than I can see.
He is very, very like me from the heels up to the head;
And I see him jump before me, when I jump into my bed.
The funniest thing about him is the way he likes to grow—
Not at all like proper children, which is always very slow;
For he sometimes shoots up taller like an India-rubber ball,
And he sometimes gets so little that there's none of him at all.
He hasn't got a notion of how children ought to play,
And can only make a fool of me in every sort of way.
He stays so close beside me, he's a coward you can see;
I'd think shame to stick to nursie as that shadow sticks to me!
One morning, very early, before the sun was up,
I rose and found the shining dew on every buttercup;
But my lazy little shadow, like an arrant sleepyhead,
Had stayed at home behind me and was fast asleep in bed.

Ask your student whether his shadow has ever behaved as this one did. Ask the following questions after these lines:

Line 4—Where would the light be if you were facing your bed and your shadow fell onto the bed? *(The light would be behind you.)*

Line 7—What time of day does your shadow shoot up tall? Why? *(When the rays of the sun shine on you from a lower position—that is, in the early morning and late afternoon—your shadow falls in an elongated shape. As the sun rises, it shines down on you instead of across and your shadow becomes shorter.)*

Line 8—What time is it when your shadow is the smallest? *(It is smallest at noon when the sun is directly overhead.)*

Line 10—In what way do you think the boy's shadow makes him feel foolish? *(The shadow can never be "caught" as in a regular game of tag.)*

Line 16—Was the shadow *really* at home in bed? Why was it not with the boy? *(If the boy arose before the sun was up, then it was dark outside. There are no shadows in the dark except those formed by streetlights or moonlight.)*

For Your Information

The size and shape of a shadow depend on the size of the light source and the size of the opaque object. If the light source is of low intensity, the shadow will be much darker because the object is able to stop all the light rays. This dark shadow is called the *umbra*. If the light source is of high intensity, the object will stop some rays but simply deflect others. Thus there will be a dark inner shadow that is surrounded by a lighter outer shadow. The lighter part is the *penumbra*.

C H A P T E R   S E V E N

Lessons 25-29

Living and Not Living

This chapter summarizes some of the distinctions between living and non-living things. Beginning with Lesson 25, each lesson emphasizes one of the following characteristics of living things: they move, they have needs, they respond, they reproduce, and they grow. Through the use of various examples of nature, and firsthand experience with seed germination, your student will develop a better perspective of how the living differs from the nonliving.

Materials

The following items must be obtained or prepared before the presentation of the lesson. These items are designated with an * in the materials list in each lesson and in the Supplement. For further information see the individual lessons.

- 6-8 bean seeds (Lesson 26)
- 1 green rubber glove (Lesson 26)
- 12 magazine pictures of different animals (Lesson 28)
- 4 chenille wires (Lesson 29)
- 1 growth chart (Lesson 29)

Lesson 25

Living Things Move

Text, pages 80-83 • Notebook, page 23

Preview

Objectives

Given proper instruction, your student will be able to

- Distinguish between living and nonliving things.
- Conclude that animals are living things that are able to move on their own.
- Conclude that plants are living things that are unable to move on their own.

Materials

Have available

- Crayons
- Felt-tip pens
- A Write It flip chart

Lesson

Introducing the Lesson

Introduce the activity. Take your student to a pet shop or to the zoo. Allow him to observe several different kinds of animals as well as the other things around them (cages, trees, rocks, food, animals' "toys," etc.). Tell your student that he will learn more about some of the things he sees in today's lesson.

Direct the activity. When back home, ask your student to tell you which animal was his favorite and why he liked it best. Write the name of the animal on the Write It flip chart. Ask the following questions: Does this animal have a cage? Is the cage important for the care of the animal? Why? *(Yes; the cage keeps the animal from running away or from getting injured by another animal.)* Under the name of the animal, write *moves*.

Now ask your student to name something else that he saw besides animals. *(He might name a rock, a building, etc. Lead him to name a nonliving thing.)* Write this item in another column on the Write It flip chart. Ask whether this nonliving item needs a cage. Why? *(no, because it cannot run away)* Under the name of this item, write *does not move*.

Ask your student to tell you some things that his favorite animal needs. *(Answers will vary, but your student will probably include food, water, shelter, and sometimes medicine.)* Ask your student why his favorite animal needs food and water. *(Without food and water the animal would die.)* Write *needs food and water* under the animal category. Ask him whether the nonliving item on the list needs food and water. Why? *(No; the item is not alive.)* On the Write It flip chart write *does not need food and water* under the nonliving item category.

Continue the activity. Ask your student to tell you some things that he saw the animals doing. *(Some possible answers are eating, sleeping, swinging, fighting with another animal, playing, licking, growling to show anger, etc.)* Under the animal category, write *responds*. Ask your student if he knows what the word *responds* means. *(how things react to the world around them)* Does the other item do any of these things? *(no)* Under the nonliving item category write *does not respond*.

Conclude the activity. Ask your student whether he remembers seeing any baby animals. Did the baby animals look like the grown animals? *(The answer will probably be "yes.")* Write *makes more babies* under the animal column on the Write It flip chart. Does the other item make more items? Why? *(no, because it is not alive)* Under the nonliving item column, write *does not make more items*.

Ask your student what he thinks will happen in the next few months to the baby animals. *(They will grow bigger.)* Under the animal category, write *grows*. Ask him whether he thinks that the other item will grow. Why? *(no, because the item is not alive)* Write under the nonliving item column *does not grow*.

Instruct your student to read aloud the list under the animal name. Write *Living* above this list. Now instruct him to read the list of things under the item category. Write *Not living* above this list. Tell your student that he will learn more about living and nonliving things in today's lesson.

"Then king Darius wrote unto all people, . . . I make a decree, That in every dominion of my kingdom men tremble and fear before the God of Daniel: for he is the living God."

Daniel 6:25-26

Look at the pictures. Which things are living? Which things are not living?

80

People are living things. Animals are living things. Plants are living things.

How are living things alike?

81

Teaching the Lesson

Direct a text activity on pages 80-83. Use the following questions to initiate your student's interest in what he is going to read.

1. How can you tell living things from nonliving things?

2. Can something be both living and nonliving at the same time?

Continue with discussion questions. After your student completes his silent reading, use the following questions and statements as a guide to discuss the pages he read.

1. Where did living things come from? *(God made all things. [Bible Promise: I. God as Master])*

2. Look at the pictures on pages 80-81. Which things are living? *(dog, flower, and people)*

3. Name some ways that animals move. *(Some possible answers are swim, fly, walk, climb, run, hop, etc.)*

4. Name at least three animals that move in more than one way. *(Some possible answers are raccoon—walk and climb; goose—walk, fly, swim; horse—walk, run, jump.)*

5. Are plants living or nonliving? *(living)*

6. How do people move plants from place to place? *(People dig up the whole plant and plant it in a new place. People put parts of plants—seeds, leaves, flowers—in other places to grow or just for decoration.)*

Living Things Move

"And God created . . . every living creature that moveth."

Genesis 1:21

Many living things can move on their own. Animals are living things that move. Animals move in many ways. Some swim. Some fly. Others climb. Some animals hop and jump. Others walk and run. What other ways can animals move?

Some animals move in more than one way. A duck can swim, fly, and walk. A raccoon can walk, run, and climb. What other animals move in more than one way?

Some living things do not move from place to place on their own. Plants stay where they are unless something moves them to another place. Plants do move in a way. Some turn to face the sun. Some have leaves or flowers that fold up when it is dark or when they are touched. How do people move plants from place to place?

82

83

name _____

Look at the picture and pick out the things that are living.
Then color *only* those living things.

Science 2
Notebook Packet

Lesson 25 | 23

Evaluating the Lesson

Direct a notebook activity on page 23. Instruct your student to study the various items in the covered wagon picture and distinguish between those that are living and those that are not living. Allow time for your student to color only the living things in the picture.

Enrichment

Make magazines, scissors, glue, and two large envelopes or boxes available to your student. Instruct him to cut out magazine pictures of living things and of nonliving things. Label one envelope or box *Living* and the other *Not living.* Your student should sort the pictures into the two categories. To check your student's work, allow time for him to show the pictures from each category to the rest of the family.

For Your Information

Most people have noticed that tulips, morning glories, buttercups, and similar flowers open during the day, close in the evening, and reopen the following morning. These openings and closings are examples of *nastic movements.* Nastic movements in plants are caused by the loss or gain of turgor in certain cells, often at the base of the petal or leaf. (Turgor is the presence of water inside a plant cell in sufficient quantity to give the cell stiffness.) Since nastic movements depend on the presence or absence of water, they are temporary, reversible changes.

Unlike the nastic movements, which are temporary, plants also respond to changes in their environment by producing different growth regulators. The regulators have a lasting effect on the movement of the plant's growth. These growth responses of plants to their environment are called *tropisms.*

Phototropism is a plant's response to light. When a plant's stem and leaves turn toward light, they demonstrate positive phototropism; at the same time, the roots are growing away from the light and demonstrating negative phototropism. *Photoperiodism* is a plant's response to the length of time it is exposed to light. A plant blooms at the time of the season when the length of each day is appropriate for its needs.

Geotropism is a plant's movement in response to gravity. Roots show positive geotropism since they grow toward the pull of gravity, and a plant stem shows negative geotropism because it grows away from the pull of gravity. You may demonstrate geotropism by placing a potted plant on its side for a few days. It will turn to grow vertically instead of continuing to grow in the same direction.

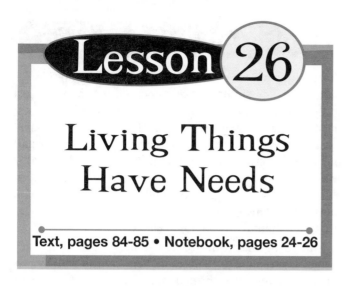

Lesson 26

Living Things Have Needs

Text, pages 84-85 • Notebook, pages 24-26

1. Get

some seeds   two paper towels   two small recloseable plastic bags   some water   some clear tape

2. Place some seeds on each paper towel.

3. Tape the seeds in place.

4. Place each towel in a plastic bag.

5. Add a half-inch of water to one bag.

6. Seal the bags.

7. Record what you did. Look at your seeds each day. Record what happens.

85

Preview

Objectives

Given proper instruction, your student will be able to

- Identify three needs of living things.
- Keep a record of the growth of bean seeds.

Materials

Have available

- 2 resealable plastic bags
- 2 paper towels
- 6-8 bean seeds*
- Masking tape
- 1 felt-tip pen
- Cellophane tape
- 1 green rubber glove*

Lesson

Introducing the Lesson

Introduce a *Finding Out* activity. Hold up your thumb and tell your student that you have a green thumb. Ask him whether he knows what that phrase means. *(that you are able to make plants grow well)* Tell your student that today he will be doing a little "gardening" of his own. He will make special "sprouting bags" and will grow seedlings.

Give your student two resealable plastic bags, a paper towel, three or four seeds, masking tape, and a strip of cellophane tape. Explain to your student that he will put together sprouting bags using the materials you have just given him. Direct his attention to page 85 and instruct him to read the steps in the *Finding Out* experiment. Ask your student what he thinks this experiment will test. *(It will test what seeds need to grow.)*

Direct the activity. Assemble the sprouting bags by demonstrating how to fold a paper towel into fourths so that it will fit into each bag. Assist your student as he follows directions using the materials you have given him. Tell your student that he will have one sprouting bag that receives water (labeled *A* on masking tape) and another bag that does not receive water (labeled *B* on masking tape). Pour about one-half inch of water into the bag labeled *A*, making sure to get the towel damp. Carefully seal the bag and place a long strip of masking tape across the top. The tape should be about one inch longer than the width of the bag so that the ends can be folded over and used as tabs. (*NOTE:* See Figure 26-1.) Hang up the bags on the side of the refrigerator or on a bulletin board.

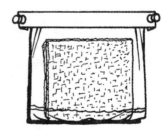

Figure 26-1

Tape the beans to the outside of the paper towel so that the growth of the seeds is visible.

Living Things Have Needs

Circle the correct word(s).

Bag A   *Answers will vary.*

Does the seed have food?   Yes / No

Does the seed have water?   Yes / No

Does the seed have air?   Yes / No

I think that the seeds in the bag (will / will not) grow.
Why?

_____

_ _

_ _

Bag B   *Answers will vary.*

Does the seed have food?   Yes / No

Does the seed have water?   Yes / No

Does the seed have air?   Yes / No

I think that the seeds in the bag (will / will not) grow.
Why?

_____

_ _

_ _

Science 2
Notebook Packet   **Lesson 26**   24

Continue the activity. Remind your student that the bag with water will be labeled *A* and the bag without water will be labeled *B*. Direct your student's attention to notebook page 24. Assist him in reading the statements on the page and instruct him to circle whether the seeds in each bag received food, air, and water. Encourage him to predict which seeds will grow and which will not grow and to give a reason for his predictions in the blanks provided.

Conclude the activity. Direct your student's attention to the two remaining notebook pages. Explain that he will keep a record of his seeds' growth. He will use notebook page 25 for bag *A* and notebook page 26 for bag *B*. Read the various descriptions listed on the page. Instruct your student to place an *X* in the box or boxes that best describe how *most* of his seeds look on *that* particular day. Guide your student as he fills out the chart for Day 1. Ask him what description best describes his seeds today. Instruct him to mark an *X* in the appropriate boxes on both notebook pages. Inform your student that for the rest of the week he will need to make time to fill out his charts regarding the growth of his seeds.

name

Seed Growth Record

Bag A		Day 1	Day 2	Day 3	Day 4	Day 5
Seeds have not changed.						
Seeds have sprouted.						
Main root has grown.						
Side roots have grown.						
Roots have become longer.						
Leaves have appeared.						
Leaves have grown larger.						

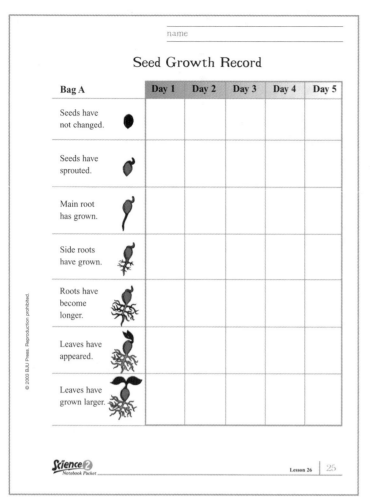

Seed Growth Record

Bag B		Day 1	Day 2	Day 3	Day 4	Day 5
Seeds have not changed.						
Seeds have sprouted.						
Main root has grown.						
Side roots have grown.						
Roots have become longer.						
Leaves have appeared.						
Leaves have grown larger.						

Teaching the Lesson

Direct a text activity on pages 84-85. Use the following question to initiate your student's interest in what he is going to read: What do living things need to stay alive?

Continue with discussion questions. After your student completes his silent reading, use the following questions and statements as a guide to discuss the pages he read.

1. Name the three substances that living things need. *(food, air, and water)*

 Reemphasize the three needs by explaining that inside each seed is a tiny plant. For the plant to begin to grow, it must have air, food, and water. The air for the seeds is in the bag. The food for the seeds is inside the seed. God created these seeds and many others with a special supply of food inside. As the tiny plant grows, it uses up the food. By the time the food stored in the seed is all used up, the plant has grown roots and leaves and can make its own food.

2. Which picture on page 84 shows someone taking air with him? *(the astronaut)*

3. Why do you think that the astronaut needs to take air with him into space? *(There is no oxygen outside the earth's atmosphere.)*

4. Which pictures on page 84 show living things getting food or water? *(The baby is getting food, and the plant is getting water.)*

5. Who provides all that is needed for all of the plants and animals? *(God)*

 Providing food for a tiny plant growing from a seed is just a small way in which God cares for the plants and animals He created. Matthew 6:26-29 reminds us that the birds do not plant seeds, tend gardens, and harvest; yet they are fed. Neither do plants work at making their colorful flowers; yet their blooms are more beautiful than a king's royal robes. If God cares enough to look after the needs of the birds and the flowers, how much more will He look after the needs of His people? (Bible Promise: H. God as Father)

Living Things Have Needs

Living things need food. They need air and water. Which picture shows someone taking air with him? Which pictures show living things getting food or water?

"Behold the fowls of the air: for they sow not, neither do they reap, nor gather into barns; yet your heavenly Father feedeth them."　　　　Matthew 6:26

84

6. Name some needs that all people have. *(food, water, clothes, place to live, love)*

Those things are all important needs, but the greatest need that people have is to receive forgiveness for the wrong things they do (sin). God loved men, women, boys, and girls so much that He allowed His Son, Jesus Christ, to die on a cross so that people could receive forgiveness for their sin. Only those who have asked Jesus to save them and forgive their sins will be able to have fellowship with God and to go to heaven and live with God someday. (BATs: la Understanding Jesus Christ; lb Repentance and faith)

Evaluating the Lesson

Introduce a review activity. Give your student a green rubber glove to put on. Explain that you will read several short stories. After each story your student should decide if the story *truly* shows that living things have needs. He should respond by holding up his green thumb for *true—living* and putting down his green thumb for *false—not living*. For each situation involving living things, ask your student what the needs are.

1. Kristen and her family went on vacation for a week and forgot about watering the plant in her room. When they returned, the plant's leaves were all wilted and droopy. *(true, needs water)*

2. All of a sudden the car began to sputter. Soon it would not run at all. The car had run out of gas. *(false)*

3. The sleeping mother woke up when she heard her newborn baby crying. It had been four hours since the last feeding, and baby Justin was hungry. *(true, needs food)*

4. The skin diver had been searching the bottom of the lake for nearly an hour. Suddenly a warning bell rang from his air tanks. The gauge showed that he had used nearly all of his air supply. It was time to swim back up to the surface of the water. *(true, needs air)*

For Your Information

Though animals and humans obviously need air and water to survive, the needs of plants may not be quite so visible. The relationships between plants and animals in providing the basic needs of each other become more and more amazing as a person considers them carefully. Animals and humans take in air (oxygen), water, and food to provide energy for all life processes. Animals and humans breathe out carbon dioxide as a waste product of those processes. Conversely, plants take in the carbon dioxide from the air. They also take in water and energy in the form of light. With these raw materials, plants make their own food—glucose—through the process of photosynthesis. People provide carbon dioxide for plants; plants provide oxygen and food for people. Thus God's creative hand again becomes evident in the ways in which He has provided for all His creation.

Family Time 27

Trapped

The following Family Time provides an outline appropriate for your family devotional time.

Materials

Have available
- A Bible

Instructions

Read II Chronicles 24 aloud. Ask your student the following questions about the passage.

1. Who is the story about? *(Joash)*
2. How old was Joash when he became king? *(seven)*
3. Who was Jehoiada? *(the high priest and also Joash's uncle)*
4. When did Joash serve the Lord? *(when Jehoiada was alive)*
5. Why did they collect money? *(to repair the house of the Lord)*
6. What did they do with the leftover money? *(They made vessels and spoons for the house of the Lord.)*
7. Did they waste any money? *(no)*
8. How old was Jehoiada when he died? *(130)*
9. Who did King Joash listen to after Jehoiada's death? *(the princes of Judah)*
10. What did the princes of Judah do to show that they did not serve God? *(They worshipped groves and idols.)*
11. What was the result of Joash's sin? *(disease, murder, war, and destruction)*

Discuss with your family members that they, like Joash, will meet people who trap others to try to become their friends and to influence them to do wrong. Encourage your family members to make sure that their friends love the Lord Jesus and want to serve Him. (BAT: 5e Friendliness) Friends that do not care about Christ can lead them astray.

Use this opportunity to name some friends, discuss whether you think that they love Christ, and pray for them.

Lesson 27

Living Things Respond

Text, pages 86-88

Preview

Objective

Given proper instruction, your student will be able to

• Identify various ways animals obtain food.

Materials

Have available

• A Write It flip chart

Lesson

Introducing the Lesson

Introduce the activity. Make a sudden, loud, startling noise (perhaps by dropping a large book on a table). Your student will probably jump or cry out. Ask your student to describe how he responded. Ask him whether he thinks a rock would respond in this same way. Why? *(no, because a rock is not living, and nonliving things do not respond)* Ask him to tell some ways that other people might have responded. *(Possible answers are jumped, looked up, squealed, dropped their pencils, hearts started pounding.)* Explain to your student that noise is just one of many things that living things respond to. Ask your student to name any other things that living things respond to. *(light, touch, smell, movement, and gravity)* Ask your student whether he believes that people respond to these things too. *(yes)* Ask whether he thinks that plants and animals respond to these things. *(yes)*

Direct the activity. Ask your student how he responds when he feels hungry. *(He gets something to eat or asks someone else to get him some food.)* Ask him what he thinks a spider does when it is hungry. *(Answers will vary, but your student will probably say that the spider grabs bugs to eat.)*

Take your student to examine a spider's web (or several different spiders' webs).

 Spiders' webs can be found in the corners of houses, on shrubbery, in the ends of clothesline poles, etc.

Ask your student to describe the shape of the web and to sketch it if possible. Are there any insects captured in the web? Name the insects. Is the spider still in the web? What is the spider doing?

 Different spiders weave different kinds of webs. Each web uses different kinds of "silk" within the same web. In an orb web the silk that spirals around and around is sticky. The rest of the silk is not sticky.

Continue the activity. Ask your student why he thinks that a spider makes a web. *(to catch food)* Ask him why he thinks that sticky silk would help make the web a better trap. *(Insects would get caught in the silk and not be able to get out.)*

Conclude the activity. Explain to your student that how an animal gets food is an *animal behavior.* Ask him whether he thinks that how an animal responds to happenings around him is an animal behavior. *(yes)* Tell your student that he will learn about these animal behaviors in today's lesson.

Living Things Respond

Living things respond to what is happening around them. Look at the pictures of the plant. How has it changed? Why has it changed?

Plants respond to changing light.

Animals respond to what is happening around them. How they respond is called *animal behavior*. Getting food and taking care of young are some animal behaviors.

Animals get food in many different ways. Some animals wait for ocean currents to bring it. Some store food for times when there isn't much food. Some animals travel to other places where they can find food. Some animals hunt, steal, trick, trap, or provide a service to get food. What ways of getting food are shown in these pictures?

Teaching the Lesson

Direct a text activity on pages 86-88. Use the following questions to initiate your student's interest in what he is going to read.

1. What are some ways that living things respond to things around them?
2. How do animals get food?

Continue with discussion questions. After your student completes his silent reading, use the following questions and statements as a guide to discuss the pages he read.

1. Look at the pictures of the mimosa plant on page 86. How has the plant changed? Why has it changed? *(The leaves respond to light by opening. They respond to darkness by closing.)*

 Certain mimosa plants also respond to touch—the leaves close when disturbed. Because of this response, the mimosa is often called the "sensitive plant."

2. What animals and their food supply systems are pictured on page 87? *(spider and birds)*

3. How do the baby birds get food? *(The mother and father birds bring insects or worms to the young and actually place the food in their open mouths.)*
4. Which word—*hunt, steal, trick,* or *trap*—best describes how the spider gets its food? *(trap)*

 Although spiders are very good trappers and hunters, we would not call them good mothers. When the tiny spiderlings hatch from their egg sac, they look like tiny adult spiders. Usually the mother has little to do with them, and they are left on their own. The mother does not teach them how to weave a web; God has given them that knowledge at birth.

Some baby animals get better care than others. Baby fish, lizards, and snakes do not get much care. They do not need much help to learn how to live. But baby birds, lions, tigers, monkeys, and bears get a lot of care. Mother cheetahs spend many hours teaching their young how to hunt. And monkeys spend a lot of time cleaning their young and teaching them how to behave.

88

Evaluating the Lesson

Direct a matching activity by writing the following words on the Write It flip chart: *hunts food, traps food, gathers food, steals food, tricks its food,* and *provides a service.* Explain to your student that you will read a short description of how six different animals get their food. Your student must decide which of the six categories on the Write It flip chart best describes the animal in each story. You might want to reward him with a sticker or small token for each correct answer.

Honeybee
The honeybee flies from flower to flower collecting nectar and pollen. It makes honey from the nectar and uses the honey and pollen as food. *(gathers food)*

Ant lion
The ant lion digs a pit in the desert sand. When an insect accidentally wanders into the pit, the sand shifts and slides, pushing the insect to the bottom where the ant lion is waiting. *(traps food)*

Red fox
The red fox depends on its eyes and ears to find its food. When it spots a mouse, it leaps high into the air and lands on the mouse with its paws and muzzle. *(hunts food)*

Man-of-war fish
Although other fish find the tentacles of the Portuguese man-of-war deadly, the small fish called the man-of-war fish lives among the tentacles without harm. Protected from larger fish that might eat it, the man-of-war fish does not leave its place of safety to find food. Instead it takes food caught in the man-of-war's tentacles. *(steals food)*

Alligator snapping turtle
This turtle uses its tongue to attract fish. At the tip of its tongue is a long thin strand of skin. Fish are fooled into thinking that the skin is a worm, and they swim after it into the turtle's mouth. *(tricks its food)*

Crocodile bird
Plagued by insects that live on its body, the crocodile gets help from the crocodile bird. The bird helps rid the crocodile of pests by feeding on the insects it finds. *(provides a service)*

Enrichment

Write the following poem on a Write It flip chart.

Little Names

What do you call a baby cat?
A kitten, of course;
Who doesn't know that?
But did you know
That's also the name
Of a wee rabbit, too—
Though he's nothing the same.
Little boy horses
Go by "colt"
And so do zebras—
But turkeys are "poults."

Pups are born to seals and dogs;
"Shoats" the term for little hogs.
Fawns are born to gentle does;
Calves are baby buffaloes.
Calves are also little whales
And little cows and elephants.
You call a baby fox a cub.
But what's the name for little ants?
Owlet, duckling, kid, and pup—
How many more can you think up?

By Elizabeth Abbott

Prepare index cards to help your student match mother animals with their babies. On the left side of each index card, write the name of a mother animal in uppercase letters. On the right side, write the name of the corresponding baby animal in lowercase letters. Cut the cards in half using a unique pattern for each card. Your student will be able to self-check his answers by fitting together the matching halves of each puzzle pattern. Instruct your student to read the poem and then match the animal cards. In addition to the animals discussed in the poem (i.e., CAT—kitten, RABBIT—kitten), you could include GOAT—kid, SHEEP—lamb, BEAVER—kit, BEAR—cub, SWAN—cygnet, FISH—fry, KANGAROO—joey, OSTRICH—chick, and GOOSE—gosling.

For Your Information

Animal behaviors are complex. The survival of some species, such as the honeybee, depends upon complicated social relationships such as exist in the honeybee hive. Other animals, such as the tiger, are solitary creatures.

Man is just beginning to understand the communication processes of animals. Many animals communicate by means of *pheromones,* or special hormones, which have only recently been studied. Each group of animals has specific ways of claiming territory, courting the females of its species, building its home, bringing up its young, obtaining food, and defending its personal space. In addition, animals operate according to daily and seasonal rhythms. Some animals are diurnal, or active in the day; others are nocturnal, or active at night.

Many animal behaviors are innate. Some are reflexes, or instant responses to something in the environment (such as a dog panting on a hot day); others are instincts, which are built-in reactions and knowledge (such as the way a Northern Oriole builds a special hanging nest). Other animal behaviors are learned. The mother oriole teaches her babies to fly when they are old enough, and when they leave the nest, she forces them to learn to find their own food. Though these behaviors may involve some instinct, they involve the learning process as well.

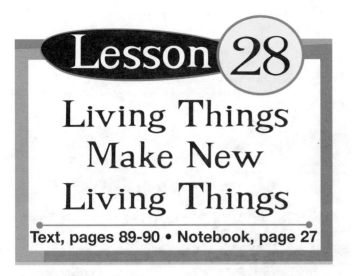

Lesson 28

Living Things Make New Living Things

Text, pages 89-90 • Notebook, page 27

Preview

Objective

Given proper instruction, your student will be able to

- Identify four characteristics of living things.

Materials

Have available

- A Write It flip chart
- 12 magazine pictures of different animals*
- 12 4" × 6" cards
- A Bible

Prepare

- The Write It flip chart by writing the following poem:

  What is a tiny treasure
  In a round and fragile box
  That has no lid or hinges,
  No keys or chains or locks?
  What keeps out wind and weather
  But lets in air and light?
  What keeps life safe a while
  But cannot hold it tight?
  What comes through many dangers
  And can roll without a nick,
  And yet will break apart
  At the tapping of a chick?
  　　　　by Dawn L. Watkins

- The 12 magazine pictures of different kinds of animals by cutting them out and gluing them on 4" × 6" cards. To make the activity self-checking, write the appropriate type of birth method (egg or mother's body) on the back of each card.

Lesson

Introducing the Lesson

Introduce the activity. Read the poem and ask your student to tell you what object is being described. *(egg)*

Direct the activity. Direct your student to sort the cards into two groups: animals whose babies hatch from eggs and animals whose babies grow inside the mother's body. Allow him to check his answers by looking at the back of each card. Tell him that in today's lesson he will learn about how living things make new living things.

Living Things Make New Living Things

The Bible says that living things bring forth after their kind. This means that apple trees produce apples. They will never make peaches or grapes. Dogs have puppies. They will never have kittens or lambs. It also means that living things make new living things.

Plants make new plants in different ways. Many plants make seeds. Then new plants grow from the seeds. Some plants make bulbs. Bulbs are tear-shaped stems, like onions. New plants grow from the bulbs. Sometimes a piece of a plant can grow into a new plant. Find the pictures of each way that plants make new plants.

89

Animals make baby animals in different ways. Many animals make eggs; then baby animals hatch from the eggs. Many animals make baby animals inside their bodies; then the baby animals are born. Find the pictures of each way.

90

Teaching the Lesson

Direct a text activity on pages 89-90. Use the following riddle to initiate your student's interest in what he is going to read: How are some plants like electric lights?

Continue with discussion questions. After your student completes his silent reading, use the following questions and statements as a guide to discuss the pages he read.

1. How are some plants like electric lights? *(They use bulbs.)*

2. Describe a flower bulb. *(tear-shaped stems, like onions)*

3. Read Genesis 1:21. What do you think "after their kind" means? *(Plants and animals can make only more plants and animals of the same species.)*

 God created all the living things on earth to follow a special plan—to make new living things (reproduce) "after their kind." (Bible Promise: I. God as Master) Because of this special plan, when the acorns fall from an oak tree, sprout, and grow, they will grow up into oak trees, not apple trees or pear trees. The baby bird that hatches from a large ostrich egg will be an ostrich, not an owl.

4. Name the three ways that plants can make new plants. *(from seeds, from bulbs, or from a piece of a plant, called a cutting)*

5. Look at the picture of the ostrich and its eggs on page 90. What animal will hatch out of each of these eggs? Why? *(ostriches, because an ostrich laid eggs to make more baby ostriches)*

6. Tell what you know about ostriches. *(Answers will vary depending upon your child's knowledge.)*

Living Things

Look at each picture. Put an *X* in the box below the words that best describe the picture.

	Moves	Has Needs	Responds	Makes New Living Things
				X
	X			
		X		
			X	
				X
	X			

Science 2
Notebook Packet

 You might want to share the following information with your child. Approximate Gestation Periods:

Hamster 16-19 days

Mouse 19-24 days

Rabbit 30 days

Skunk 62 days

Dog 63 days

Cat 63 days

Guinea pig 67-68 days

Lion 105-13 days

Sheep 143-59 days

Chimpanzee 227 days

Cow 280 days

Horse 330 days

Sperm whale 480-510 days

Elephant 607-730 days

9. Which do you think would take longer to grow inside its mother—a baby mouse or a baby elephant? Why? *(an elephant, because it is much larger than a mouse)*

 A mother elephant (cow) usually has only one baby at a time. When her calf is born, it weighs about two hundred pounds and stands about three feet tall. On the other hand, a mother mouse may have four to seven babies at one time. The mice are so small that each one could fit inside a teaspoon.

The ostrich is the largest living bird. Although it has feathers, it cannot fly. The eggs of the ostrich are large and can weigh as much as three pounds and measure about seven inches long.

7. Do you think that birds are the only animals that lay eggs? *(no)* Name some other animals that lay eggs. *(Some examples are fish, turtles, alligators, insects, frogs, and certain snakes and sharks.)*

8. What is another way that some animals make baby animals? *(inside their bodies)*

10. Name the characteristics of living things that you have learned so far. *(Living things move, have needs, respond, and make new living things.)*

11. Do you think that human babies hatch from eggs like those in your refrigerator or grow inside the mother's body and are born? *(grow inside the mother's body and are ready to be born after nine months)*

12. Do you think that new plants hatch from eggs like those inside your refrigerator or develop inside the mother plant? *(Plants do neither of these. They grow from seeds, from bulbs, or from cuttings of the root, stems, or leaves of other plants.)*

Evaluating the Lesson

Direct a notebook activity. Explain to your student that notebook page 27 reviews what he has learned from the last four science lessons. Point out the column of pictures on the left. Tell your student that he should look at each picture and decide which of the four characteristics on the right *best* describes it. Once he matches a picture to a characteristic, he should mark the box below with an *X*.

For Your Information

Marsupials are mammals that carry developing young in pouches on the outside of their bodies. Kangaroos, for example, give birth only thirty or so days after conception. The newborn kangaroo—about the size of a bee—has no eyes, ears, or back legs. This fragile bit of life travels to the mother's pouch by grasping her hair with its front feet and wiggling. When it reaches the pouch, it attaches itself to a mammary gland. There it continues to grow for several months. When it is fully developed, the joey begins to spend some time outside the pouch, playing and exploring. But until the joey is almost one-fourth his mother's size, the pouch remains a snug, safe retreat from the world.

The following paragraphs give information about interesting animals that lay eggs.

Green sea turtle: The only time the large green sea turtle leaves its ocean home is to lay eggs. During the night the mother turtle climbs up to the sandy beach, where she digs a large nest for her 100 or more eggs. Before the sun rises, the mother crawls back to the sea, leaving her eggs behind.

King cobra snake: Unlike most snakes, the king cobra builds a nest for her eggs. From the forest floor, the cobra gathers grass and leaves and builds a nest that may be 18 inches high. Within the nest there may be several chambers. The mother cobra lays her eggs in one of these chambers and then stays in an upper chamber to keep watch over her eggs.

Sunfish: The father sunfish begins early to prepare a nest for the eggs. By moving his tail like a fan, he clears a small bowl-shaped area at the bottom of a lake or stream. After the mother sunfish lays her eggs in the nest, she swims away, but the father sunfish stays and guards the eggs and provides them with extra air by fanning them. After the eggs hatch, the baby fish (fry) rise to the top of the water, and the father fish leaves them to care for themselves.

Monarch butterfly: During the fall of each year large groups of monarch butterflies fly south to spend the winter. They may travel over 2,000 miles to reach their southern home. When winter is over and spring arrives, it is time for the monarchs to make their return trip north. As they travel north, the mother monarchs lay their tiny pale eggs on milkweed plants along the way. No other plant is suitable since the monarch young eat only from the milkweed plant. A special sticky material laid with the eggs helps hold the eggs to the plants. When a mother monarch finishes laying all her eggs, she dies.

Lesson 29

Living Things Grow

Text, pages 91-92 • Notebook, pages 28-30

Preview

Objectives

Given proper instruction, your student will be able to
- Identify the four stages of a butterfly's life cycle.
- Properly sequence the four stages of a butterfly's life cycle.

Materials

Have available
- Baby record book and/or baby photographs of your student
- 1 current photograph of your student
- 1 bathroom scale
- 1 growth chart*
- Home Teacher's Edition, p. A12
- 1 egg carton
- Scissors
- Tape
- Glue
- 4 chenille wires*
- Crayons
- A Write It flip chart

Prepare
- The egg carton by cutting it into the following sections: Sections A, B, and C—1 compartment each; Section D—3 compartments (lengthwise); Section E—6 compartments (lengthwise). (See Figure 29-1.)
- The Write It flip chart with the names of the four stages—*egg, pupa, larva, adult butterfly*—of the butterfly's life cycle.

Lesson

Introducing the Lesson

Introduce the activity. Provide a bathroom scale, a growth chart, a current picture of your student, and a baby picture of him. Also make available the birth statistics about your student.

Direct the activity. Direct your student's attention to the Class Album Sheet (Appendix, page A12). Instruct your student to glue his pictures in the designated boxes on the page. Give him time to neatly copy his birth height and weight on the lines below his baby picture.

Continue the activity. Instruct your student to weigh himself on the bathroom scale. Point out that the needle on the scale should point to 0 before he measures his weight. Measure his current height by having him place his heels against the wall, aligning his body with the growth chart. Give him an opportunity to record his current height and weight on the record sheet.

Conclude the activity. Ask your student to tell how he knows that he has grown. *(He weighs more and is taller.)* Ask him how he thinks he will change as he grows older. *(He will grow taller, gain more weight, and develop stronger muscles for approximately ten more years.)* Direct your student's attention to the pictures on his record sheet. Instruct him to look at his photographs and describe some of the ways he has changed. *(Now he has more hair; his face is narrower; his face is longer; he is not as chubby.)* Comment that just as people grow and change, animals and plants grow and change. Tell your student that he will learn more about the changes of living things in today's lesson.

Living Things Grow

All living things get bigger. They grow. Have you grown? Do plants grow? Do animals grow? How can you tell?

Some baby animals and plant seedlings grow up faster than others. Those animals that do not need much help learning how to live grow up quickly.

Some baby animals and plant seedlings look like their parents. When they are born, baby cows and baby giraffes look like their parents. But tadpoles have to change as they grow to look like their parents. Caterpillars change too.

Rabbits can leave their mothers six weeks after they are born. And within six months they can have babies of their own.

91

Plants and animals grow in different ways. Plants grow all their lives, but animals stop growing at some point. Also, plants grow new parts and animals do not. Plants keep making buds that grow into branches and leaves. But animals always have the same number of parts. Cats have four legs and one tail. They do not grow any more. What would happen if all living things grew in the same way?

92

Teaching the Lesson

Direct a text activity on pages 91-92. Use the following question to initiate your student's interest in what he is going to read: Do all living things grow in the same way?

Continue with discussion questions. After your student completes his silent reading, use the following questions and statements as a guide to discuss the pages he read.

1. Name some other animals that grow up quickly. *(Some possible answers are insects, fish, snakes, and spiders).*

2. Do you think that these fast-growing animals need much help learning how to live? Why? *(No; God gives them the instincts that they need to survive on their own.)*

3. Name some animals that grow up slowly. *(Most mammals will grow up slowly and require some help learning how to live.)*

4. How do tadpoles change as they grow? *(They grow to become frogs.)*

This special type of changing growth is called *metamorphosis*. The following paragraph explains the different stages of a butterfly's life cycle. We recommend that you read the paragraph to your child using pictures from an encyclopedia, if possible, to show each stage described. As you read, write the name of each stage on the Write It flip chart.

A butterfly begins as an *egg* as small as the head of a pin. From it a *larva* (or caterpillar) hatches. The larva feeds continuously on leaves and other plant parts while it slowly moves about. In time it stops eating and begins looking for a place to rest. During this third stage of growth, the larva changes to a *pupa*. Unlike the caterpillar (larva) stage, the pupa does not eat or move about. The outer covering of the pupa is called a chrysalis (pronounced kris´ə•ləs). It may be rough, smooth, or fuzzy, and it is often colorful. Inside the chrysalis, the insect undergoes many changes. Finally, the *adult butterfly* breaks out of the chrysalis. It is equipped with large, delicate, and colorful wings that it uses for flying. When the adult butterfly feeds, it does not eat leaves; instead, it sips liquid nectar from flowers using its coiled, strawlike mouth.

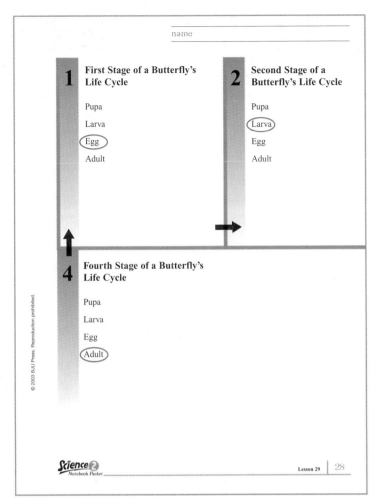

name

1 **First Stage of a Butterfly's Life Cycle**

Pupa

Larva

(Egg)

Adult

2 **Second Stage of a Butterfly's Life Cycle**

Pupa

(Larva)

Egg

Adult

4 **Fourth Stage of a Butterfly's Life Cycle**

Pupa

Larva

Egg

(Adult)

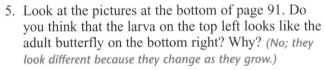

Science 2
Notebook Packet

Lesson 29 | 28

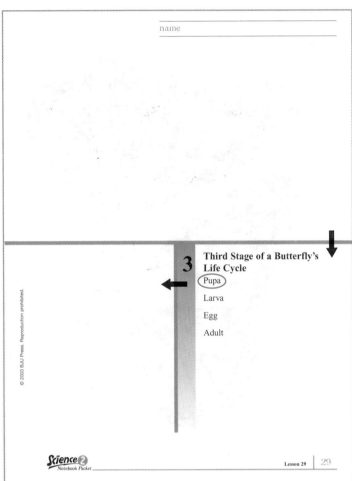

name

3 **Third Stage of a Butterfly's Life Cycle**

(Pupa)

Larva

Egg

Adult

Science 2
Notebook Packet

Lesson 29 | 29

5. Look at the pictures at the bottom of page 91. Do you think that the larva on the top left looks like the adult butterfly on the bottom right? Why? *(No; they look different because they change as they grow.)*

6. Which stage of the butterfly's growth is not pictured? *(The egg stage is not pictured.)*

7. Think back to the water cycle that you studied in Grade 1. What does the word *cycle* mean? Give some other examples of cycles. *(A cycle is something that happens over and over. The seasons of the year and the days of the week are both examples of cycles.)*

8. Name the four stages in the human life cycle. *(baby, child, teenager, adult)*

9. Name in order the four stages of the butterfly's life cycle. *(egg, caterpillar [or larva], pupa, and adult butterfly)*

10. Do animals grow new parts and grow all their lives as plants do? *(no)*

11. Look at the cartoon on page 92. How different would the world be if the growth of plants and the growth of animals were alike in every way? *(Some very unusual plants and animals would be formed.)*

Evaluating the Lesson

Introduce the activity. Direct your student's attention to notebook pages 28-30. Instruct him to remove pages 28-29, tape them together, and circle the correct answer next to each number.

Give your student four chenille wires and the sections of the egg carton. (*NOTE:* See Figure 29-1 as well as the *Materials* section at the beginning of this lesson.) Explain to your student that each of the five sections of the carton work together to represent one of the stages in a butterfly's life cycle.

Section A with one compartment represents the egg.

Sections B and C with one compartment each represent the pupa.

Section D with three compartments represents the adult butterfly.

Section E with six compartments represents the larva (caterpillar).

Direct the activity. Instruct your student to glue together the two sections of carton used for the pupa to make it look more like a chrysalis. Assist him in adding a chenille wire antennae for both the larva and butterfly sections of the carton. Instruct him to cut out the butterfly wings on page 30 and glue them to the butterfly section of his carton.

Conclude the activity. After your student assembles each of the egg carton stages, instruct him to glue each corresponding section in the space provided next to each numbered stage.

name

Science 2
Notebook Packet

Lesson 29 | 30

For Your Information

Summary of Differences Between Butterflies and Moths

Butterfly
Pupa in chrysalis
Adult antennae thin with knobs on ends
Adult body slender
Wings usually held vertically while at rest

Moth
Pupa in a spun silk cocoon
Adult antennae feathery
Adult body thick and often appears furry
Wings usually held horizontally while at rest

An organism grows as it takes nonliving materials and makes them into the living substances of its body. This process is different from the "growth" of things such as rocks or buildings. They are nonliving things and grow by having more material added to them. True growth is done *by* an organism, not *to* an organism. Digested food is re-assembled into the various parts of an animal's or human's body. Plants grow by taking in water and minerals from the soil and gases from the air and assembling them into the materials of the plant.

Growth does not always affect the size of an organism. It can mean simply the replacement of worn-out parts or the repair of injured parts. An adult does not continue to grow in size, but it does grow new cells and parts of cells until it dies.

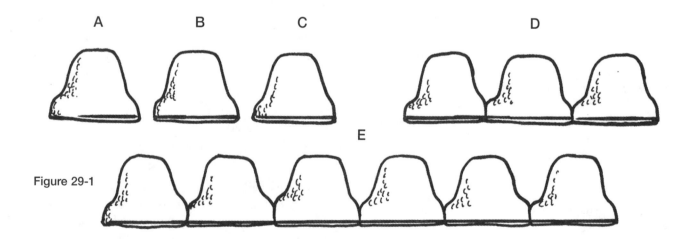

A   B   C   D

E

Figure 29-1

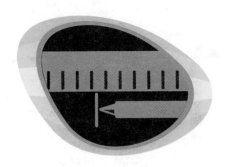

CHAPTER EIGHT

Lessons 30-33

How Long Is It?

In this chapter your student will learn various ways to measure objects using a variety of units of measure. Through discussions and activities he will learn that the two main reasons for measuring are to identify and to classify objects. Your student will have ample opportunity to identify and to classify common objects in the home and in nature.

Materials

The following items must be obtained or prepared before the presentation of the lesson. These items are designated with an * in the materials list in each lesson and in the Supplement. For further information see the individual lessons.

- 1 piece of poster board (Lesson 31)
- 1 4" × 6" card (Lesson 31)
- 1 meter stick (Lesson 31)
- 10 rocks ranging from about $\frac{1}{8}$" to more than 10" in diameter (Lesson 32)

8

Lesson 30

How Long Is It?

Text, pages 94-95 • Notebook, pages 31-32

Preview

Objective

Given proper instruction, your student will be able to

- Use units to measure.

Materials

Have available

- 1 package of paper clips
- Home Teacher's Edition, pp. A13-A17

Prepare

- The animal prints from the Home Teacher's Edition by cutting along the bold lines around each print. Hide the prints around the room.

Lesson

Introducing the Lesson

Introduce the activity. Tell your student that hidden throughout the room are a number of different animal prints. Instruct your student that at the signal *go* he should hunt for the animal prints. Allow time for him to examine the prints; then ask him to briefly describe each print. *(He may mention the shape, the number of toes, the presence or absence of claw marks, or the size of the print.)* Explain to your student that all of those points may be used to describe an animal print but that in this lesson he will pay special attention to size.

Direct the activity. Instruct your student to place the prints in categories according to size, matching all the large prints, all the small prints, etc. Tell your student that his animal prints are very close to the size of the actual prints that

these different animals make. Ask your student how he thinks the size of an animal print would help a tracker. *(The size of the print is one way people determine which animal made a certain print.)*

Beside one print that your student considers big, place another animal print that is bigger. Ask your student which print is bigger when he sees the two together. *(the bigger print)* Now beside a print that your student considers small, place another print that is smaller. Ask your student which print is small when he sees the two together. *(the smaller animal print)* Remind your student that the best way to describe big and small things is to measure them with a standard unit.

 If your child has difficulty comparing big and small things and sees everything that is larger than his own foot as big, allow him to use the largest track in the field guide as a point of comparison.

Continue the activity. Allow your student to select one animal print for you to attach to the wall where he can see it. Instruct him to hold a paper clip against the print, beginning with the bottom edge of the "heel." Tell your student to see how many paper clip widths it takes to cover the length of the animal print by placing the clips beside each other and "measuring off" the print to the outside edge of the "toe" of the print. (*NOTE:* See Figure 30-1.)

Figure 30-1

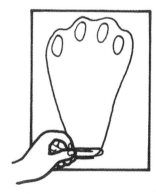

Ask your student how many paper-clip widths long his print is. (*"about _____ paper-clip widths long"*) Ask him what we call the activity he just completed. *(measuring)* Explain that he used each of the paper clips as a *unit*, or an amount, for measuring.

Conclude the activity. Instruct your student to measure a few more animal prints, using the paper clips as the units. Remind him to place the clips close together as he measures. Ask him which prints are as short as or shorter than one paper-clip width long. Ask him which print is the longest.

"I lifted up mine eyes again, and looked, and behold a man with a measuring line in his hand. Then said I, Whither goest thou? And he said unto me, To measure Jerusalem, to see what is the breadth thereof, and what is the length thereof."

Zechariah 2:1-2

Is a cow heavier than a horse? Is a semi truck longer than a train car? Is a train faster than a boat? How much lemonade will a pitcher hold? How can you find out? You measure.

94

How Do You Measure?

You use units to measure. An inch is a unit. So is a foot. A gallon and a pound are units too. Even the width of your finger can be a unit because a unit is an amount. How do people use units to measure?

When people measure, they compare a unit with something else to see how many units equal that thing.

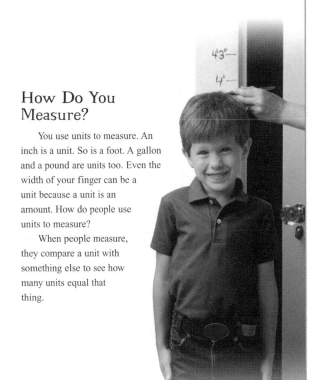

95

Ask your student which method of measuring he thinks is more accurate—just saying "big" or "small" or using the paper clip as a unit. *(using the paper clip as a unit)*

 Collect the prints for use in the enrichment activity and in Lesson 33.

Teaching the Lesson

Direct a text activity on pages 94-95. Use the following questions to initiate your student's interest in what he is going to read.

1. How can you tell whether a cow is heavier than a horse?

2. How can you tell how much lemonade a pitcher will hold?

Continue with discussion questions. After your student completes his silent reading, use the following questions and statements as a guide to discuss the pages he read.

1. How can you tell whether a cow is heavier than a horse? *(weigh both of them and compare their weights)*

2. How can you tell whether a tractor-trailer truck is longer than a train car? *(measure the lengths of both of them and compare their lengths)*

3. How can you tell whether a train is faster than a boat? *(clock the speed of both a train and a boat and compare the speeds)*

4. How can you tell how much lemonade a pitcher will hold? *(pour the contents of the pitcher into a measuring cup to see how much liquid the pitcher holds)*

5. Look at the picture on page 95. What measurement tool is being used? *(a growth chart)*

6. Name some units of measurement that you know. *(Answers will vary, but your student might include inch, foot, pound, gallon, quart, pint, liter, minute, hour, second, etc.)*

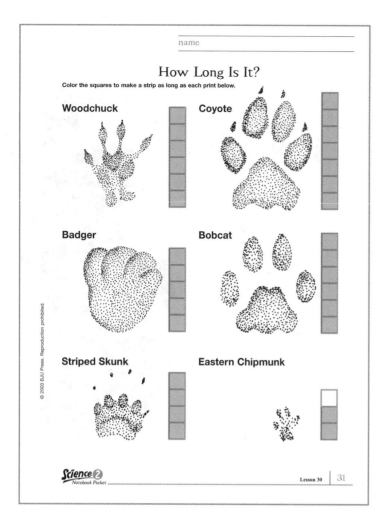

How Long Is It?

Color the squares to make a strip as long as each print below.

Woodchuck

Coyote

Badger

Bobcat

Striped Skunk

Eastern Chipmunk

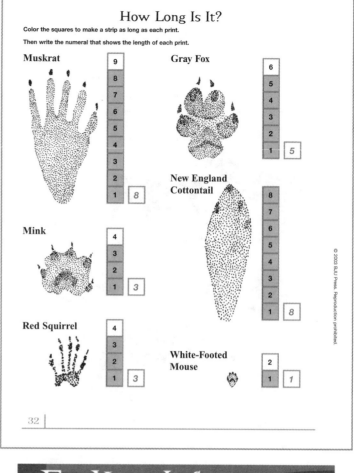

How Long Is It?

Color the squares to make a strip as long as each print.

Then write the numeral that shows the length of each print.

Muskrat — 8

Gray Fox — 5

Mink — 3

New England Cottontail — 8

Red Squirrel — 3

White-Footed Mouse — 1

Evaluating the Lesson

Direct the activity. Direct your student's attention to page 31 of his notebook packet. Instruct him to follow the directions on the page, coloring in the squares to correspond to the lengths of the prints.

Now direct his attention to page 32 of the notebook packet and instruct him to fill in each blank with the number that indicates the length of the print. (*NOTE:* Although each square measures one centimeter, we will not refer to the centimeter as a unit of measure in this lesson.)

Enrichment

Place your student's copies of the animal prints in a box. Write these instructions on the lid of the box: *Arrange the animal prints in order by length. Put the smallest print first and the largest print last.*

To illustrate how long a rod might have been years ago, you might allow your student to measure (in inches) his father's right foot. (See *For Your Information* below.) Then add several combinations of sixteen measurements to see how inaccurate the standard was.

For Your Information

Standards for a measurement must meet certain requirements. First it must have a constant value; it cannot vary. At one time, for example, a rod was determined as the combined length of the right feet of the first sixteen men coming out of church each Easter Sunday. Every year, then, the value changed.

Standards must also be easy to preserve. A Popsicle stick, for example, is not a good unit of measure. Standards must be easy to copy exactly. Otherwise everyone would have to use the original. And standards must be easy to use. They must suit the size of the measurement. It would be inconvenient, for instance, to use a yardstick to measure everything from grains of sand to football fields.

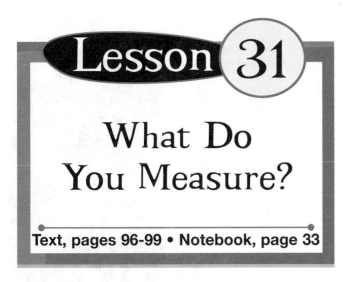

Lesson 31

What Do You Measure?

Text, pages 96-99 • Notebook, page 33

Preview

Objectives

Given proper instruction, your student will be able to
- Measure objects with a one-foot ruler.
- Measure objects with a centimeter ruler.

Materials

Have available
- A Write It flip chart
- 1 4" × 6" card*
- 1 one-foot ruler
- 1 centimeter ruler

 Often a ruler has inch/foot measurements on one side and centimeter measurements on the other side.

- 1 tape measure
- 1 piece of poster board*
- 1 yardstick
- 1 meter stick*
- Cellophane tape or masking tape

Prepare
- A 4" strip cut from a 4" × 6" card.

Lesson

Introducing the Lesson

Introduce the activity. Instruct your student to place his hand with his fingers spread apart against a page of the Write It flip chart. Draw a straight line reaching from his little finger across to his thumb (as illustrated on page 96 in the text) to indicate his span. Place your hand on a page of the Write It flip chart and draw a line to indicate your span. Ask your student why your line is longer than his line. *(Your hand is larger than his hand.)*

Give your student a 4" strip cut from a 4" × 6" card and tell him to fold it in half two times. When unfolded, the strip will have four spaces of the same size. Give time for your student to measure his science textbook with the unfolded strip to see how many small spaces the book measures.

Direct the activity. Give your student a one-foot ruler and ask him to examine it. Ask him whether he thinks that all one-foot rulers are the same length. Why? *(yes, because the foot is a standard unit of measure)* Ask him what the little marks with numbers above them are called. *(inches)* Direct your student to measure the length of a table using his one-foot ruler. Assist him with locating his starting and ending points as he measures.

Now place a yardstick next to the one-foot ruler on a table. Instruct your student to compare the yardstick with his one-foot ruler to see how many one-foot rulers equal one yardstick. *(three)* Ask your student to write an addition equation on the Write It flip chart to illustrate that three one-foot rulers would equal one yardstick. *(12 + 12 + 12 = 36)* Ask your student which he thinks would be better to use for measuring the length of the room—a one-foot ruler or a yardstick. Why? *(It is better to use a yardstick to measure long distances because more of the space could be measured at one time.)* Instruct your student to measure the length of a room using his yardstick.

Continue the activity. Select some small items from around the house for your student to measure. Hold up one of the objects, such as a pencil, and ask which unit—the inch, the foot, or the yard—would be best for measuring the pencil. *(the inch, because the foot and the yard are both much longer than the pencil)* Hold the pencil, eraser end on the table top, as your student holds his ruler next to it to measure the length of the pencil. Ask how many inches long the pencil is.

Conclude the activity. Show your student a meter stick and ask him what he thinks it looks like. *(a yardstick)* Place the meter stick next to the yardstick to compare their lengths. Ask which is longer. *(the meter stick)* Explain that in

In Bible times, one unit used for measuring was a span. A span is the length of the space between the tip of a man's thumb and the tip of his little finger.

Another unit used in Bible times was the cubit. A cubit is the length of the space from a man's elbow to the tip of his middle finger. Look at the man and his son measuring the same board. Will they get the same measurement? Why not?

The father and his son would not get the same measurement because the father's arm is longer than the son's arm. What could they do to get the same measurement? They could use units that are the same. Units that are the same are called standard units.

96

You could make a standard unit by folding a piece of paper in half two times. The folds would make four spaces of the same size. Suppose you measured your book with your standard unit and found it to be five standard units long by three standard units wide. Would you ask the clerk at the bookstore for a book cover to fit a book five standard units long by three standard units wide? Why not?

You could not use your standard unit when talking to the clerk at the bookstore because she would not know your standard unit. If you want to tell people how long or wide something is, you should use a standard unit that they know.

Can you name some standard units that people know?

97

countries that use the metric system the meter is used instead of the yard to measure large objects. Write the word *meter* on the Write It flip chart.

Allow your student to examine the meter stick. Point out the one hundred small numbered units and the *cm,* the symbol for *centimeter.* Write the word *centimeter* on the Write It flip chart and pronounce it with your student.

Cm is a short way to write *centimeter,* but it is not an abbreviation; that is why it does not end with a period.

Relate *centimeter* with *cents* by writing the following information on the Write It flip chart, underlining *cent* each time.

100 <u>cent</u>s = one dollar

100 <u>cent</u>imeters = one meter

Teaching the Lesson

Direct a text activity on pages 96-99. Use the following questions to initiate your student's interest in what he is going to read.

1. What is a span?
2. What is a cubit?
3. What is the best way to measure Mom's tablecloth?

Continue with discussion questions. After your student completes his silent reading, use the following questions and statements as a guide to discuss the pages he read.

1. What is a span? *(the length of the space between the tip of a man's thumb and the tip of his little finger)*
2. Is the span the same measurement for everybody in your family? Why? *(no, because the size of each person's hand is different)*
3. Is the span an accurate measurement? Why? *(no, because the measurement of each person's hand is different)*

4. What is a cubit? *(the length of the space from a man's elbow to the tip of his middle finger)*

5. Is the cubit the same for your father and for your grandfather? Why? *(no, because the length of each of their arms is different)*

6. Why do you think it is important to use standard units when measuring? *(so that everybody will get the same measurement; so the measurement will be accurate)*

7. Why couldn't you ask a clerk at a store for a book cover that is five standard units long and three standard units wide? *(The clerk would not know which standard units you used to measure your book.)*

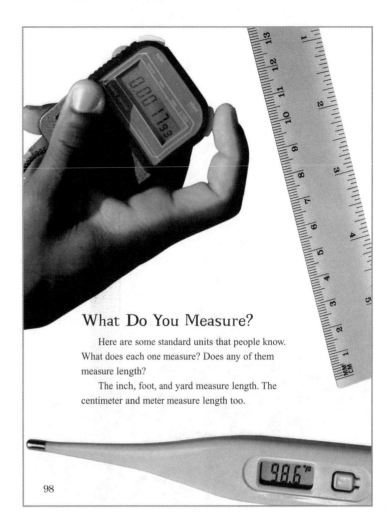

What Do You Measure?

Here are some standard units that people know. What does each one measure? Does any of them measure length?

The inch, foot, and yard measure length. The centimeter and meter measure length too.

98

Finding Out...

How to Measure Length

1. Get

    your foot ruler   your centimeter ruler

2. Get

    a pencil   your notebook page

3. Measure three objects in the room with your foot ruler.

4. Record the measurements on your notebook page.

5. Measure the same three objects in the room with your centimeter ruler.

6. Record the measurements on your notebook page.

99

---

name

What Do You Measure?

Use your foot ruler to measure these things.
Record the results.

Answers will vary.

1. Your shoe

    _____

2. Your largest book

    _____

3. Your smallest pencil

    _____

Use your centimeter ruler to measure these things.
Record the results.

Answers will vary.

1. A piece of chalk

    _____

2. The wall from floor to window

    _____

3. The width of that window

    _____

Science 2
Notebook Packet

Lesson 31   33

Evaluating the Lesson

Direct a *Finding Out* activity on page 99 and notebook page 33. Instruct your student to follow the directions given on page 99 to measure things around the house with his one-foot ruler and with his centimeter ruler. After he finishes measuring and recording his findings, allow him to display his notebook page on the refrigerator or on a family bulletin board.

Enrichment

On a table that you have pushed against the wall, set a house plant that grows vertically (as opposed to a trailing plant like ivy). Affix a tape measure to the wall with the one-inch end even with the top of the dirt in the pot. Tape or glue Ernie Inchworm to a large paper clip that you can slide up the measuring tape as the plant grows. *(NOTE:* See Figure 31-1.) Alongside the tape measure affix a strip of paper on which you can mark the height of the plant at intervals.

For Your Information

The inchworm (or measuring worm or looper) is really the caterpillar of the cankerworm moth family. It makes a delicate cocoon in the ground.

The inchworm moves by bringing its hind feet up to its front feet and then stretching itself forward and bringing its hind feet up again. The movement makes it look as if it were measuring. An old superstition held that an inchworm on a person was a bad sign: the worm was measuring him for a shroud.

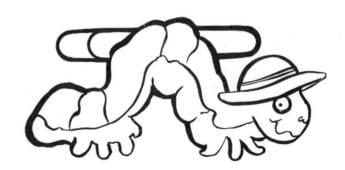

Figure 31-1

Lesson 32

Why Do You Measure?

Text, pages 100-103 • Notebook, page 34

Preview

Objective

Given proper instruction, your student will be able to

- Classify rocks by measuring them.

Materials

Have available

- 1 one-foot ruler
- 1 centimeter ruler
- 1 pencil
- 1 paper plate or plastic meat tray
- Large assortment of buttons
- 10 rocks ranging from about $\frac{1}{8}$" to more than 10" in diameter*

Introducing the Lesson

Introduce a classifying activity. Give your student a paper plate and fifteen assorted buttons. Tell him to sort the buttons into three groups any way he likes. Do not give your student any criteria for his classifying.

Ask your student to show his buttons and to explain why he divided them as he did—by color, type, shape, or size. Tell your student that he will learn more about classifying in the following steps.

You might want to display the buttons by groups. Give your child some stiff cardboard or fabric-covered board and ask him to form a design with the buttons of each group. Attach the buttons with clear silicon sealant.

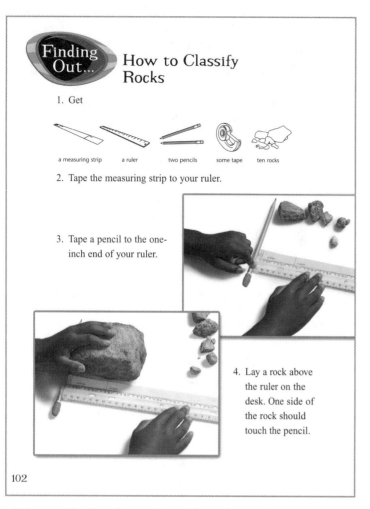

Finding Out... How to Classify Rocks

1. Get

a measuring strip   a ruler   two pencils   some tape   ten rocks

2. Tape the measuring strip to your ruler.

3. Tape a pencil to the one-inch end of your ruler.

4. Lay a rock above the ruler on the desk. One side of the rock should touch the pencil.

5. Hold another pencil against the other side of the rock.

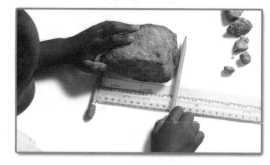

6. Look at the measuring strip. Record the type of each rock on your notebook page.

7. Display your rocks.

Direct a *Finding Out* activity. Direct your student's attention to pages 102-3. Read through the steps orally as your student follows along in his book. Assist your student as he gathers his materials, makes his calipers, and measures his rocks.

To make a measuring strip for the *Finding Out* activity:

1. Cut a strip of paper two inches by eleven inches.
2. Draw a line parallel to the eleven-inch side of the paper one-half inch from the edge.
3. Draw four perpendicular lines from the edge of the paper to the parallel line using the following measurements:

      one-eighth inch from end
      one-quarter inch from end
      two and one-half inches from end
      ten inches from end.

4. Label the sections as shown below.

sand grain	pebble	cobble		boulder
1" **end**		Tape this part to back of ruler		

name _____

Measure to Classify

Answers will vary.

Types of rock	Put an X in the correct box for each rock that you measure.										
sand											
grain											
pebble											
cobble											
boulder											

Types of rock	Put an X in the correct box for each rock that you measure.										
sand											
grain											
pebble											
cobble											
boulder											

Answers will vary.

Science 2
Notebook Packet

Lesson 32 | 34

Why Do You Measure?

Tell why the people are measuring length in these pictures.

A carpenter measures to make things fit together. An artist measures to make things fit into a certain space. A sports judge measures to see who wins.

100

Conclude the activity. Direct your student's attention to page 34 of the notebook packet. Assist your student if necessary with the recording of the type of rock on the top half of the notebook page. (*NOTE:* See *Evaluating the Lesson* for use of the bottom of the notebook page.) When your student finishes measuring and recording the width of all his rocks, he will have a chart that tells how many of each type of rock he has.

Teaching the Lesson

Direct a text activity on pages 100-103. Use the following questions to initiate your student's interest in what he is going to read.

1. Why do people measure things?
2. How can the measurement of a rock determine what kind of rock it is?

Continue with discussion questions. After your student completes his silent reading, use the following questions and statements as a guide to discuss the pages he read.

1. Look at the pictures on page 100. What is being measured in each picture and why? *(The carpenter is measuring the pieces of wood to make sure they fit together properly. The artist is measuring the space on his paper to make sure his drawings will fit. The sports judge is measuring the length of the jump to see who the winner is.)*
2. Name some other people who measure length as a part of their jobs. *(seamstresses, salespeople, nurses, carpet layers)*
3. What is classifying? *(putting things into groups)*
4. What is the correct way to measure a rock? *(measure across it at the widest spot)*

Why do scientists measure length? Sometimes scientists measure length to put things into groups. When they do that, they are classifying. Measuring length helps scientists classify rocks.

When scientists measure a rock, they measure across it at the biggest spot. They use a special tool called a caliper. Look at the picture of someone using a caliper on a rock. Can you see how it is used?

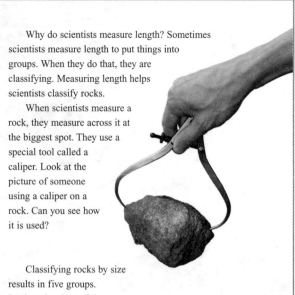

Classifying rocks by size results in five groups. Look at the chart of the groups.

Boulders	>10 inches across
Cobbles	$2\frac{1}{2}$ inches to 10 inches
Pebbles	$\frac{1}{4}$ inch to $2\frac{1}{2}$ inches
Granules	$\frac{1}{8}$ inch to $\frac{1}{4}$ inch
Sand	$<\frac{1}{8}$ inch

101

5. What is the name of the tool pictured on page 101? *(a caliper)*

6. Which is smaller—a pebble or a cobble? *(pebble)*

7. What kind of rock is more than 10 inches across? *(boulder)*

Evaluating the Lesson

Direct an evaluating activity. To check the measuring, fold your student's notebook page in half on the center line in order to conceal his measurements. This time you or another family member will measure the rocks and record the results on the chart on the bottom half of the page. When the measuring is finished, your student should compare his measurements with your measurements. If any of the numbers are different, try to find out why. Together measure again those rocks whose measurements were different for you and for your student.

Make available some blank books for giving your student more practice with classifying. One set of books might have the following titles: *Huge Things* and *Tiny Things*. Another set might be called *Tall Things* and *Short Things*. Provide scissors, glue, and some magazines from which your student may cut appropriate pictures for pasting on the blank pages of the various books.

For Your Information

Some quantities cannot be described or defined in terms of smaller or simpler parts. These quantities are called the *fundamental properties* of nature. The only way to describe such quantities is by how they are measured.

Three fundamental properties are length, mass, and time. Other quantities such as speed and volume are called *derived units* because they are combinations of fundamental units.

Lesson 33

Why Do You Measure?

Text, page 104 • Notebook, page 35

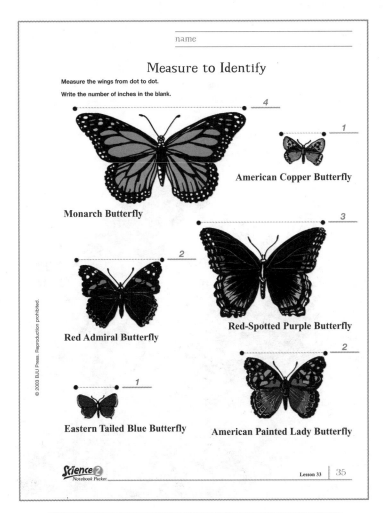

name _____

Measure to Identify

Measure the wings from dot to dot.

Write the number of inches in the blank.

4

Monarch Butterfly

1

American Copper Butterfly

2

Red Admiral Butterfly

3

Red-Spotted Purple Butterfly

1

Eastern Tailed Blue Butterfly

2

American Painted Lady Butterfly

Science 2
Notebook Packet

Lesson 33 | 35

Preview

Objective

Given proper instruction, your student will be able to

- Identify animal prints by measuring.

Materials

Have available

- 1 one-foot ruler
- 1 centimeter ruler
- Home Teacher's Edition, pp. A18-A21

Prepare

- The Field Guide from the Home Teacher's Edition by stapling it together to make it usable for your student.

Lesson

Introducing the Lesson

Direct a notebook activity on page 35. Select a couple of butterflies from the page and ask your student to describe them to you. Then instruct him to follow the directions on the page to measure each butterfly. Which two factors did he use as part of his scientific identification? *(description and measurement)* Ask him to name the two butterflies whose wingspans measure two inches. *(the American Painted Lady Butterfly and the Red Admiral Butterfly)* Ask what descriptions would help to tell the differences between the two butterflies. *(The American Painted Lady Butterfly has more color and design on its wings.)*

 At this point, you might want to look up these varieties of butterflies in an encyclopedia.

Conclude the activity. Ask your student why scientists measure. *(to identify and to classify)* Tell your student that in today's lesson, he will learn more about why we measure.

Sometimes scientists measure length to find out which group things belong to. When they do that, they are identifying. Measuring length helps scientists identify trees, butterflies, and prints.

When scientists measure a leaf, they measure its length from top to bottom. Ponderosa pines have needles five to eight inches long. Loblolly pines have needles six to nine inches long. And long-leaf pines have needles eight to eighteen inches long.

104

Make available a variety of identification books about butterflies, insects, animal prints, leaves, trees, rocks, etc. Include some empty shoeboxes into which your student may put specimens that he collects for identification. From time to time, you may want to take your student on a leaf or insect hunt to collect specimens for measuring and identifying.

For Your Information

At best, all measurements are approximations. They have to be made by human beings with less-than-perfect instruments. To minimize inaccuracy, you should do a measurement several times and record the average.

The *precision* of your measurements can be checked. First, find the difference between all individual measurements and the average. Then add the differences and divide by the number of times you took measurements. The result is the average of the individual differences.

Teaching the Lesson

Direct a text activity on page 104. Use the following question to initiate your student's interest in what he is going to read: How do you correctly measure a leaf?

Continue with discussion questions. After your student completes his silent reading, use the following questions and statements as a guide to discuss the pages he read.

1. How do you correctly measure a leaf? *(by measuring its length from top to bottom)*

2. Look at the picture on page 104. Judging from the length of the needles, what kind of pine do you think this is? *(ponderosa pine)*

Evaluating the Lesson

Introduce the activity. Give your student the animal prints and the Field Guide. Remind him that he will have to think about what the print looks like, as well as how long it is, in order to identify it.

Direct the activity. Instruct your student to measure each print in centimeters and to write the measurement near the track. He should then refer to the Field Guide to assist him in deciding which animal made each print. Instruct him to write the name of the animal near the track also.

CHAPTER NINE

Lessons 34-37

How Earth Moves

These lessons show the importance of the earth's rotation in relation to day and night, time zones, and the seasons. Your student will learn to differentiate between the earth's rotation and its revolution around the sun. This chapter will also introduce the calendar, its division into months and seasons, and leap year.

Materials

The following items must be obtained or prepared before the presentation of the lesson. These items are designated with an * in the materials list in each lesson and in the Supplement. For further information see the individual lessons.

- 1 globe† (Lessons 34 and 36)
- Plastic tack (Lesson 34)
- 4 electric or spring-wound clocks (Lesson 35)
- 1 Judy Mini-Clock† (Lesson 35)
- 1 basketball or volleyball (Lessons 35 and 36)
- 1 large United States map† (Lesson 35)
- Several calendars, with at least one being for a year whose number is divisible by four—1992, 1996, 2000, 2004, etc. (Lesson 37)

9

137

Lesson 34

Day and Night

Text, pages 106-8 • Notebook, page 36

Objective

Given proper instruction, your student will be able to

- Demonstrate that the rotation of the earth causes night and day.

Materials

Have available

- 1 globe*†
- 1 flashlight
- Plastic tack*
- 1 large paper plate (10" to 12")
- 1 small paper plate (6" to 8")
- Metal brads
- 1 black or dark blue crayon
- A Write It flip chart

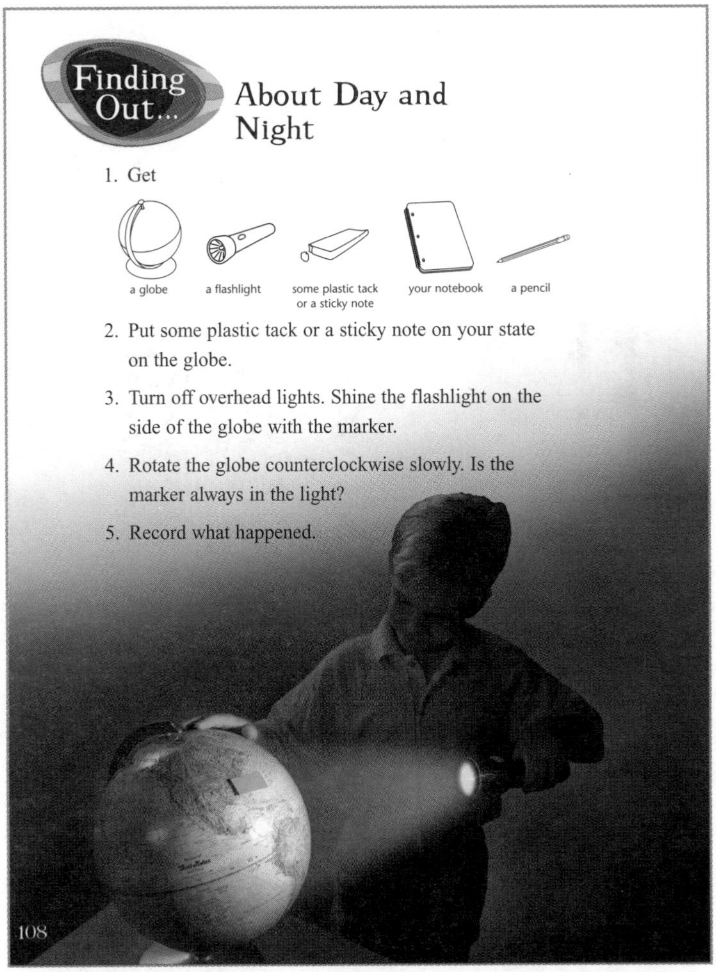

Finding Out... About Day and Night

1. Get

a globe | a flashlight | some plastic tack or a sticky note | your notebook | a pencil

2. Put some plastic tack or a sticky note on your state on the globe.
3. Turn off overhead lights. Shine the flashlight on the side of the globe with the marker.
4. Rotate the globe counterclockwise slowly. Is the marker always in the light?
5. Record what happened.

108

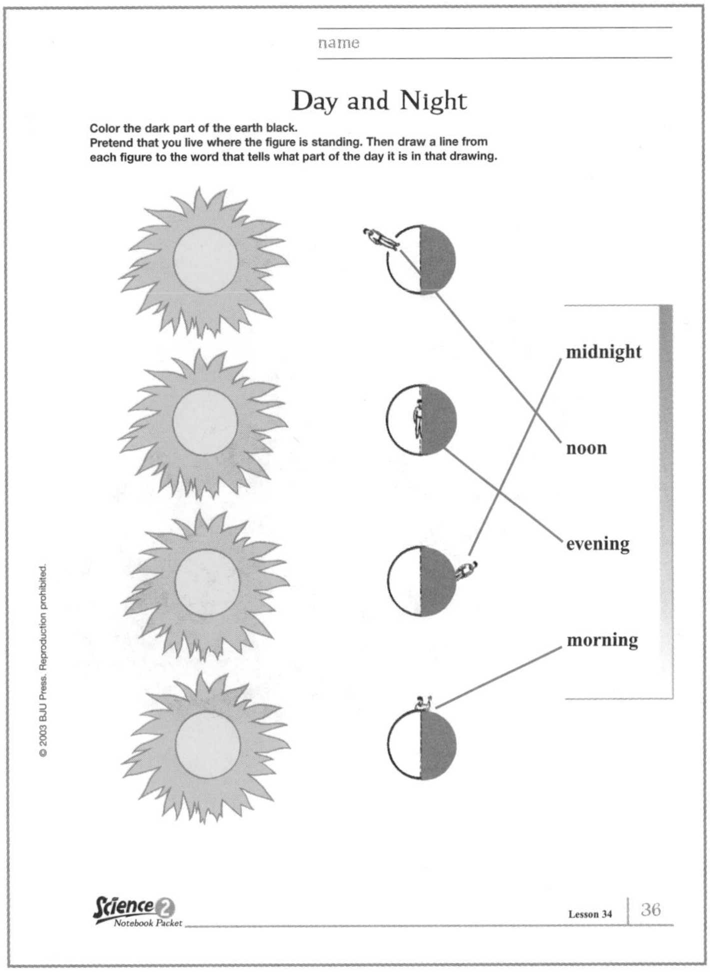

name

Day and Night

Color the dark part of the earth black.
Pretend that you live where the figure is standing. Then draw a line from each figure to the word that tells what part of the day it is in that drawing.

midnight
noon
evening
morning

© 2003 BJU Press. Reproduction prohibited.

Science 2 Notebook Packet — Lesson 34 | 36

Lesson

Introducing the Lesson

Introduce the activity. Ask your student to demonstrate different ways of moving yet staying in one place. *(hopping, jumping, marching in place, spinning around)* Ask whether he knows which way of moving is called rotation. *(spinning around)* Instruct your student to stand and slowly turn around. Explain that the earth moves like that, making one full turn every day. Write *rotation* on the Write It flip chart and direct your student to repeat the word after you.

Direct a *Finding Out* activity on page 108. Read the steps with your student. Place the globe where he can see it; then rotate it slowly, counterclockwise. Explain that the earth moves like that, around and around, all the time.

At certain points as your student rotates the globe, ask him whether the plastic tack (the place where he lives) is in the light or in the darkness. Ask him whether he thinks that the light curves around to the back of the globe. Why not? *(It does not curve around to the back of the globe because light travels in a straight line.)*

Continue the activity. Ask your student what the light time is called *(day)* and what the dark time is called. *(night)* When the plastic tack is in the center of the light, ask him to tell what people call that time. *(noon)* What name is given to the time when your area is just moving into the darkness? *(evening)* When the plastic tack is in the center of the darkness, ask him what we call that time. *(midnight)* What name is given for the time when your area is just moving into the light? *(morning)*

Conclude the activity. Direct your student's attention to notebook page 36. Instruct him to follow the instructions on the page and to color the dark part of the globe in each picture; then match the picture with the word that tells what that time is.

If time permits, discuss what would be different if the earth did not rotate. *(One half would be light all the time, and one half would be dark. Plants could grow on one half, but not on the other.)*

Can you move but stay in one place? Yes, you jump and hop. Can you move from place to place? Yes, you can skip and run. You move in many different ways.

The earth moves in different ways too. But it does not hop or jump or skip. Do you know how it does move?

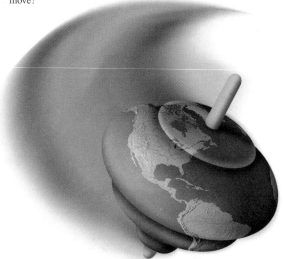

A Rotating Earth

The earth spins like a top. It goes around and around. It rotates. What other things rotate? Does a globe? Does a merry-go-round?

Because the earth rotates, there is a time of light and a time of darkness. The times of light and darkness happen over and over. Each cycle of light and darkness is called one day.

"And God called the light Day, and the darkness he called Night. And the evening and the morning were the first day."   Genesis 1:5

Teaching the Lesson

Direct a text activity on pages 106-8. Use the following question to initiate your student's interest in what he is going to read: Which cycle changes time but does not take you anywhere?

Continue with discussion questions. After your student completes his silent reading, use the following questions and statements as a guide to discuss the pages he read.

1. Which movements can you make without moving to a different place? *(hopping, jumping, running or walking in place, moving your arms)*

2. Who created the sun, the moon, the stars, and the earth and started all of those things in motion? *(God)*

3. What did God name the light time? *(day)* What did He name the dark time? *(night)*

4. What is a cycle? *(something that happens over and over again)*

5. Which cycle changes time but does not take you anywhere? *(the cycle of light and darkness that we call a day)*

6. What is the earth shaped like? *(a ball)*

7. Where do people live on the earth? *(all around the surface of the ball-shaped earth)*

8. What do we use as a model of the earth? *(a globe)*

9. Where is the North Pole? *(at the "top" of the earth)*

10. Where is the South Pole? *(at the "bottom" of the earth)*

Evaluating the Lesson

Introduce the activity. Give your student a large and a small paper plate, a black or dark blue crayon, and a metal brad. Instruct your student to draw a line across the middle of the large plate and then to color one half of the plate black (or dark blue). On the edge of the small plate, your student should choose a spot and draw a small figure to represent himself. He should then draw a curved arrow that points counterclockwise. (*NOTE:* See Figure 34-1.)

Figure 34-1

Demonstrate how your student should attach the small plate on top of the large plate with a metal brad through the center of both plates. Wiggle the brad so that the small plate can move freely.

Direct the activity. As your student looks at his plates, tell him to pretend that the metal brad is the North Pole. Ask him to guess what each plate would represent if he were looking down at the North Pole. *(The small plate is the earth, and the large plate is light and darkness or night and day.)*

Conclude the activity. Remind your student that he drew a figure on his earth to represent himself. Tell him that you will give him a word and that he should rotate his earth plate the way the arrow is pointing so that his figure is standing where it is that time of day or night. Demonstrate how he should have his figure stand in the middle of the white side when you say *noon.* Then give him the following times—midnight, morning, evening, night, day, lunch time, supper time, breakfast time—and give him opportunity to set his "earth clock." Check the time on the "clock" as you go along. Continue the activity until your student demonstrates that he understands that the earth's rotation brings about night and day.

There are proofs—occurrences that can be explained only one way—that the earth rotates. One proof is the slightly bulging shape of the earth. Planets that are spinning slowly are the most nearly round. Earth is slightly flattened at the poles and bulged at the equator.

Another proof is the way long-range projectiles move. Missiles launched from earth have to be aimed ahead of or behind their targets in order to hit them. If the earth were not moving, such *leading* of targets would not be necessary.

The best proof, of course, is direct observation. The astronauts on the moon could see different parts of the earth facing them every day. The moon does not travel fast enough to have given them these views. The only explanation is that the earth rotates.

Lesson 35

Time Zones

Text, pages 109-10 • Notebook, page 37

Preview

Objective

Given proper instruction, your student will be able to

- Demonstrate the time differences across the United States.

Materials

Have available

- 4 electric or spring-wound clocks*
- 1 Judy Mini-Clock*†
- 1 basketball or volleyball*
- 1 large map of the United States*†
- 2 sheets of construction paper

Prepare

- The four clocks by setting one at the correct time and the others at three different times, one hour apart (i.e., 8 o'clock, 9 o'clock, 10 o'clock, 11 o'clock). Place the clock with the earliest time at your student's left and the other three clocks in time order across the room. Each clock will represent one of the four time zones in the United States throughout the day or as long as you prefer.
- Cut both sheets of construction paper in half; then fold each section in half again. Write one of the names of the time zones on each section of construction paper to stand up in front of the time-zone clocks.

Introducing the Lesson

Introduce the activity. Give your student a basketball, instructing him to represent the sun. Direct him to stand to the right of you (the east), holding the ball over his head. Ask him what time he thinks the clock should read when the sun is directly overhead. *(12:00 noon)* Instruct the "sun" to walk slowly across the front of the room, holding the ball over his head as he walks, and stopping when you tell him. Stop him in front of each clock, asking him to tell what each clock should read when the sun is directly overhead. *(12:00 noon)*

Direct the activity. Set up the large United States map and outline with your hands the four time zones of the continental United States as illustrated on the map on page 110 in the textbook. (Do not include Alaska and Hawaii.) As you point out each zone, instruct your student to place a time-zone label in front of each clock. (Eastern, Central, Mountain, and Pacific)

Though we refer to the names of the time zones, it is not necessary for your child to learn these names at this time.

Continue the activity. Direct your student's attention to the clocks set up in the room, and tell him that each clock represents a time zone in the United States. Read the labels giving the names of the zones if you wish. Ask your student to examine the time set on each clock and to read each time for you. Ask him what the difference in time is from one clock to another. *(The clocks are exactly one hour apart.)* Assist him in figuring out what the difference in time is from the clock on the far left of the room to the clock on the far right of the room. *(The clock on the far left of the room is three hours earlier than the one on the far right.)* Ask your student to tell what he usually does at the time that each clock indicates. *(Answers will depend on the time you begin this activity and how you structure your school day.)*

Conclude the activity. Instruct your student to set his mini-clock to 6:00. Assist him in figuring out at what time each of the other time-zone clocks should be set. Assist him in setting each of the wind-up or electric clocks to represent each of the four time zones in the continental United States. (*NOTE:* From the left to the right, each time is one hour later than the one before it; therefore your student needs to add one hour to each clock as he progresses to the right.)

Because the earth rotates, the sun seems to move across the sky. The sun seems to move across the sky fourteen miles each minute. When the sun is right overhead, we say the clock time is noon. But the United States is so big that the states cannot all have the sun right overhead at the same time. So how do we decide when noon is in each state?

To make telling time easier, the whole earth is divided into twenty-four bands. They are called time zones. All the clocks in each band have the same time.

109

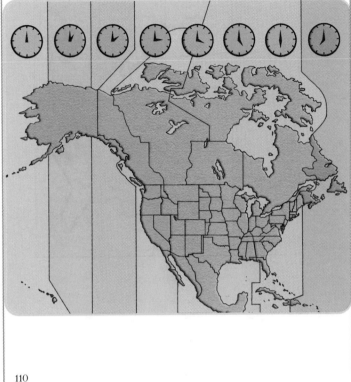

Look at the map. How many time zones are in Canada? How many are in the United States? How many are on this map?

110

Teaching the Lesson

Direct a text activity on pages 109-10. Use the following questions to initiate your student's interest in what he is going to read.

1. Which time zone do you live in?
2. What does the illustration on page 109 mean?

Continue with discussion questions. After your student completes his silent reading, use the following questions and statements as a guide to discuss the pages he read.

1. Why does the sun seem to move across the sky?
   (because the earth rotates)

2. Why are there so many different time zones in the United States? *(The land is so big that all places in it cannot have the sun directly overhead at the same time.)*

3. How many time zones are there for the whole earth? *(twenty-four)*

4. Look at the map on page 110. How many time zones are there in Canada? *(six)*

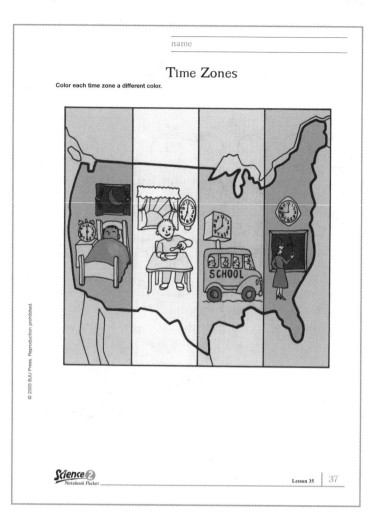

name _____

Time Zones

Color each time zone a different color.

© 2003 BJU Press. Reproduction prohibited.

Science 2
Notebook Packet _____   Lesson 35 | 37

Enrichment

In a convenient space, set up the United States map with four clocks arranged at the different time zones. Also place an electric clock set at the correct time in your own time zone. Encourage your student to periodically set all the clocks to correspond with the time in his time zone. If you have family members or friends living in these other time zones, your student could "report" what time it is where Grandma lives, where Uncle Bill lives, and so on.

For Your Information

The circles of longitude divide the earth into the twenty-four time zones. Each zone is 15 degrees wide. The 180-degree meridian is the International Date Line. If you cross the Date Line going east, you subtract a day. If you cross it going west, you add a day. The prime meridian passes through Greenwich, England. Traveling west from the prime meridian, you lose one hour per meridian crossed until you reach the International Date Line.

Evaluating the Lesson

Direct an evaluating activity on notebook page 37. Instruct your student to color each time zone on the United States map a different color. Set the mini-clock at a certain time. Instruct your student to set one of his clocks for the same time as yours and to set the rest of the clocks for each of the time zones in the continental United States. As soon as your student finishes setting his clocks, check each one to see whether the times are correct.

144 | Chapter 9

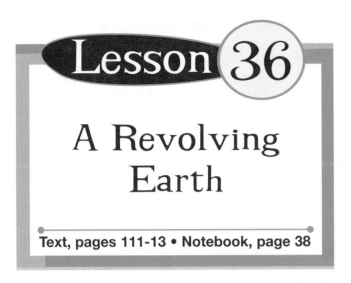

Lesson 36

A Revolving Earth

Text, pages 111-13 • Notebook, page 38

A Revolving Earth

The earth travels around the sun. It revolves. What other things revolve? What happens because the earth revolves?

111

Preview

Objectives

Given proper instruction, your student will be able to

- Demonstrate revolving and rotating.
- Mark the parts of the earth where the sun shines during various stages of the earth's revolution.

Materials

Have available

- 1 basketball or volleyball*
- 1 globe*†
- A Write It flip chart
- Home Teacher's Edition, p. A22

Prepare

- Page A22 of the Home Teacher's Edition by cutting out the symbols of the seasons.

Lesson

Introducing the Lesson

Introduce the activity. Ask your student to define *rotate* and to tell you some examples of things that rotate. *(to spin all the way around; the earth, a top, a globe, a merry-go-round, a record)* Then ask him to demonstrate how something rotates.

Direct the activity. Place a volleyball or a basketball in the center of an open space outdoors. Tell your student that he should pretend that the ball is the sun. Ask him to represent the earth, standing about six feet away from the ball and rotating as the earth does, slowly, for one full turn. Ask your student what happens on the earth during that one full turn. *(Earth experiences one day and one night.)*

Conclude the activity. Tell your student that the earth also moves in another way. Instruct him to walk in a circular path around the ball, and explain that his movement is called revolving. Tell your student that while the earth is revolving, it is also rotating. Ask your student to try to demonstrate that combination of movements—rotating and revolving.

Teaching the Lesson

Direct a text activity on pages 111-13. Use the following questions to initiate your student's interest in what he is going to read.

1. How long do you think it takes the earth to revolve around the sun one time?
2. What happens because the earth revolves?

Continue with discussion questions. After your student completes his silent reading, use the following questions and statements as a guide to discuss the pages he read.

1. Besides the earth, what things revolve? *(Answers will vary: a tetherball, a toy airplane on a string, merry-go-round horses, etc.)*
2. How long does it take the earth to rotate one full turn? *(one day and night, or twenty-four hours)*

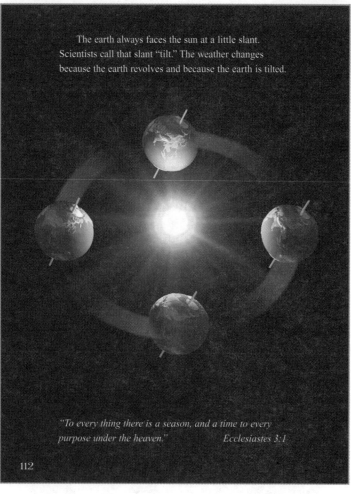

The earth always faces the sun at a little slant. Scientists call that slant "tilt." The weather changes because the earth revolves and because the earth is tilted.

"To every thing there is a season, and a time to every purpose under the heaven." Ecclesiastes 3:1

3. What do scientists call the slant of the earth? *(tilt)*

 You can illustrate the tilt of the earth by showing a globe and pointing out the way it is suspended on its stand. God created the earth, started it in motion, and designed the motion and the tilt to cause the different seasons of each year. (Bible Promise: I. God as Master)

4. What are the results of the earth's movement and its tilt? *(weather changes, seasons, and the passing of the year)*

5. Name the four seasons in order as they appear at the beginning of each new year. *(winter, spring, summer, and fall [autumn])*

As your child names each season, write its name on the Write It flip chart, forming a circle of seasons. (*NOTE:* See Figure 36-1.)

6. Describe the weather that you think of for each season. *(Answers will vary depending upon the region in which you live.)*

7. Do the seasons always come in the same order? What name is given to something that happens over and over again in the same pattern? *(Yes, the seasons are always in the same order. It is called a cycle.)*

 You and your child might enjoy making a list of the special days and holidays in each season. You may refer to a calendar for a monthly listing of holidays. Then glue one of the season symbols from page A22 of the Home Teacher's Edition on each month's calendar page to indicate the season.

Figure 36-1

name

A Revolving Earth

Think about where the sun shines as the earth revolves around it. Cut out the darkened figures and paste them to show where no light is shining on the earth figures.

Science 2
Notebook Packet

Lesson 36 | 38

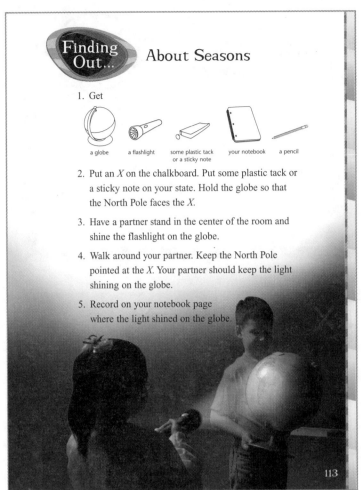

Finding Out... About Seasons

1. Get

a globe   a flashlight   some plastic tack or a sticky note   your notebook   a pencil

2. Put an *X* on the chalkboard. Put some plastic tack or a sticky note on your state. Hold the globe so that the North Pole faces the *X*.

3. Have a partner stand in the center of the room and shine the flashlight on the globe.

4. Walk around your partner. Keep the North Pole pointed at the *X*. Your partner should keep the light shining on the globe.

5. Record on your notebook page where the light shined on the globe.

113

Evaluating the Lesson

Introduce the activity. Direct your student's attention to the *Finding Out* activity on page 113. Read the steps with your student and allow him to help you gather the necessary materials. Follow directions to prepare the globe and mark the Write It flip chart.

Direct the activity. You will need to take the part of the science partner, shining the flashlight on the globe. Encourage your student to keep the globe with the North Pole pointed toward the *X* on the Write It flip chart at all times as he walks. Tell your student to mark on his notebook page each place on the globe where the light shines.

Conclude the activity. When your student finishes his notebook page, discuss the markings on the globe and check to see whether your student correctly transferred to the page what he saw in the demonstration.

For Your Information

Solstice means "sun stop." In the summer and winter solstices, the sun appears to stand still over the Tropic of Cancer (summer) and the Tropic of Capricorn (winter). On these dates the sun seems to reverse its direction, starting to move back across the sky about one degree each day.

The spring and fall *equinoxes* occur about March 21 and September 21. *Equinox* means "equal night." On these dates, day and night are equal everywhere on earth.

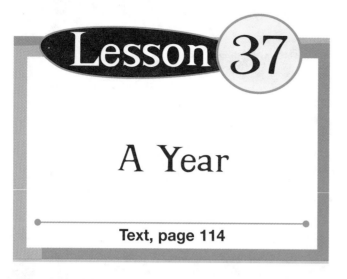

Lesson 37

A Year

Text, page 114

Preview

Objective

Given proper instruction, your student will be able to

- Identify each cycle of season changes as a year.

Materials

Have available

- Several calendars (If possible, obtain at least one calendar for a year whose number is divisible by four—1996, 2000, 2004.)*
- 4 index cards or paper strips for labeling
- Construction paper
- Scissors
- A piece of drawing paper

Prepare

- 1 large construction paper circle cut into quarters, with each quarter labeled $\frac{1}{4}$.
- 4 cards or strips by writing *365* on each.
- A chart-paper copy of the poem printed in *Introducing the Lesson* (optional).

Lesson

Introducing the Lesson

Introduce the activity. Read the following poem to your student:

> Thirty days hath September,
> April, June, and November.
> February has twenty-eight alone,
> And all the rest have thirty-one,
> Excepting leap year; that's the time
> When February's days are twenty-nine.

 You may want to challenge your child to memorize the poem about the months.

Direct the activity. Distribute calendars to your student, allowing time for him to check the days of the months against the poem. Ask your student whether any of his calendars show February with twenty-nine days. Then discuss whether he knows anyone who was born on February 29. Ask your student whether he thinks that person would have a birthday only in the years when February has 29 days. *(No, he would still have a birthday every year.)* Ask your student what he thinks a person born on February 29 would do to celebrate his birthday in the years when February has only 28 days. *(Some people in this situation celebrate their birthdays either on February 28 or on March 1.)*

 If your child seems curious about why there is a leap year, explain that each year contains a little bit more time than 365 days. This little bit of extra time is "saved up" for four years when it can then all be combined to make an extra day. Thus leap year contains 366 days.

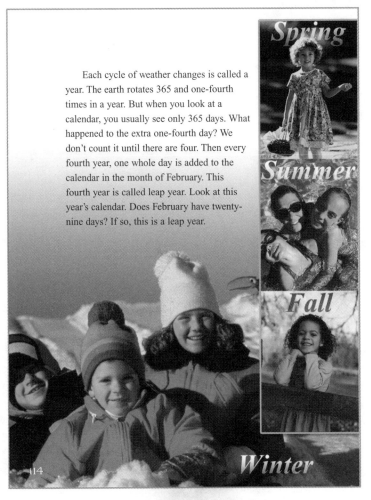

Each cycle of weather changes is called a year. The earth rotates 365 and one-fourth times in a year. But when you look at a calendar, you usually see only 365 days. What happened to the extra one-fourth day? We don't count it until there are four. Then every fourth year, one whole day is added to the calendar in the month of February. This fourth year is called leap year. Look at this year's calendar. Does February have twenty-nine days? If so, this is a leap year.

Spring

Summer

Fall

Winter

Teaching the Lesson

Direct a text activity on page 114. Use the following question to initiate your student's interest in what he is going to read: What is leap year?

Continue with discussion questions. After your student completes his silent reading, use the following questions and statements as a guide to discuss the page he read.

1. Describe the cycles of weather in a year, beginning with January. *(Answers will probably be similar to these: cold, snowy, icy; then warmer, windy, and sometimes rainy; next hot, sunny; finally cool, crisp, and breezy.)*

2. How many times does the earth rotate each year? *(365 $\frac{1}{4}$ times)*

3. What happens to the extra one-fourth day? *(We do not count it until the fourth year when the calendar "catches up"; then we add one extra day to the month of February.)*

4. What special name do scientists give to this fourth year? *(leap year)*

5. Do you think that leap year is a good name for this fourth year that has one extra day? Why? *(Actually we "leap" over the one-fourth day for three years and add on the extra day in the fourth year.)*

Evaluating the Lesson

Allow your student to write his birth date at the top of a piece of drawing paper. Then tell him to decide the season in which his birthday falls and to draw a picture of an activity that he enjoys during that season. At the bottom of his picture he should write the name of the season that he has illustrated.

 You might want to encourage each family member to do the activity described above. Then allow your child to compile the illustrated months in order in a family seasonal booklet.

For Your Information

Leap years are attempts to make a calendar year the same as a solar year. An extra day is added to every calendar year that can be evenly divided by four. The exceptions are the turn-of-the-century years, such as 1900. To be leap years, these years must be divisible by 400.

C H A P T E R   T E N

Lessons 38-41

Your Muscles

In this chapter your student will learn to distinguish between the different types of muscles. He will examine and discuss the various tasks muscles perform in the body, such as movement of bones, blood, and food. In addition, your student will participate in activities designed to stimulate interest in God's intricate design of the body and its functions necessary for life.

Materials

The following items must be obtained or prepared before the presentation of the lesson. These items are designated with an * in the materials list in each lesson and in the Supplement. For further information see the individual lessons.

- 1 skein of yarn, any color (Lesson 38)
- A thin piece of raw steak or chicken, enough for six slides (Lesson 38)
- A darning needle (Lesson 38)
- 1 microscope slide† (Lesson 38)
- 1 cover slip (a small piece of glass or plastic)† (Lesson 38)
- 1 magnifying glass† (Lesson 38)
- A rag doll (Lesson 39)
- 1 box of round toothpicks (Lesson 41)

Lesson 38

Names and Structure of Muscles

Text, pages 116-19 • Notebook, page 39

Preview

Objectives

Given proper instruction, your student will be able to

- Differentiate between voluntary and involuntary muscles.
- Recognize the three kinds of muscles.
- Observe muscle fiber under a magnifying glass.

Materials

Have available

- A watch with a second hand
- 1 skein of yarn, any color*
- A thin piece of raw steak or chicken*
- 1 darning needle*
- 1 microscope slide*†
- 1 cover slip (small square piece of glass or plastic)*†
- Red and blue food coloring
- Rubbing alcohol
- 1 small bottle (baby food jar, olive jar, etc.)
- 1 tablespoon
- 1 magnifying glass*†
- 1 pencil

Lesson

Introducing the Lesson

Introduce the activity. Instruct your student to blink his eyes three times and then immediately begin to hold his eyes open for as long as he can. Tell him not to roll his eyes. Time how long your student is able to hold his eyes open without blinking.

Ask your student whether he knows what part of the eye helps him to hold his eyes open without blinking. *(muscles in the eye)* Ask your student what else muscles help him do. *(Some possible answers are walk, run, sit, and write.)* Tell your student that muscles that we can control are called voluntary. Ask him what name we could give to muscles that cannot be controlled. *(Answers will vary, but scientists call these types of muscles* involuntary.*)*

 Involuntary muscles move blood through a person's blood vessels, help him breathe, and make up most of his digestive system. The muscles located around the eye are voluntary. Some muscles, like the diaphragm, are both voluntary and involuntary. The diaphragm separates the chest cavity from the abdomen.

Direct the activity. Tell your student that the diaphragm is a special muscle that separates the chest cavity from the abdomen. Show him where the diaphragm is by placing your flattened hand between your chest and abdomen and parallel to the floor. Instruct your student to locate his diaphragm. Ask him to feel the movement of the diaphragm as he breathes in and out. Ask him what he thinks is the job of the diaphragm. *(It aids the lungs in breathing.)* Ask him to try to control the movement of this special muscle called the diaphragm.

 Usually, the diaphragm works on its own (involuntary muscle), but sometimes you can control it (voluntary muscle) when you want to breathe faster or slower or hold your breath.

Ask your student whether he thinks about his diaphragm moving as he breathes in and out and as he talks and moves around. *(no)*

Finding Out... About Muscle Fibers

1. Get

a short, thin piece of raw steak or chicken   a darning needle   two microscope slides   red and blue food coloring

rubbing alcohol   a small bottle   a tablespoon   a magnifying glass

2. Put one drop of red and one drop of blue food coloring in a tablespoon. Fill up the rest of the spoon with rubbing alcohol. Store in the bottle.

3. Put the piece of meat on a microscope slide. Pick the muscle fiber apart with a darning needle. Put several drops of stain on the meat. Put a second slide on as a cover.

4. Look at the muscle with a magnifying glass. In your notebook, sketch what the fibers look like.

118

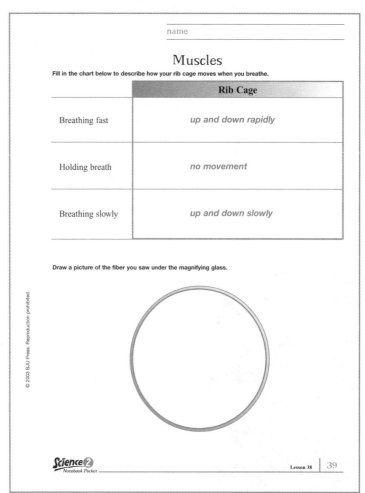

Muscles

Fill in the chart below to describe how your rib cage moves when you breathe.

	Rib Cage
Breathing fast	*up and down rapidly*
Holding breath	*no movement*
Breathing slowly	*up and down slowly*

Draw a picture of the fiber you saw under the magnifying glass.

Science 2 Notebook Packet

Lesson 38   39

Continue the activity with notebook page 39. Instruct your student to place one of his hands on his rib cage. Tell him to breathe very fast and feel the way his rib cage moves. Then tell him to breathe slowly, and finally, to take a deep breath and hold it as long as he can. Allow time for him to fill in the chart on the top of notebook page 39, describing how his rib cage moved.

Conclude the activity. Direct your student's attention to the *Finding Out* activity on page 118. Allow your student to help you gather materials and prepare the microscope slide, following the steps given. Give him the prepared microscope slide and a magnifying glass. Instruct him to use the magnifying glass to observe the muscle fiber on the slide. Explain to him that, with the aid of the magnifying glass, he will see a fiber of meat on the slide. If he looks closely, he will see a square plastic or glass piece over a section of the slide. He should use the magnifying glass to look carefully at the fiber *under* that cover slip.

 Be sure to use the magnifying glass to find the fiber before placing the cover slip on the slide. The fiber will look like a strand of hair. The stain will have colored it light purple.

Direct your student's attention to the circle at the bottom of notebook page 39. Instruct him to draw in that circle the muscle fiber as he sees it under the magnifying glass. Make sure he understands that he should draw the fiber larger than it actually is.

Has anyone ever said to you, "Make a muscle?" What did you do? You probably made a fist and bent your arm. Then your "muscle" came up as a hump on your upper arm. But that is only one of the many muscles God put in your body.

Names of Muscles

Each muscle has a name. The name may be a long, hard word, but it tells something about the muscle. For example, the name *pectoralis major* tells the place and size of the muscle. *Pectoralis* means "chest area" and *major* means "large." The name *deltoid* tells the shape of the muscle. It means "triangular."

Structure of Muscles

Muscles are made of long, thin threads. Each thread is called a fiber. Have you ever seen the fibers in chicken muscle? They look like the strands of fiber in a rope.

Teaching the Lesson

Direct a text activity on pages 116-19. Use the following questions to initiate your student's interest in what he is going to read.

1. Where are the muscles in the body?
2. What kinds of muscles do I have?
3. How many muscles do I have?

Continue with discussion questions. After your student completes his silent reading, use the following questions and statements as a guide to discuss the pages he read.

1. Look at the picture on page 116. Which type of muscle is the boy using? *(voluntary)*

 Some voluntary muscles move the bones of the skeleton. Some voluntary muscles are connected directly to the bones. Some voluntary muscles, like the face muscles, are connected to other muscles.

2. What are muscles made of? *(long, thin threads called fibers)*
3. Look at the illustration on page 117. Do these muscle fibers work alone or are they closely bound

to other muscle fibers? *(closely bound to other muscle fibers)*

Fibers lie close together to form little bundles that make up a muscle group. Use the skein of yarn to illustrate how individual fibers of yarn are twisted together to form the thread of yarn. These threads then bunch together to form a bundle, or skein. Muscles are similar in that the tiny fibers of muscle lie close to each other to form the muscle. Many muscles bunch together to form a muscle bundle or group. Muscle groups allow movement when a person is playing or working.

4. How many kinds of muscles do you have? *(three)*
5. Name the three kinds of muscles. *(skeletal, smooth, and cardiac)*
6. What do skeletal muscles look like? Where are they found and what job do they have? *(They are striped or grooved like a plowed field. Skeletal muscles are found in the arms, legs, eyes, face, etc. They help control the skeleton.)*

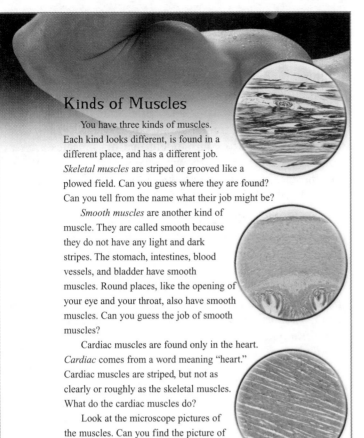

Kinds of Muscles

You have three kinds of muscles. Each kind looks different, is found in a different place, and has a different job. *Skeletal muscles* are striped or grooved like a plowed field. Can you guess where they are found? Can you tell from the name what their job might be?

Smooth muscles are another kind of muscle. They are called smooth because they do not have any light and dark stripes. The stomach, intestines, blood vessels, and bladder have smooth muscles. Round places, like the opening of your eye and your throat, also have smooth muscles. Can you guess the job of smooth muscles?

Cardiac muscles are found only in the heart. *Cardiac* comes from a word meaning "heart." Cardiac muscles are striped, but not as clearly or roughly as the skeletal muscles. What do the cardiac muscles do?

Look at the microscope pictures of the muscles. Can you find the picture of each kind of muscle?

119

---

7. What do smooth muscles look like? Where are they found and what job do they have? *(They are smooth with curvy lines, not straight lines. Smooth muscles are found in the organs and blood vessels. They are involuntary muscles.)*

8. What do cardiac muscles look like? Where are they found and what job do they have? *(They are unevenly striped and are found only in the heart. Cardiac muscles help to pump the blood in and out of the heart.)*

 The cardiac muscles are involuntary. A person cannot make his heart skip a beat. The heart is made up of groups of muscle fibers working together. These muscle fibers look different depending on the type of muscle.

9. Look at the microscope pictures of the muscles on the bottom of page 119. Identify each of the kinds of muscles correctly. *(The top picture shows skeletal muscle, the middle picture shows smooth muscle, and the bottom picture shows cardiac muscle.)*

Evaluating the Lesson

Introduce a review activity. Tell your student that you are going to name some common muscles. He is to determine if the muscle you name is voluntary or involuntary. If the muscle is voluntary, he should stand up. If the muscle is involuntary, he should sit down or remain seated.

Direct the activity. Read the following phrases aloud one at a time, allowing your student to respond after each item.

1. arm muscles *(voluntary)*
2. small intestine *(involuntary)*
3. heart *(involuntary)*
4. leg muscles *(voluntary)*
5. lungs *(involuntary)*
6. eyelids *(voluntary)*
7. neck muscles *(voluntary)*
8. blood vessels *(involuntary)*

For Your Information

Muscle tissues have three other important characteristics necessary for movement: *irritability, elasticity,* and *extensibility.* Irritability is the muscle's ability to respond to the nervous system, such as when you touch a hot stove. Elasticity is the muscle's ability to return to its previous shape after contracting, and extensibility allows one group of muscles to contract as another group of muscles stretches to allow movement. Generally, a person is not aware of the normal contractions and relaxations of muscles. However, when these contractions become prolonged or severe, with no relaxation of the muscles, cramps may result.

As in the case of all living cells, muscle fibers need energy to work properly. They get this energy from the foods that a person eats. Enzymes in the body break down the food into energy for muscles. The most important food sources for energy are fats and carbohydrates. Many long-distance runners will eat a meal of high fat and carbohydrates immediately prior to a run in order to provide their muscles with the necessary energy.

When muscles work, they release lactic acid as waste. If a muscle works too hard, lactic acid will build up inside the muscle and, as a result, the muscle fibers will lose some of their ability to contract and will tire. Strength will be lost, and the muscles will need to rest in order to remove the lactic acid.

Lesson 39

Muscles Move Bones

Text, pages 120-21

Preview

Objectives

Given proper instruction, your student will be able to

- State the function of muscles in relation to the skeleton.
- Identify at least one pair of muscles and describe how those muscles work together through contraction and relaxation.
- State what happens when muscles are not exercised properly.

Materials

Have available

- A rag doll*
- A piece of drawing paper
- Crayons

Lesson

Introducing the Lesson

Introduce the activity. To make your student aware of the importance of muscles, show him a rag doll. Pick up one of the doll's arms and let it drop. Do the same with one of the doll's legs. Ask your student to try to make the doll remain upright. After several attempts, it will be obvious that the doll will not remain upright without help. Ask your student why the rag doll cannot remain upright and why its limbs have no control. *(It is not alive. It has no bones or muscles.)*

Ask your student what people would be like without working muscles. *(We would be just like the rag doll, unable to hold our arms out or hold ourselves upright.)*

Direct the activity. To help your student understand what his muscles do, instruct him to stand and put his arms out

to his sides. Tell him to let his arms drop loosely to his sides. Repeat the action and then direct your student to sit down.

Ask your student to describe the difference he felt between extending his arms and letting them hang loosely. Ask if his arms felt tighter at one point. *(yes, when they were extended)* Explain to your student that his muscles are responsible for the up-and-down movement of his arm. Without muscles, his arms would hang loosely, unable to move up or down.

Continue the activity. To let your student feel his muscles in action, instruct him to extend one leg straight out in front of him. After a few seconds, ask him whether he can feel the leg muscles that are holding his leg in the air. Ask him where he thinks the muscles are located. *(in the calf and thigh)* Instruct him to move the suspended leg back and forth. Then ask whether he can feel the muscles in the leg controlling the action. *(yes)* Instruct your student to put his leg down and then put out his right hand and wiggle his fingers. Instruct him to place his left hand on his right forearm to see whether he can feel the muscles which move his fingers. *(Yes, he can feel the muscles moving.)* Ask your student whether he thinks the muscle is getting tighter or relaxing loosely. *(getting tighter)* Tell him that the action of the muscle when it tightens is called contraction. During muscle contraction, the muscle tightens and grows shorter. Ask your student what he thinks a muscle does when it relaxes. *(It slackens or "sags" a bit.)*

 Most muscles work in pairs to create movement. While one muscle contracts, another relaxes, and the movement is possible.

Conclude the activity. Instruct your student to put the fingers of his right hand on the upper part of his left arm. Ask him what he feels as he bends his left arm slowly upward. *(He can feel his muscles contract.)* Ask your student whether he knows the names of these large arm muscles. *(biceps muscle and triceps muscle)*

As your student straightens his left arm, explain that now the triceps muscle contracts and the biceps muscle relaxes. To locate the triceps muscle and feel it contract, instruct your student to rest his arm, palm up, on the table. Direct him to press his arm down hard on the desk. As he does this, tell him to touch the back of his upper arm with his other hand. Ask him whether he feels the triceps contract. *(yes)* Tell him that the contraction of the triceps moves the arm down. The teamwork of the biceps and triceps is just one example of muscles working together to create movement.

Jobs of Muscles

As you may have already guessed, skeletal muscles move your bones. But they move other body parts too, like your eyes and tongue. Most of the time skeletal muscles work in pairs.

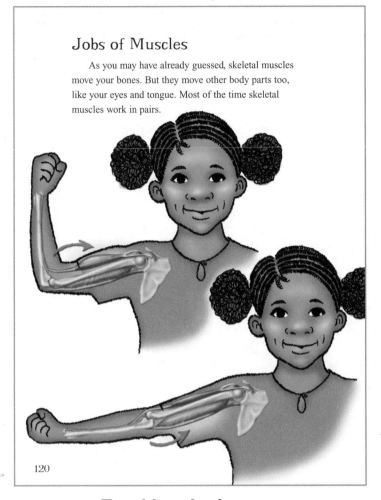

120

One muscle in a pair will tighten and pull a bone in one direction. Then it relaxes, and the other muscle in the pair will tighten and pull the bone in the other direction.

Look at the drawings of muscle pairs in action. Which muscle in the pair is doing the action?

121

Teaching the Lesson

Direct a text activity on pages 120-21. Use the following question to initiate your student's interest in what he is going to read: How do muscles work in pairs?

Continue with discussion questions. After your student completes his silent reading, use the following questions and statements as a guide to discuss the pages he read.

1. Look at the pictures on page 120. Which picture illustrates the use of the biceps? *(the top one)*

2. How do the triceps look in the top picture? *(tightened)*

3. Look at the pictures on page 121. Which muscles are being used? *(A muscle under the leg [rectus femoris, rek'tes fem ´ər•əs] contracts to flex the thigh and extend the leg as the boy gets ready to kick. The muscle on top of the leg [biceps femoris] contracts to flex the leg and extend the thigh.)*

 The muscles that move bones are voluntary muscles because a person decides when to use them. Unused muscles lose their strength.

6. Have you ever worn (or known someone who has worn) a cast or a sling because of a broken bone? How do you think the muscles feel after the cast or sling is removed? *(weak)*

 Immobilized muscles often require special exercises called therapy to get their strength back.

7. What do you think will happen if we do not exercise our muscles? *(They will become weak.)*

8. Name some exercises that you enjoy. *(Answers will vary, but here are some possibilities: jumping jacks, pushups, chin-ups, sit-ups, bicycling.)*

 We need to make our muscles expend more effort than our ordinary daily activities require. Dynamic exercise such as calisthenics (jumping jacks, pushups, sit-ups) is a good way to strengthen muscles. Dynamic exercise makes our muscles move against resistance and heightens their own ability to resist. Exercise is necessary for muscle strength, and muscle strength is necessary for movement.

Evaluating the Lesson

Direct an activity. Give your student a piece of drawing paper and crayons. Instruct him to draw an example of muscles in action. Perhaps he can draw a figure exercising or playing a sport. After the illustration is complete, give your student opportunity to explain his picture and tell what the muscles are doing. This activity will illustrate the many actions that muscles control.

For Your Information

A person depends on his muscles for movement. In fact, simply taking one step requires the work of over 300 muscles. Just as a man cannot function without his muscles, those muscles cannot function without energy. Muscles receive energy after cells have prepared the energy for them through a process called *cellular respiration.* Proteins in the cell, called *enzymes,* break down large food molecules, which are the fuel for energy. As the fuel is broken down, it releases its chemical energy. This freeing of trapped energy is called *respiration.* As soon as the energy is free, it joins with an adenosine diphosphate bond (ADP), which then becomes an adenosine triphosphate (ATP) molecule. The ATP molecule uses the transferred energy to produce muscular movement, and you take a step.

Lesson 40

Muscles Move Food

Text, page 122

Preview

Objective

Given proper instruction, your student will be able to

- Identify the parts of the digestive system and their functions.

Materials

Have available

- 1 pair paper lips made of construction paper
- 1 small bowl or butter tub
- 1 cardboard tube (from a paper towel roll)
- 2 balloons
- 1 vacuum cleaner hose
- 2 dishpans or medium-sized bowls
- 1 sponge
- 1 bucket
- 1 paper circle
- Masking tape

Prepare

- The esophagus and trachea for the model. Tape the cardboard tube (the trachea) to the top of the vacuum cleaner hose. Cut a small paper circle to cover the opening of the trachea and tape it so that it can flap open or shut. This flap will represent the epiglottis. At the back of the cardboard tube, tape two partially inflated balloons, representing lungs. (*NOTE:* See Figure 40-1.)
- The mouth by taping the paper lips to the small bowl.

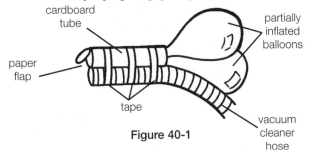

cardboard tube

paper flap

tape

partially inflated balloons

vacuum cleaner hose

Figure 40-1

Lesson

Introducing the Lesson

Introduce the activity. Place the materials for the model of the digestive system in front of you. Explain to your student that he will help you build a model of the digestive system as you discuss each part.

Ask your student where digestion begins. *(in the mouth)* Hold up the small bowl with the lips taped to it. Ask your student what two things in the mouth aid in digestion. *(teeth and tongue)* Ask what the teeth do to food. *(They bite and chew the food.)* Ask what happens when several teeth, in particular the front two teeth, are missing. *(It is harder to eat and chew food.)* Tell what foods you could eat and what foods you could not eat if your front two teeth were missing. *(could eat soft, creamy foods; could not eat corn on the cob, apples, or any foods that you need to bite)*

 The teeth are used for biting, tearing, crushing, and grinding food. The first set of teeth usually begins to fall out when a child is six years old. The two front teeth on the top and bottom are used mostly for biting and grasping food. Usually only soft foods can be eaten until the second set of teeth come in. The tongue is a muscle that is used in digestion. It is important in chewing, in swallowing, and in tasting. The tongue contains the taste buds that allow a person to taste his food.

Direct the activity. Show your student the prepared vacuum cleaner hose. Explain that the cardboard tube represents the windpipe. Ask your student whether he knows the purpose of the windpipe. *(It allows air to go to the lungs.)* Ask what he thinks the two balloons represent. *(the lungs)* Direct your student's attention to the small flap. Ask him whether he knows the important job of this part on the windpipe. *(It prevents food being swallowed from entering the windpipe.)* Ask what would happen if food *did* enter the windpipe. *(Food particles might end up in the lungs, causing choking.)* Ask your student whether he has ever choked when food or liquid went down the "wrong pipe."

Ask your student which part of the model he thinks represents the food pipe. *(the vacuum cleaner hose)* Ask him whether he thinks food drops into the stomach through the food pipe. *(no)* Tell him that food is moved down the food pipe by a wave of contractions. Ask your student to define *contractions. (movements of muscles pulling together and becoming shorter)* Ask him whether these digestive organs are muscles. *(yes)* Food is moved quickly, but systematically, down the food pipe.

Continue the activity. Place the flap end in the "mouth" and the windpipe end in the first pan. Ask your student to guess what the first pan represents. *(the stomach)* Explain that in the stomach, special juices break down the food. The grinding and mashing of the powerful stomach muscles also pound the food, making it easier to carry into the next part of the digestive system.

Ask your student what he thinks the second pan represents. *(the small intestine)* Explain that this part with its three main sections is the most important part of the digestive tract. Ask your student what he thinks the job of the small intestine is. *(The parts of the small intestine further break down the food and complete digestion.)*

 Nutrients are soaked up into the cells of the small intestine and then passed into the bloodstream.

Ask your student whether he thinks the small intestine is really small. *(No; if it were stretched out from end to end, it would be twenty-two to twenty-eight feet long.)*

 You might want to assist your child as he measures to see the length of the small intestine.

Ask your student how long it takes food to get to the small intestine to complete digestion. *(It takes an average of four hours for a meal to pass through the small intestine.)* Ask him why he usually gets hungry every four hours that he is awake. *(because digestion is complete for food previously eaten and the stomach "feels" hungry again)*

Conclude the activity. Now show your student the sponge and the bucket. Ask him what part of digestion he thinks these represent. *(the large intestine)* Ask your student what he thinks the job of the large intestine is. *(Its main job is to soak up water.)* Ask him why it is necessary for the large intestine to soak up water. *(to make the food break down)* Tell your student that he will continue to learn in today's lesson about how these muscles move food.

 About nine quarts of water are needed every day to allow the digestive system to work smoothly. That is one of the reasons doctors emphasize the importance of drinking six to eight glasses of water a day.

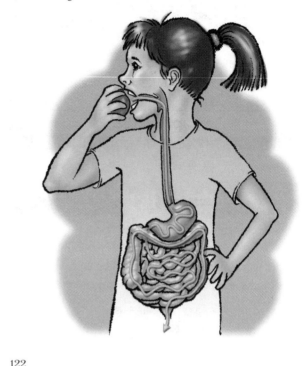

The smooth muscles are in charge of moving things such as food in the body. Use one finger to follow the path of the food on the drawing of the digestive system. Can you see how the muscles keep the food moving along?

122

Teaching the Lesson

Direct a text activity on page 122. Use the following question to initiate your student's interest in what he is going to read: How does the food you eat reach all parts of your body and help it to grow?

Continue with discussion questions. After your student completes his silent reading, use the following questions and statements as a guide to discuss the page he read.

1. Look at the illustration of the digestive system on page 122. Use your fingers to trace the path that the food takes in completing digestion.

2. What is the name of the long tubelike part in the throat? *(esophagus)*

3. Point to the stomach and the large and small intestines in the diagram on page 122.

Evaluating the Lesson

Introduce the activity. Tell your student that you will ask questions about digestion. Reward him with stickers or small candies for each correct answer.

1. Where does digestion begin? *(in the mouth)*

2. What helps you to taste your food and aids in digestion? *(the tongue)*

3. What kind of tissues are the digestive organs? *(muscles)*

4. Are the muscles of the digestive system voluntary or involuntary? Why? *(involuntary, because they cannot be controlled)*

5. Which organ is the most important in the digestive system? *(the small intestine)*

6. How long is the small intestine? *(twenty-two to twenty-eight feet)*

7. What prevents food from going into the windpipe? *(a tiny flap, the epiglottis)*

8. How many glasses of water should you drink every day? *(six to eight glasses)*

For Your Information

Denticles are small teeth or teethlike projections. Snakes must swallow their food whole because their teeth are sharp like needles and are not good for chewing. A snake can separate its top and bottom jaws in order to swallow an animal two or three times as thick as its own head. Once a snake has begun to swallow its prey, the muscles in its body begin to contract, pushing the food into its stomach. When the animal is in the stomach, the strong digestive juices digest all of the animal except feathers and hair.

A person's involuntary muscles in his digestive system work in a similar way, pushing food down the esophagus, through the stomach, and into the small and large intestines.

The small intestine is divided into three parts: the duodenum (doo´ə•dē´nəm), the jejunum (jə•joo´nəm), and the ileum (ĭl´ē•əm). The duodenum (eight to ten inches long) mixes food from the stomach with the secretions from the liver and the pancreas. The jejunum is the main site of homogenization (process of making liquid uniform in consistency) and the mixing of intestinal contents. The ileum is responsible for absorbing vitamin B-12, bile acids, and the remaining amino acids and fats. Both the jejunum and the ileum are responsible for absorption of water. Together, the jejunum and ileum measure twenty-one to twenty-seven feet.

Approximately 8.9 quarts (8.5 liters) of water enter the gastrointestinal tract per day. Of that amount about 1.57 quarts (1.5 liters) of water are taken through the mouth. The rest is secreted into the tract from other parts of the body.

Family Time 41

The Heart

You might want to use the following Bible verse and discussion as part of your family devotional time. Direct the questions that follow to different family members. This will include everyone and not single out your second grader.

Materials

Have available

• A Bible

Instructions

Ask your child whether he has ever heard an adult say, "It broke my heart." Ask whether he thinks the heart can really be broken in two pieces. *(no)* Ask him what he thinks that person might mean. *(that he has hurt feelings or is concerned about something)* Ask other family members to describe other feelings that are usually "felt" in the heart. *(love, friendship, loneliness, hurt, tenderness, sentiment)*

Ask whether people are talking about the organ in the body when they talk about a broken heart. *(no)* Ask your child to tell you the function of the heart in the body. *(The cardiac muscles of the heart pump blood throughout the body.)* Ask him whether he knows what this special system of blood flow is called. *(the circulatory system)* Instruct your child to place his hand over his heart and to describe the sound and movement that he feels as the heart pumps blood through the body. *(a regular beating or pounding)*

Read Proverbs 23:7a. Ask how other people know whether we are angry or sad or happy just by looking at us. *(The expression on the face reveals the emotions of the heart.)* Ask your child why, according to the Scripture, it is important to think about good, pure things. *(The verse says that what we think about affects the kind of person we are. Thinking about good, pure things, rather than evil, unkind things, helps us to be good, pure, and kind.)* Ask your child whether he knows what attitudes are. *(Answers may vary. Attitudes are ways of thinking, feeling, or acting about someone or something.)* Ask whether people can see what attitudes are in the hearts of other people. *(No, only God can see what is in a person's heart.)* Ask your child whether a person's actions always reveal what that person really feels, what his attitude is. *(no)* Ask your child to give an example of a time when he obeyed but inside was grumbling or angry with the person in authority. Allow several of your family members to tell of some instances. Read Proverbs 23:7 again. Ask your child whether God sees a wrong attitude even if the action does not reveal the wrong attitude. *(Yes, God sees the sin of a wrong attitude, even though we may have obeyed in action.)*

Ask your child how we can be sure to have the right attitudes and actions. *(Only through the Lord Jesus Christ can a person have the right attitudes and thoughts.)* Once Jesus has cleansed someone's heart from sin, He can and will help that person to think clean, kind thoughts and to have pleasing attitudes toward parents, teachers, and friends. (BAT: Ib Repentance and faith) Our wonderful God created our bodies and helps us to control them and care for them for His own glory.

Lesson 41

Muscles Move Blood

Text, pages 123-24 • Notebook, page 40

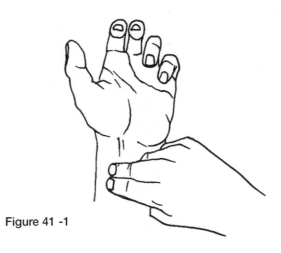

Figure 41 -1

Preview

Objectives

Given proper instruction, your student will be able to

- Differentiate between arteries and veins.
- Locate his pulse.
- Use exercise to change his heart rate.

Materials

Have available

- 1 box of round toothpicks*
- 1 thumbtack
- 1 stopwatch or watch with a second hand
- 1 red crayon
- 1 blue crayon

Prepare

- One pulse indicator for your student by taping a toothpick to the point of a thumbtack. (*NOTE:* See Figure 41-2.)

Lesson

Introducing the Lesson

Introduce the activity. Ask your student what carries blood from the heart to other parts of the body. *(arteries)* Tell him that as the heart pumps (contracts), the arteries produce a steady throbbing. Ask your student what that throbbing is called. *(a pulse)*

Direct the activity. Demonstrate the following procedure and instruct your student to do as you do, step by step. Make a fist and notice the cords (tendons) that pop up on the wrist. Place two or three fingers into the hollow along the side of the cord on the thumb side of the wrist. (*NOTE:* See Figure 41-1.) Tell your student not to use his thumb to find his pulse because the thumb has its own pulse.

Figure 41-2

Once your student has located his pulse, give him a pulse indicator that you have prepared. Instruct him to place the thumbtack (head down) on his pulse. (*NOTE:* See Figure 41-2.) Adjust the position of the thumbtack until your student can see the toothpick moving with his pulse. Direct him to rest his hand and/or arm on the table and to keep it as steady as possible. If the arm is kept really steady, the heartbeat will be more noticeable.

Continue the activity. Ask your student whether exercise affects the heart rate. *(yes)*

Exercise causes large muscle groups to work. Muscles need a great amount of oxygen to work correctly. That is why people begin to breathe faster and pant when running or playing hard.

Ask your student what he thinks the word *fitness* means. *(being in good physical shape)* Ask your student to name some exercises that contribute to making a person fit. *(jogging, walking, running, aerobics, etc.)*

In recent years, people have become increasingly aware of how important fitness is to the proper working of the heart. When a person is in good physical shape, his heart and lungs (cardiovascular system) can make and use oxygen very well. The oxygen is carried to the muscles, where it is used for energy.

Conclude the activity. Instruct your student to find his pulse (heart rate) again. Tell him to count the number of beats his heart makes when you say "start" and to stop counting when you say "stop." Time him for twenty seconds. Allow time for him to write the number on his notebook page 40.

Direct your student to stand. Tell him to run in place for one minute, starting when you say "start" and stopping when you say "stop." Instruct your student to find his heart rate as soon as you say "stop" and to begin counting his heart rate when you say "start." Time him for twenty seconds. Allow him to write the number in his notebook.

Your child may find his pulse easier in his neck. Instruct him to place his hand on either side of his throat about an inch and a half below his chin in order to count his pulse. *(NOTE:* See Figure 41-3.)

The cardiac muscles move blood through the heart. They pump blood out into the long hollow tubes called *blood vessels*. This system of the heart and blood vessels is called the *circulatory system*. How is it a little bit like a circle?

123

Figure 41-3

Finding Out... About Heart Rate

1. Get

   a stopwatch   your notebook

2. Have your teacher find your heart rate. Record this number on your notebook page.

3. Have a partner time you while you run in place for thirty seconds. Let your teacher find your heart rate again. Record this number on your notebook page.

4. Fill in the bar graph on your notebook page. Did your heart rate go up or down? Why?

"For bodily exercise profiteth little: but godliness is profitable unto all things, having promise of the life that now is, and of that which is to come."
I Timothy 4:8

124

---

name _____

My Heart Rate

Fill in the first blank. Then listen to your teacher's directions.   *Answers will vary.*

Resting Heart Rate	Heart Rate After Exercise
_____ (20 seconds)	_____ (20 seconds)
_____	_____
+ _____	+ _____
_____ (1 minute)	_____ (1 minute)

Color the bar graph to match your 1-minute heart rate. Follow your teacher's directions. Use the color code.

Blue =

Red =

Resting Heart Rate
80 85 90 95 100 105 110 115 120 125 130 135 140

Heart Rate After Exercising
80 85 90 95 100 105 110 115 120 125 130 135 140

Science 2
Notebook Packet   Lesson 41   40

Teaching the Lesson

Direct a text activity on pages 123-24. Use the following question to initiate your student's interest in what he is going to read: How is the circulatory system a little like a circle?

Continue with discussion questions. After your student completes his silent reading, use the following questions and statements as a guide to discuss the pages he read.

1. Locate the heart in the illustration on page 123. What are the colored lines that are coming out of the heart? *(blood vessels)*

2. Describe blood vessels. *(long, hollow tubes coming out of the heart)*

3. What is the circulatory system? *(the system of the heart and the blood vessels)*

Evaluating the Lesson

Introduce the activity. Direct your student's attention to the top of notebook page 40. The first blank in the resting heart rate column is where he should have written his heart rate while resting. Instruct him to write it two more times and then add all three numbers together to get his heart rate for one minute. The first blank in the exercising heart rate column is where he should have written his heart rate after running in place. Again, instruct him to write it two more times and add the three numbers together to get his heart rate for one minute.

Direct the activity. Now direct the student's attention to the bar graph at the bottom of the page. Tell him that each little square represents one beat of the heart per minute. Instruct him to count to the line that matches his heart rate. Then instruct him to draw a blue line on that line and to color the boxes up to that line. That bar will show him his resting heart rate. For instance, if his heart rate were ninety-three, he would draw a line three lines above the darker line labeled ninety.

Next, direct your student to use his red crayon to color the bar graph illustrating his heart rate after exercising.

Compare the resting and after-exercise heart rates of your student. Ask him why there is a difference in his heart rates. *(The heart must work harder during exercise, so it pumps blood faster.)* Ask your student why it is easier to feel his pulse after exercising. *(His heart is beating faster to get oxygen to his muscles.)*

Conclude the activity. If time permits, check your student's heart rate after various intervals of exercise: one minute, two minutes, five minutes. Let your student record the times. His heart rate should level off and remain constant until exercise is completed. Within five minutes of completing exercise, the heart rate should be back to the normal resting heart rate. Keep into account any physical limitations (doctor's orders against strenuous exercise, extreme overweight, etc.) before starting this activity.

For Your Information

No manmade pump has ever come close to the efficiency of the heart. It pumps about seventy times per minute when a person is at rest. At that rate, it pumps forty-two hundred times an hour, one hundred thousand times a day, and over thirty-seven million times a year.

The blood leaves the heart traveling about 330 feet per minute. As it branches out into smaller and smaller vessels, called capillaries, the speed decreases. The blood travels to the lungs, back to the heart, out to other body tissues, and finally returns to the heart—all in about twenty-three seconds!

Veins are much thinner than arteries and therefore have greater blood-pooling capacity. The presence of one-way valves in veins prevents the blood from flowing in the wrong direction. These valves, the "milking" action of the muscles, and the constriction of the veins, all aid in returning the blood to the heart.

CHAPTER ELEVEN

Lessons 42-45

Layers of the Earth

In this chapter your student will study about the layers of the earth and will learn to describe the features of the earth's crust. Your student will "build" his own map of the earth's crust using imaginative names for mountains, islands, continents, and oceans.

Materials

The following items must be obtained or prepared before the presentation of the lesson. These items are designated with an * in the materials list in each lesson and in the Supplement. For further information see the individual lessons.

- A volcano made of play dough (Lesson 42)
- A picture of Mount St. Helens (Lesson 43)
- A globe† (Lessons 44 and 45)
- 1 recipe of play dough, divided and tinted three colors as described in Lesson 7 (Lesson 44)
- An apple (Lesson 44)

11

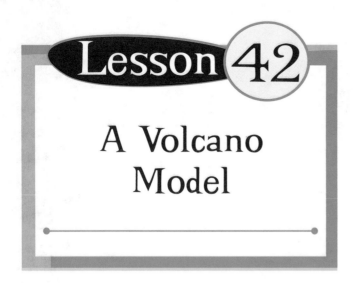

Lesson 42

A Volcano Model

Preview

Objective

Given proper instruction, your student will be able to

- Identify some parts of a volcano.

Materials

Have available

- Play dough. (*NOTE:* See Lesson 7 for the recipe for home-made play dough.)*

 The volcano prepared during this lesson is necessary for Lesson 43. The volcano must be made two or three days ahead of time so that the play dough will have dried sufficiently when the volcano "erupts." Do not try to bake the volcano at a low temperature because the play dough will crack.

Lesson

Introducing the Lesson

Introduce the activity. Gather the materials needed as given in Lesson 7. Allow your student to combine the ingredients in the saucepan and to stir them together thoroughly. As the ingredients "cook," you will need to stir them until a ball forms. (*NOTE:* Refer to Lesson 7 for further instructions as well as for some alternate recipes to use.)

Direct the activity. After the mixture has cooled, assist your student in shaping the dough into a cone, leaving a substantial hole (crater) at the top. (*NOTE:* You will put the baking soda into this hole for the "eruption.") Place the completed volcano on a board or small, covered table, ready for further use in Lesson 43.

Notes

You may prefer to make your volcanic cone from papier-mâché or plaster of Paris. These materials would make a more permanent volcano that could be used from year to year.

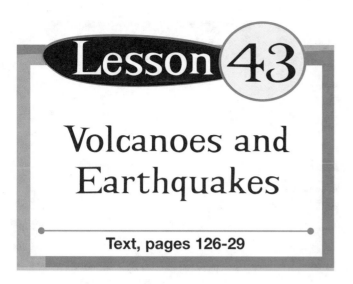

Lesson 43

Volcanoes and Earthquakes

Text, pages 126-29

Preview

Objectives

Given proper instruction, your student will be able to

- Describe what scientists can and cannot observe about the earth.
- Identify some ways that scientists can learn about the inside of the earth.

Materials

Have available

- A volcano made of play dough* (*NOTE:* See Lesson 42.)
- 1 box of baking soda
- 1 bottle of vinegar
- Red and yellow food coloring
- A picture of Mount St. Helens*
- 1 ball, any size

Lesson

Introducing the Lesson

Introduce the activity. Hold up a round ball. Ask your student what he thinks the surface is made of. *(Answers will vary depending on the ball used.)* Ask him whether it was easy or hard to tell what the surface looked like. *(easy)* Why? *(because he can see it)* Ask your student whether he thinks it would be easy to study the inside of the ball. *(no)* Why? *(It cannot be seen.)*

Show your student the play dough volcano. Ask him to predict what might have made the sides of a real volcano look like a mountain. *(Answers may vary. Some students may*

Direct the activity. Put baking soda inside the cone of your model volcano and tint the baking soda with several drops of red and yellow food coloring. You may want to place the cone in a dishpan or on old newspapers to protect your floor. Pour vinegar over the baking soda. You will get a realistic-looking "lava eruption." Adding more vinegar will cause more foaming.

Continue the activity. Ask your student whether he thinks scientists can look into the earth. *(no)* Ask him why the material that comes out of the inside of a volcano is valuable to a scientist. *(The scientist can study the volcanic material and find out about the make-up of the inside of the earth.)*

Conclude the activity. Show your student the picture of Mount St. Helens. Ask him to listen to the following story to find the name of this famous volcano.

Mount St. Helens was a beautiful, tree-covered mountain in the state of Washington. People often camped on the mountain, especially along the shores of Spirit Lake at the top of Mount St. Helens.

One day Mount St. Helens began to have earthquakes. Scientists quickly moved in to study the mountain. People quit going there for picnics and camping because no one knew what might happen. The government even asked the people who lived on Mount St. Helens to move away so that they would be safe.

On May 18, 1980, Mount St. Helens erupted. Gas, ash, and rocks flew into the air. Trees were flattened like toothpicks, and many animals died. Much of the mountain's top blew away, and Spirit Lake filled with ash and mud. The ash spread for many miles and made people cough.

Lava and ash have come out of Mount St. Helens several times during the past few years. But slowly the mountain is settling down. Trees are beginning to grow again. Animals are coming back. Perhaps someday people will again be able to camp and have picnics on a beautiful Mount St. Helens.

What do you think is in the very middle of the earth? Do you think there is sand? Do you think there is water? Do you think there is ice? Or do you think the earth is empty at the core? For a long time writers and scientists have tried to guess what might be there.

One writer named Jules Verne made up a whole book about some people going to the middle of the earth. But that is only a story. Scientists want to know the facts.

How Scientists Find Out About the Earth's Inside

It is not hard to find out about the outside of things. Let's say you get a birthday present. You know it's a birthday present because it's in birthday wrapping paper. You know something about its size just by looking at it. In one way, the earth is like a birthday present. Scientists can find out quite a lot about the outside part because they can see it.

To find out about the inside of things, however, is a different problem. To find out what's in your present, you open it. But in another way, the earth is not like a birthday present. You cannot just open it and look inside. How do scientists know anything about the middle of the earth?

Signs from Inside

Most of what scientists know about the inside of the earth they learn from earthquakes and volcanoes.

When there is an earthquake, scientists measure how much and how long the ground shakes. What they record helps them tell what kind of rock is under the surface.

Sometimes volcanoes throw out melted rock called *lava*. This rock comes from much farther down in the earth than man has ever been able to dig. What can scientists learn about the inside of the earth from lava?

Teaching the Lesson

Direct a text activity on pages 126-29. Use the following questions to initiate your student's interest in what he is going to read.

1. What is in the very middle of the earth?
2. What information does lava give scientists?

Continue with discussion questions. After your student completes his silent reading, use the following questions and statements as a guide to discuss the pages he read.

1. Name some things inside the earth that scientists study. *(rocks and lava)*
2. What two occurrences give scientists the most information about the inside of the earth? *(earthquakes and volcanoes)*
3. How do scientists get information about the inside of the earth during an earthquake? What information do they get? *(They measure how much and how long the earth shakes to help determine what kind of rock is under the surface.)*
4. What is lava? *(melted rock thrown out of an erupting volcano)*

5. What do scientists record about rock samples? *(what kind of material the rock samples are, what layers they are in, and how deep in the earth they were found)*
6. When Mount St. Helens erupted, what came out of the volcano? *(ash)*
7. Do you think ash can give scientists any information about the inside of the earth? *(yes)*
8. What were divining rods supposed to do? Did divining rods really locate water? *(They were supposed to shake when they were carried over ground that had water under it. No, it was just superstition.)*
9. What is "doodlebugging?" *(foolish ways of finding what is underground)*

Men drill holes in the earth and pull out samples of rock. Have you ever put a straw into a drink and closed off the top of the straw with your finger? What happened when you lifted the straw up? Some of the drink stayed in the straw, didn't it? Something very much the same happens when scientists drill into the earth for rock samples. Then they study the sample and record the kind of material it is, what layers it is in, and how deep in the earth it was.

Sometimes men go under the ocean to drill holes in the earth. Why do you think they go to the ocean floor to drill?

128

A long time ago, many people tried to find underground water by cutting forked tree branches and walking around with them pointed down. These branches are called "divining rods." Divining rods were supposed to shake when they were carried over ground that had water under it. Do you think underground water would make a branch shake?

Oil men sometimes try to find oil underground with magnets and machines that vibrate. These ways of trying to find out what is underground are called "doodlebugging." "Doodle" means "fool." What do you think the name tells about divining rods and other gadgets like it?

129

➤ **Why do you think they go to the ocean floor to drill?** *(Almost two-thirds of the earth's surface is under water. Some of the best sites for drilling are on the ocean floor.)*

Evaluating the Lesson

Direct a review. Using your picture of Mount St. Helens, a picture of some other volcano, or the photos of Mount St. Helens and the lava and ash on page 125 in the student text, conduct a review using the following questions and pointing activities.

1. Point to a place where scientists cannot see to study the inside of the earth. *(the bottom of the picture, under the ground)*

2. Point to something that scientists can study to learn about the inside of the earth. *(lava or ash)*

3. Point to a place where an earthquake could happen. *(the ground)*

4. What is something besides lava that could come out of a volcano? *(ash)*

5. How can scientists learn about the inside of the earth besides studying volcanoes and earthquakes? *(drilling)*

6. Point to a place where scientists might drill into the earth. *(the ground)*

For Your Information

Scientists are able to learn much about the center of the earth from earthquakes. Whenever and wherever an earthquake occurs, it sends waves through the earth. These waves are picked up by seismographs monitored by scientists all over the world. Different earthquake waves pass through different types of material. Primary (P) waves are able to pass rapidly through both solids and liquids. Secondary (S) waves travel slower and will pass only through solids. Long (L) waves are the slowest, and they travel only on the surface of the earth. By studying the pattern of the P, S, and L waves, scientists have indirectly been able to determine the general boundaries of the crust, mantle, and core and have been able to learn more of the earth's structure.

Lesson 44

The Layers of the Earth

Text, pages 130-32 • Notebook, page 41

Preview

Objectives

Given proper instruction, your student will be able to

- Name the three layers of the earth.
- Describe the thickness and temperature of the three layers.

Materials

Have available

- A globe*
- 1 recipe of play dough, divided and tinted three colors (*NOTE:* See Lesson 7.)*
- 1 two-foot length of thread
- 1 apple*
- 1 knife
- Crayons

Lesson

Introducing the Lesson

Introduce the activity. Show the apple to your student. Ask him to describe what he would find if he bit or cut into an apple. *(white fruit)* Ask him whether he could ever cut into an apple and find red peeling or skin all the way through the apple. Why? *(No; the skin is thin.)* Ask him what he will always find in the center of an apple. *(a core)* Tell your student that today he is going to look at how an apple can be a model of what the earth looks like on the inside.

Direct the activity. Cut the apple in half and give one half of it to your student. Point out the skin of the apple. Ask your student whether the skin is thick or thin. *(thin)* Tell your student that the skin of the apple represents the crust of the earth.

Show your student the globe. Point out the place on the globe where you live. Ask your student whether he is living on the crust of the earth. *(yes)* Then ask whether he is living on the thin part or the thick part of the earth. *(thin)*

Continue the activity. Ask your student why we do not fall into the earth since we live on the thinnest "skin" of the earth. *(There is a thick layer underneath.)*

 The crust of the earth is actually miles thick, but it is considered "thin" when compared to the mantle and the core.

Ask him whether he knows the name of the thickest layer of the earth. *(mantle)* Instruct your student to look at his half of the apple. Ask him what part of the apple he thinks would represent the mantle. *(the main part of the white fruit)* Tell your student that the mantle of the earth is made of hot rock. Ask him how he thinks the rock of the mantle helps keep us safe. *(It keeps us from falling through the earth.)*

Conclude the activity. Ask your student what part of the apple he has not looked at yet. *(the core)* Allow your student to eat his half of the apple before proceeding. Tell him that he will continue to compare the apple and the earth in today's lesson to learn more about the earth.

What Scientists Find Out About the Earth's Inside

Layers of the Earth

Scientists think the earth is made of three layers. The top layer of the earth is mostly solid rock called the crust. How thick is the crust? If the earth were an apple, the crust would be as thin as the apple's skin. The crust is about 2 to 4 miles thick under the oceans. Under some mountains, the crust can be up to 44 miles deep.

Under the crust is the layer of earth called the mantle. It is about 1,800 miles thick. If we again compare the earth to an apple, the mantle would be as thick as the white part under the skin of the apple. Geologists believe the earth's mantle is as hot as 3,000 degrees Fahrenheit.

130

Deep in the center of the earth is the third layer called the core. If we compare the earth to an apple once again, the earth's core is as thick as the center, or core, of the apple. The earth's core is about 4,200 miles from one side to the other. Temperatures there are probably as high as 7,200 degrees Fahrenheit.

131

Teaching the Lesson

Direct a text activity on pages 130-32. Use the following questions to initiate your student's interest in what he is going to read.

1. How thick is the earth's crust?
2. Where is the earth the hottest?

Continue with discussion questions. After your student completes his silent reading, use the following questions and statements as a guide to discuss the pages he read.

1. Do scientists know for sure how many layers the earth has? *(No, they think the earth has three layers.)*
2. Name the three layers of the earth. *(crust, mantle, and core)*
3. Which layer is the thinnest? *(the crust)*
4. What do you think a geologist is? *(a scientist who studies the earth)*
5. How hot do geologists think the mantle is? *(3,000 degrees Fahrenheit)*
6. How thick and how hot is the core of the earth? *(It is 4,200 miles thick from one side to another, and the temperature is as high as 7,200 degrees Fahrenheit.)*

7. Is the core inside or outside of the mantle? *(inside)*

 The core is the hottest part of the earth. It is probably more liquid than the mantle.

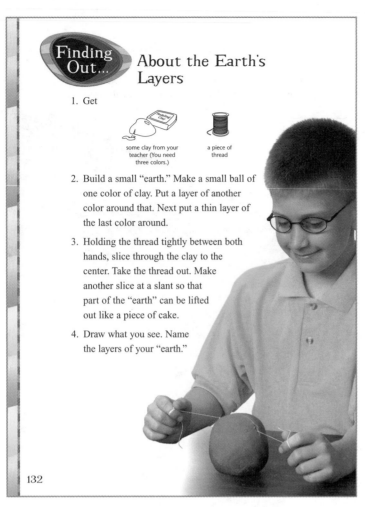

Finding Out... About the Earth's Layers

1. Get

some clay from your teacher (You need three colors.)

a piece of thread

2. Build a small "earth." Make a small ball of one color of clay. Put a layer of another color around that. Next put a thin layer of the last color around.

3. Holding the thread tightly between both hands, slice through the clay to the center. Take the thread out. Make another slice at a slant so that part of the "earth" can be lifted out like a piece of cake.

4. Draw what you see. Name the layers of your "earth."

132

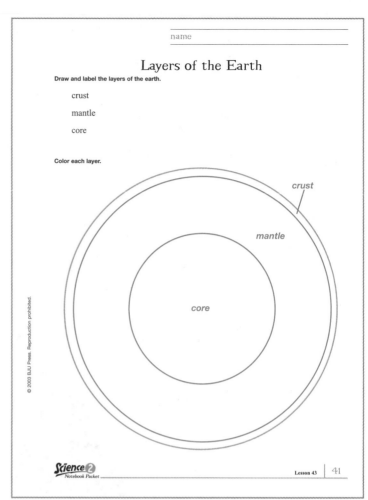

name _____

Layers of the Earth

Draw and label the layers of the earth.

crust

mantle

core

Color each layer.

crust

mantle

core

Science 2 Notebook Packet

Lesson 43   41

Evaluating the Lesson

Direct a *Finding Out* activity on page 132. Using three colors of play dough and following the directions given, assist your student in building the model of the earth.

Red, yellow, and green are good, clear colors to use. Green is especially appropriate for the crust. Thread works much better than a knife for cutting out a wedge of the earth.

Supervise as your student completes Step 3 of the activity. Assist him as he lifts out the wedge so that the structure will not collapse. The completed model with wedge removed provides an excellent view of the probable appearance of the inside of the earth.

Conclude the activity. Direct your student's attention to notebook page 41. Using the model of the earth that he just made, instruct your student to color and label the drawing of the layers of the earth.

For Your Information

Because the crust of the earth is only about three miles thick at the bottom of oceans (as compared to thirty-seven miles under some mountain ranges), scientists have theorized about the possibilities of getting through the crust to learn more about the mantle. They have been attempting to reach the *Moho,* which is the boundary between the crust and the mantle. (The Moho is named for a Yugoslavian scientist, Andrija Mohorovičić, who discovered it in the early 1900s.) In 1961, scientists from the United States began Project Mohole, an ambitious attempt to drill through the crust. But when the project ran out of funds, it was discontinued by Congress. At this time, no one has obtained a sample of material from the mantle of the earth.

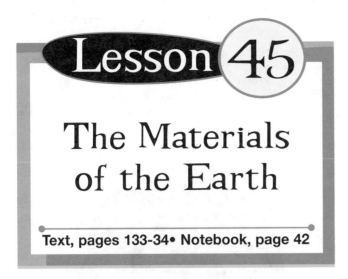

Lesson 45

The Materials of the Earth

Text, pages 133-34• Notebook, page 42

Preview

Objective

Given proper instruction, your student will be able to
- Describe features of the earth's crust.

Materials

Have available
- A globe*†
- 1 nickel
- 1 shallow dishpan
- Sand for the dishpan*

Prepare
- The dishpan by filling it about half full of sand and then adding water. The water should only slightly cover the sand.

Lesson

Introducing the Lesson

Introduce the activity. Show your student the globe and ask him what a globe represents. *(the earth)* Does it represent the crust, the mantle, or the core of the earth? *(the crust)* If your globe is a relief globe or has shading to show differences in land features, point out those differences to your student. Tell your student that you will be using the globe as you study about what makes up the crust of the earth.

Direct the activity. Use the following questions to direct a discussion about the features on the globe.

1. What color makes up most of the globe? *(whatever color represents oceans on your globe)*
2. What does that color represent? *(oceans)*
3. What do the other colors represent? *(land)*
4. What are the big landmasses called? *(continents)*
5. Is all the land on the earth in the continents? *(No, some is in smaller pieces.)*
6. What do you call these smaller lands in the oceans? *(islands)*
7. Of which is there the most—oceans, continents, or islands? *(oceans)*
8. What do you think the crust is made of? *(rocks and soil)*

Continue the activity. Ask your student what the other two parts of the earth are. *(the mantle and the core)* Ask whether he remembers what the mantle is made of. *(rock)*

Show your student the nickel. Tell him to imagine a huge pile of nickels, melted down. Ask what part of the earth is made of something that is like melted nickels. *(the core)* He should be able to see now why the core is the hottest part of the earth.

Conclude the activity. Give your student a dishpan filled with sand. Tell your student to design a sand map. His map should include continents, islands, and oceans. He may add rivers, mountains, and lakes if he desires. He should name his continents and islands.

 The project works best with a small amount of water since the sand soaks it up so easily. With too much water, the sand will not stay formed. Your child should leave his map intact after completion for use during the evaluation.

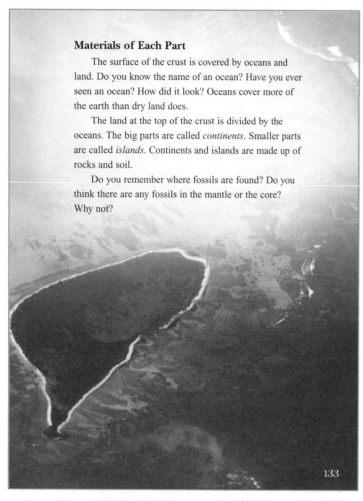

Materials of Each Part

The surface of the crust is covered by oceans and land. Do you know the name of an ocean? Have you ever seen an ocean? How did it look? Oceans cover more of the earth than dry land does.

The land at the top of the crust is divided by the oceans. The big parts are called *continents*. Smaller parts are called *islands*. Continents and islands are made up of rocks and soil.

Do you remember where fossils are found? Do you think there are any fossils in the mantle or the core? Why not?

133

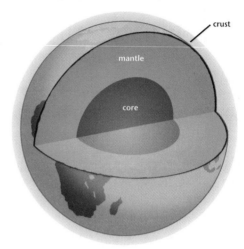

The mantle is probably made of a rock called *iron magnesium*. This rock is a mixture of a heavy metal and a lighter one that can burn brightly.

Scientists think that the outer part of the core is melted iron and nickel. Nickel is a silver-colored metal that can be made magnetic. The very center of the core is most likely almost solid iron.

Can you imagine how heavy the earth must be?

crust

mantle

core

"In the beginning God created the heaven and the earth. And the earth was without form, and void; and darkness was upon the face of the deep."   Genesis 1:1-2

134

Teaching the Lesson

Direct a text activity on pages 133-34. Use the following questions to initiate your student's interest in what he is going to read.

1. What are the parts of the earth's crust?

2. How heavy is the earth?

Continue with discussion questions. After your student completes his silent reading, use the following questions and statements as a guide to discuss the pages he read.

1. Name some oceans that you know about. *(Atlantic, Pacific, Indian, Antarctic)*

2. Which covers more of the earth—water or land? *(water)*

3. What are the big parts of land called? *(continents)*

4. What are the small parts of land called? *(islands)*

5. What is the mantle probably made of? *(iron and magnesium)*

6. Describe iron magnesium. *(rock that is a mixture of a heavy metal and a light metal that can burn lightly)*

7. What do scientists think the outer part of the earth's core is made of? *(melted iron and nickel)*

➤ Do you think there are any fossils in the mantle or the core? *(no)* **Why not?** *(Fossils are found in the top of the earth's crust. There cannot be fossils in the mantle or core because these parts of the earth are probably made of melted rock and solid iron.)*

8. Describe nickel. *(a silver-colored metal that can be made magnetic)*

9. What do scientists think is in the very center of the earth's core? *(solid iron)*

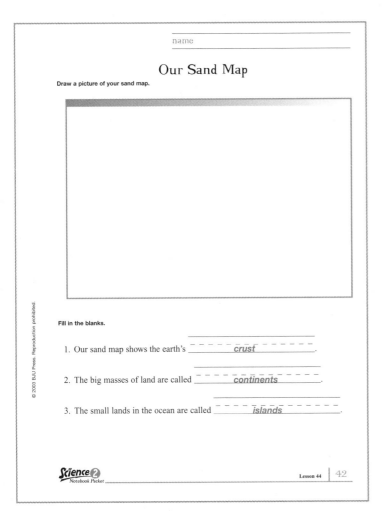

name _____

Our Sand Map

Draw a picture of your sand map.

Fill in the blanks.

1. Our sand map shows the earth's _____ *crust* _____.

2. The big masses of land are called _____ *continents* _____.

3. The small lands in the ocean are called _____ *islands* _____.

Science 2
Notebook Packet — Lesson 44 | 42

Evaluating the Lesson

Direct a notebook activity on page 42. Guide the use of the notebook page. Your student will use his map to draw what he has built. He will also complete the review statements on the bottom of his notebook page.

If play dough is left over from Lessons 42 and 43, help your student use it to make a relief map on plywood or poster board.

For Your Information

Man has never been able to study directly the mantle or core of the earth. The earth's crust is all that he has ever been able to observe. Scientists believe that two layers of rock cover the earth: a layer of basaltic rock under the oceans and continents, and an additional layer of granite that makes up the thickness of the continents. It is this granite that is responsible for land forms, such as mountains, with which we are familiar. The earth's crust contains 197,000,000 square miles. Twenty-nine percent of that mass is land, and the other seventy-one percent is water. The seven continents make up most of the landmass, and many islands account for the rest. The study of land features is known as topography.

Lessons 46-49

Where Things Live

Your student will discriminate between living and nonliving parts of an environment. He will observe and discuss the differences in animal homes and become acquainted with terms such as *habitat, environment, biome, community,* and *population.* He will discover the importance of soil, sunlight, water, and wind on animals in a given environment. Finally, he will realize the importance of water to all living things.

Materials

The following items must be obtained or prepared before the presentation of the lesson. These items are designated with an * in the materials list in each lesson and in the Supplement. For further information see the individual lessons.

- 1 manila file folder (Family Time 46)
- Laminating film or clear Con-Tact paper (optional) (Family Time 46)
- 1 piece of poster board (Lesson 46)
- 6 live earthworms, available from a bait-and-tackle shop or from your backyard (Lesson 47)
- 4 colored stakes (Lesson 48)
- A location in your yard that contains at least one anthill (Lesson 49)

12

Family Time 46

Spin an Animal Home

Appendix, pages A23-A25

Prepare the following game for use in *Evaluating the Lesson* for Lesson 46.

Materials

Have available
- Home Teacher's Edition, pp. A23-A25
- Laminating film or clear Con-Tact paper (optional)*
- 1 manila file folder*
- Glue
- 1 metal brad
- Tape
- Stiff cardboard the size of the spinner
- 1 envelope
- 1 resealable plastic bag
- 1 colored button for each player

Instructions

First, to assemble the **game board,** glue pages A23-A24 of the Home Teacher's Edition side by side to the inside of a manila file folder. Laminate the board or cover it with clear Con-Tact paper.

Next, make one copy of the **spinner** sheet. Affix the copy to a stiff cardboard. After laminating, cut out the numbered square and the dial. Assemble the spinner by pushing a metal brad through the X on the dial and then through the center of the numbered square. To let the dial spin freely, bend the prongs of the brad $\frac{1}{8}$" from the head. Tape the prongs to the back of the square to keep the brad from spinning with the dial. For additional spinning ease, bend the square slightly away from the dial. The square will curve slightly downward, and the dial will spin freely.

Finally, cut out the column of answers from page A25 and place it in an envelope labeled *Challenges.*

Put the *Challenges* envelope and spinner into a resealable plastic bag or an envelope and attach the bag or envelope to the back of the game board folder. You will also need colored buttons to serve as game markers.

Lesson 46

Homes for Living Things

Text, pages 136-38

Preview

Objectives

Given proper instruction, your student will be able to

- Describe some of the differences in animals' homes.
- List three biomes.

Materials

Have available

- A few old magazines that include pictures of outdoor places
- 1 piece of poster board*
- Glue
- Scissors
- Felt-tip pens or crayons
- A Write It flip chart
- The "Spin an Animal Home" game that was prepared in Family Time 46

 Magazine sources include *National Geographic*, outdoor magazines, travel magazines and brochures, science periodicals, and many general-interest publications.

Notes

The discussion of biomes has been limited to three general ones: desert, forest, and grassland. There are several kinds of *forest* biomes. These have not been explained for the sake of simplicity; however, they are included in the enrichment game, along with the *jungle* biome.

Water, although home for many animals, is termed an *ecosystem* rather than a biome.

Lesson

Introducing the Lesson

Introduce the activity. Ask your student the following questions:

1. Could a bird live in a hive?
2. Could a mouse live at the bottom of the ocean?
3. Could a fish live in a tree?

Ask your student why none of these could occur. *(Birds must have nests. Bees live in a hive, etc.)* Point out to your student that God provides each of His creatures with a special home and gives each animal exactly what it needs to live in that home. (Bible Promise: I. God as Master) Tell your student that in this chapter he is going to learn about animals' homes.

Direct the activity. Write the words *Biomes—Different Homes* on the Write It flip chart. Then write each of the following words on a separate page of the Write It flip chart—*Desert, Forest,* and *Grasslands*. As you ask the following questions, write your student's responses under the correct category, thereby giving characteristics of each biome.

Continue the activity. Ask your student what he thinks of when he hears the word *desert*. *(hot land with endless miles of sand)* Ask him what kind of plants he would expect to find in the desert. *(cactuses)* Ask him what kinds of animals live in the desert. *(snakes, insects, spiders, and any other animals that do not need much water)*

Now, ask your student to describe a *forest*. *(area with many trees and other plants)* Ask him whether a limited number of animals live in the forest. *(No, a great variety of birds and mammals live there.)*

Finally, ask your student what grasslands look like. *(area with many grasses and fields)* Ask him what animals live on the grasslands. *(buffalo, horses, prairie dogs, gophers, and pheasants)*

Conclude the activity. Give your student a piece of poster board and instruct him to divide it into three columns. Then give him time to copy the names of the three biomes listed on the Write It flip chart—one title for each of his columns. Give your student some magazines and instruct him to look through the magazines to find pictures of various biomes. He should cut the pictures out and glue them in the proper columns on his poster.

"The foxes have holes, and the birds of the air have nests."

Matthew 8:20

Kinds of Homes

God made every living thing to live in a particular place. He made each living thing able to get what it needs from that place.

Habitats

Name some places where animals live. Have you seen some wild animal homes? The place where an animal or plant lives is a *habitat*. Three habitats for animals are water, air, and soil. Can you think of animals that live in each of these places? Most animals live in one of these places.

136

Some animals live on or in other living things. A tick lives on another animal, often a dog. The skin of a dog can be a tick's habitat. A tapeworm lives inside another animal. Its habitat may be the stomach of that animal.

Environment

Everything that is around an organism in a habitat is called the *environment*. The word comes from two words that mean "to put in a circle." Look at the picture of the raccoons. What is their environment?

> A habitat has what the organism, the living thing, needs to live. It has the right temperature, the right food, and the right amount of light or darkness.

137

Teaching the Lesson

Direct a text activity on pages 136-38. Use the following questions to initiate your student's interest in what he is going to read.

1. What is a habitat?
2. Can you name an animal whose habitat is another animal?

Continue with discussion questions. After your student completes his silent reading, use the following questions and statements as a guide to discuss the pages he read.

1. Read again the verse given on page 136. Tell how this verse explains that God prepares different homes for different animals. *(He said that the foxes live in holes and the birds live in nests.)*

2. Why could a fox not live in a nest? *(because the fox could not get up a tree, could not fly, could not fit in a nest, etc.)*

3. Where does a prairie dog live? *(in a tunnel under the ground)*

4. What is a habitat? *(a place where an animal or a plant lives)*

5. Name some habitats mentioned or pictured on pages 136 and 137. *(a rotting tree stump, a dog, the stomach of another animal, etc.)*

6. Look around the room. Name some things that surround you. *(Possible answers might be walls, bookshelves, furniture, and potted plants.)*

7. If you were at the beach, what would be your surroundings? *(Possible answers might be sand, water, umbrellas, seagulls, and shells.)*

8. What do scientists call the surroundings of living things? *(environment)*

9. Would seagulls from the ocean be able to live in the environment of your home? Why? *(No; they need a different environment.)*

10. Do you think that each living thing needs its own unique environment? Why? *(Yes; God has provided each living thing with characteristics suitable for a particular, unique environment that aid the animal's growth and reproduction.)*

11. Look at the illustrations on page 138. What looks strange or out of place about the illustrations? *(Cactuses do not belong in the forest. Polar bears do not belong in the desert.)*

12. What do scientists call a large land area with all the plants and animals of its environment? *(a biome)*

13. Since a cactus does not belong in the forest, what biome does it belong in? *(desert)*

Biomes

Many plants and animals can share the same place. A large area that takes in all the plants and animals in the same environment is a *biome*. Some biomes are on land, and others are in the water.

Two land biomes are a desert and a forest of evergreen trees. Would a polar bear live in a desert? Would a cactus grow in an evergreen forest? Why are the bear and the cactus out of place in these pictures?

One water biome is a lake. What living things would have a habitat there?

138

Evaluating the Lesson

Introduce the activity. Introduce the "Spin an Animal Home" game for you and your student to play together. Other family members may join in too. Explain each game piece. First, show your student the **game board.** Explain that the squares on the board form a winding path from the *Start* square at the left to the *Finish* square at the right. Point out that on each square is pictured the name of a plant or an animal that belongs to one of the types of animal homes. Explain that there are two water ecosystems listed—the ocean and the freshwater (lakes and ponds) ecosystems. Point out that the jungle biome has been included also. (The animals and plants included for these should be familiar to your student and should be enriching rather than confusing to him.) Explain to your student that after spinning, he is to move to the next space on the board that contains an animal or plant from the type of animal home that his spin indicated.

Second, demonstrate how to use the **spinner.** Place the spinner on the top of a flat surface and hold the edge of the numbered square with one hand. Then place the middle finger of your other hand against one of the dial points and flick your finger toward you, spinning the dial.

Third, show the colored buttons to be used as game pieces.

Direct the activity. Explain that the object of the game is to be the first player to reach the end of the trail. All players start with their game markers on the *Start* square. Each player spins once; the highest number goes first. In turn, each player spins and then looks at the game board to determine which space contains the right animal or plant for that type of animal home. He then moves his game piece to that square. If he lands on the "Free Animal Home" square, he should move to the nearest corresponding space on the board.

Continue the activity. The other players will act as "monitors" to check correct answers. If there is a dispute, any player may challenge the other player's decision. The player will then refer to the answer card in the envelope labeled *Challenges.* If the player is correct, he may move his piece ahead two more spaces, and the incorrect challenger must move his piece back two spaces. If the player is incorrect, he must move back to the square where he began that turn, and the challenger may move his game piece ahead two spaces.

Conclude the activity. Play continues until one player reaches the end space by spinning the "Free Animal Home" space on the spinner.

For Your Information

The term *water ecosystem* includes two distinct categories. Approximately seventy percent of the earth's surface is covered with *marine* or saltwater ecosystems in the form of oceans. Different organisms live in different areas of the ocean; for example, the organisms that live near the continents could not live in the dark ocean depths. The other kind of water ecosystem is *freshwater.* It too has many different subcategories: lakes, swamps, and rivers are some.

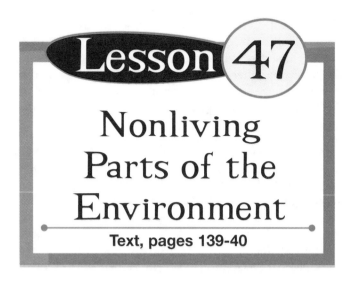

Lesson 47

Nonliving Parts of the Environment

Text, pages 139-40

Preview

Objective

Given proper instruction, your student will be able to

- Describe some of the nonliving parts of the environment: soil, water, and sunlight.

Materials

Have available

- 6 live earthworms, available from a bait-and-tackle shop or from your backyard*
- 1 foil pie plate
- 2 paper towels
- 1 small piece of aluminum foil
- Some dirt or sand
- A Write It flip chart

Prepare

- The pie plate by lining half of it with a dry paper towel.

Notes

Wind is also a nonliving part of the environment, but it will be discussed in the next lesson.

Worms have proven to be excellent lab specimens. Your student can easily observe the worms' behavior and study their environmental needs.

Lesson

Introducing the Lesson

Introduce the activity. Put the earthworms on the dry paper towel in the pie plate. Cover the other half of the pie plate with aluminum foil. Instruct your student to observe the worms for a few minutes. Ask him whether the worms

stay on the light side of the pan or move to the dark side. *(move to the dark side)* (*NOTE:* The worms may move underneath the dry paper towel, but the point will still be made.) Ask your student why he thinks the worms move. *(They like to be in darkness.)* Ask your student why he thinks the worms like the darkness. *(It keeps them from drying out.)* Ask him to name some other animals that prefer the darkness. *(owls, moles, opossums, bats, raccoons)* Ask your student whether he thinks light affects where and how animals live. *(yes)*

Direct the activity. Instruct your student to remove the foil from the pie plate. Return the earthworms to the dry paper towel. Line the opposite half of the pie plate with a wet paper towel; then instruct your student to observe the worms again. Ask him whether he thinks the worms prefer the dry half of the pie plate or the wet half. *(the wet half)* Ask him what this tells him about some animals and their need for water. *(Some need to live in or near water.)* Ask your student to name other animals that either live in water or prefer a wet environment. *(fish, turtles, salamanders, ducks)* Ask him whether he thinks there are any animals that do not need water at all. *(no)* Ask him whether he thinks that different animals need different amounts of water in their environments. *(yes)*

Continue the activity. Return the earthworms to the dry paper towel again and remove the wet paper towel from the pie plate. Then fill the other half of the pie plate with the dirt or sand and instruct your student to once again observe the behavior of the worms. Ask your student what the worms do in this situation. *(They burrow into the dirt.)* Ask your student why he thinks the worms like to be in the dirt. *(It is moist and keeps them wet; they are safer in the dirt; they can find food.)* Point out to the students that the worms are happiest in moist dirt because that is the environment for which God created them. Ask your student to name some other animals that like to live underground. *(groundhogs, shrews, moles)*

Ask your student whether he has ever seen different kinds of soil. Tell him to describe different types. Ask him whether he thinks that different soils support different plants and animals. *(yes)*

Conclude the activity. Write the headings *Living* and *Nonliving* at the top of a page on the Write It flip chart. Ask your student what scientists call the surroundings of an organism. *(environment)*

Ask your student to think of things around him that he needs in order to keep himself alive or to live comfortably. Tell your student that you are going to make a list from the things that he mentions. The list may include such things as the following:

1. Living: food, parents, shade trees
2. Nonliving: water, air, soil, house, heater, bed

Parts of an Environment

Scientists study how everything in a habitat acts together. They call this study *ecology*. That word means "the study of the home."

Parts that Are not Living

The sun is important to most environments. How brightly the sun shines and how long it shines will determine what plants can live in a place. The sun also can cause the animals to stay or leave. If a place got too hot, the animals might go somewhere else. What would happen to the plants?

139

Soil is another part of the environment. Not all soils are alike. Some soil will grow only certain kinds of plants. Those plants can then be food for only certain kinds of animals.

Let's say that a place has the kind of sunlight and soil that grows only grass. Animals that live mostly on grass could live there. But could animals that eat fruits live there? Why not?

140

Look at the list that you made. Ask your student whether both the living things and the nonliving things around him are part of his environment. *(yes)* Tell your student that during this lesson you will be looking together at how some of the nonliving parts of the environment affect living things.

 This might provide a good opportunity to discuss with your child that God created humans with the intelligence to use things in the environment for comfort, safety, etc. Man is capable of adjusting and surviving in many different environments.

Teaching the Lesson

Direct a text activity on pages 139-40. Use the following question to initiate your student's interest in what he is going to read: What are some important parts of the environment?

Continue with discussion questions. After your student completes his silent reading, use the following questions and statements as a guide to discuss the pages he read.

1. What happens to plants if their environments get too hot? *(They will probably wither and die.)*
2. Are there plants in the desert? *(yes, a few plants that do not require much moisture)*
3. Name some animals that cannot live in an environment where only short grass grows. *(Some possible answers are monkeys, parrots, and beavers.)*
4. What will affect which plants will grow in a certain environment? *(how brightly and how long the sun shines)*

Evaluating the Lesson

Direct an identifying activity. Read the following sentences aloud, instructing your student to identify which part of the environment is important in the situation described—soil, water, or sunlight.

1. Some kinds of cactuses bloom after rain, but the flowers do not last long. *(water)*
2. Tiny crabs washed in by the tide quickly burrow into the beach so that they will not be seen. *(soil)*
3. Leaves that drop off the trees in the fall decay to make the forest floor richer. *(soil)*

4. There are some kinds of birds that you will never see unless you travel on the ocean because they never come to land. *(water)*

5. On a nice summer morning, a turtle will come out of his hiding place to sit on a smooth rock away from the trees. *(sunlight)*

6. Grasslands occur in areas where there is not enough rainfall for a forest. *(water)*

7. There are some kinds of fish that live so far down in dark caves that they do not have well-developed eyes. *(sunlight)*

8. Big trees cannot grow on sandy beaches. *(soil)*

9. In some forests the trees are so thick that animals who live on the forest floor live in the shade all the time. *(sunlight)*

Enrichment

Direct an activity dealing with water. Get a cactus and cut a slice from its top. Place the cactus on a table and encourage your student to examine it from time to time to see how it conserves water. You may need to make a fresh cut periodically.

Direct an activity dealing with sunlight. Put several sheets of construction paper (not fadeless paper) and several pennies or flat objects somewhere in the room. Tell your student to place a penny or two on a piece of construction paper and to find a place in the house to leave the paper for a day or two in direct sunlight. After the time has passed, he should go back and observe what has happened. The sun will fade the paper around the objects but not under them.

For Your Information

Certain factors in the environment work in harmony to establish a unique biome. The water cycle is a good example of this harmony in nature. Water evaporates from the environment and cools high in the atmosphere. It condenses and forms precipitation, falling to the ground as rain, sleet, snow, or hail. Some of this water evaporates again, and some runs into the ground by gravity to provide the water needed for wells, deep plant roots, and ponds. Nature uses the water over and over to prevent waste in the environment.

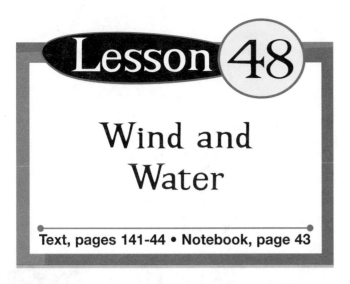

Lesson 48

Wind and Water

Text, pages 141-44 • Notebook, page 43

Preview

Objectives

Given proper instruction, your student will be able to

- Tell how wind affects organisms.
- Detect differences in wind speed and wind direction.

Materials

Have available

- 2 small pieces of paper
- One foot from an old nylon stocking
- Wire coat hanger
- Rubber cement or glue
- 4 colored stakes*

Prepare

- The hosiery by cutting off one foot up to about an inch above the heel.

Notes

This activity should be conducted on a day when there is at least a slight breeze.

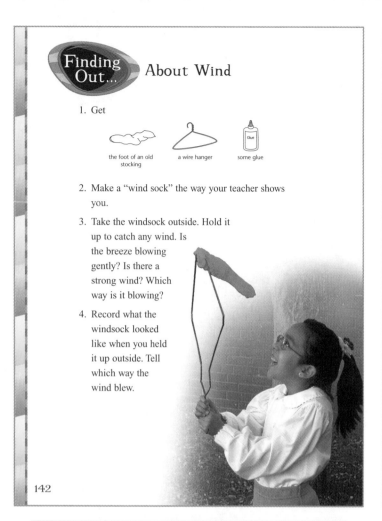

Finding Out... About Wind

1. Get

the foot of an old stocking   a wire hanger   some glue

2. Make a "wind sock" the way your teacher shows you.

3. Take the windsock outside. Hold it up to catch any wind. Is the breeze blowing gently? Is there a strong wind? Which way is it blowing?

4. Record what the windsock looked like when you held it up outside. Tell which way the wind blew.

142

Wind can also help determine which plants and animals live in a place. Many organisms cannot stand hard winds all the time. Along ocean coasts the wind blows nearly all the time. Seagulls do well on ocean coasts. They sail along on the wind. But how do you think a small wren would do?

Only certain plants can live in wind. Look at this picture. How have these trees grown because of the wind in their environment? Which way does the wind always blow there?

How does wind change the environment of water biomes? Have you ever seen waves tossed by wind? High waves will make life harder for some organisms and easier for others.

141

Lesson

Introducing the Lesson

Introduce a *Finding Out* activity. Tell your student that today you are going to use a *windsock* to learn about the speed and direction of the wind. Direct his attention to page 142 and instruct him to read the steps for the activity. Gather all of the materials.

Direct the activity. Tell your student to hold the hook end of a hanger in one hand and to push on the opposite side of the hanger to make it elongated. Put a dab of glue along the elongated end of the wire. Attach the piece of hosiery so that it is spread out along the end but dangles freely.

Continue the activity. Take your student outside. Set up the stakes around the yard so that they represent the four different directions—north, south, east, and west. Tell your student to hold his windsock out from his body so that it will catch the wind. Remind him to hold the sock both low and high. He should notice toward which stake the wind blows the sock and how high the wind blows it.

Conclude the activity. Once back in the house, instruct your student to lay one or two small pieces of paper and his closed textbook on the table. Tell him to pick up the pieces of paper and blow them with small puffs. Then direct him to blow on his textbook in the same manner. Ask your student whether he knows what part of the environment he is mimicking. *(the wind)* Ask him how the "wind" that he blew affected the tiny pieces of paper. *(It made them fly up.)* Ask your student why the pieces flew into the air. *(They were very light.)* Ask him whether the "wind" affected his book. *(no)* Why not? *(The book was too heavy to be affected by that small amount of wind.)* Tell your student that he will learn more about wind and also some about water in today's lesson.

The most important part of an environment is water. How much rain falls and when it falls make a place a desert or a thick jungle. Jungles get more rain than deserts.

143

Some environments are all water. Is a pond all water? How about a river?

What happens to a swamp when there is no rain? Does it become some other kind of environment? What will happen to the plants and animals?

Do you help water your garden or lawn? Why do you water it?

144

Teaching the Lesson

Direct a text activity on pages 141-44. Use the following question to initiate your student's interest in what he is going to read: What is the most important part of the environment?

Continue with discussion questions. After your student completes his silent reading, use the following questions and statements as a guide to discuss the pages he read.

1. Look at the picture of the trees on page 141. What has the wind done to these trees? *(It has bent them into unusual positions.)*

2. How can the wind bend trees into unusual positions? *(It is a strong force, and the trees are weaker.)*

3. Do you think the wind could bend a big oak tree as much as it bent the trees pictured on page 141? Why? *(No; the big oak tree is stronger.)*

4. What is the most important part of the environment? *(water)*

5. Is a pond all water? *(no)*

6. Is a river all water? *(no)* What else is part of that environment? *(plants, fish, turtles, etc.)*

➤ **Does it become some other kind of environment?** *(The environment changes as the water levels change.)*

➤ **What will happen to the plants and animals?** *(Whether they lose water from lack of rain or from man's work, swamp plants dry or become scarce. Animals that need the plants to live must go elsewhere or die as well.)*

7. What happens to a swamp when there is no rain? *(It loses much of its water.)*

8. Why do you think it is important to water your garden or lawn? *(to help the grass and other plants grow)*

name

Making a Windsock

When we held the sock high,

Answers will vary.

the wind blew toward _ _ _ _ _ _ _ _ _ _ _ _.

The wind blew _ _ _ _ _ _ _ _ _ _ _ _ _ _ _.

When we held the sock low,

the wind blew toward _ _ _ _ _ _ _ _ _ _ _ _.

The wind blew _ _ _ _ _ _ _ _ _ _ _ _ _ _.

When we held the sock _ _ _ _ _ _ _ _ _ _ _ _,

the wind blew toward _ _ _ _ _ _ _ _ _ _ _ _.

The wind blew _ _ _ _ _ _ _ _ _ _ _ _ _ _.

Science 2
Notebook Packet

Lesson 48 | 43

For Your Information

Wind is caused primarily by the uneven heating of air masses. When air at the equator is heated by the sun, it rises and moves toward the poles. As it cools, it begins falling back toward the earth and the equator. The rotation of the earth then causes those air masses to move around the earth directionally as well. Smaller, local winds are also affected by the positions of mountains and bodies of water. The wind is important ecologically because it affects which organisms will live in a particular area. In the ocean, wind is replaced by the movement of water currents.

Evaluating the Lesson

Conduct a notebook activity on page 43. Your student should record the observations that he made while using his windsock. You can either direct your student to take the notebook page outside with him or wait until he returns to the house to complete the page.

Lesson 49

Communities and Populations

Text, pages 145-48 • Notebook, page 44

name

Populations

Record the following populations.   *Answers will vary.*

1. The ants in the anthill _____

2. The people in the classroom _____

3. The fish in the aquarium _____

4. The trees in the school yard _____

5. _____

6. _____

7. _____

8. _____

What populations make up the community of this school?
_____
_____
_____
_____

© 2003 BJU Press. Reproduction prohibited.

Science 2
Notebook Packet   Lesson 49   44

Preview

Objective

Given proper instruction, your student will be able to

• Discriminate between a community and a population.

Materials

Have available

• A location in your yard or neighborhood that contains at least one anthill*

• A piece of string

Prepare

• The notebook page for this lesson by making a list of names of populations (groups of living things) that will individualize the page for your particular setting.

Notes

Animals and plants in your home, such as potted plants or fish in an aquarium, will supply examples of populations as you teach this lesson.

There are several blank lines on the notebook page because each educational setting is in a different habitat and therefore has different plants and animals to be included as populations.

Lesson

Introducing the Lesson

Direct an outdoor activity and a notebook activity on page 44. Take your student outside to the anthill you have located. Instruct him to bring his pencil and notebook page. Put a string around the anthill to mark its boundaries, and tell your student that he is going to count the population of ants that appear during a set time. Direct your student to count as best as he can the number of ants that appear. Instruct your student to record this number as the first entry on the notebook page. Tell your student that he has just recorded the population of ants in that anthill.

Continue the activity. Instruct your student to look around the yard or the house to record the populations referred to in items 2 through 4.

Teaching the Lesson

Direct a text activity on pages 145-48. Use the following questions to initiate your student's interest in what he is going to read.

1. What is a community?
2. What is a population?

Continue with discussion questions. After your student completes his silent reading, use the following questions and statements as a guide to discuss the pages he read.

1. Look at the pictures of the aquarium on page 145. What kinds of living things can you see in these pictures? *(a boy, fish, coral, and a turtle)*

2. What do scientists call all the living things in an area? *(a community)*

3. Look around the house. Name some of the living things that you see. (*NOTE:* If you do not have living plants or animals in your house, you might direct your student's attention to the living things he can see outside the window.)

4. Look at page 146 and find the term that scientists use for all the living things of just one kind. *(population)*

5. What living things make up various populations in your town? *(people, oak trees, ants, dogs, etc.)* Are people, trees, and dogs all part of the same population? Explain. *(No; all people in the town make a population of people. All trees in the town make a population of trees, etc.)*

6. Look at the picture on pages 146-47 and try to count the number of plant populations in the garden. *(ten)*

7. Look at the picture on page 148. Why would it be difficult to take a population count of the animals in the photograph? *(The picture does not reveal all of the animals in the field, so an accurate count could not be taken.)*

8. If you were actually in this field, why would it still be difficult to take a population count of the animals? *(They would be moving around, and some animals would be grouped together so that an accurate count could not be taken very easily.)*

Parts That Are Living

All living things in an area make a community. We can see most of the living things in an environment. But a few living things are too small to see.

Name all the living things you can see in the picture.

145

Choose one kind of flower in the picture.
How many flowers of that kind are there in
the picture? You have just found one plant
population.

All living things of one kind in an area
make up a *population*. All plants of one
kind are called a plant population. All
animals of one kind make up an animal
population.

How many different plant
populations are shown in the picture?

146

147

When you count how many of one kind of animal or plant live in an area, you do a population count. How would you like to do a population count here?

"Are not five sparrows sold for two farthings, and not one of them is forgotten before God?"   Luke 12:6

148

Evaluating the Lesson

Continue the notebook page activity. Tell your student to write on the blank lines the populations that you have added from your neighborhood's habitat. Instruct your student to count the populations of the various things listed and record the numbers on the page.

All the populations of a biotic community affect each other. Various animal populations eat various plant populations. Fungal and bacterial populations break down organic materials from dead animals and plants. The bee population pollinates clover; the clover puts nitrogen into the soil for use by other populations. When a population of plants or animals becomes extinct, it upsets the delicate balances of all the other organisms in an area. Therefore, conservation is important.

Enrichment

A terrarium is an excellent tool to reinforce the concepts of habitat, environment, and communities. An old aquarium makes an ideal container. Your student may study the terrarium's interactions whenever he has opportunity. The bottom layer, made of small pebbles, should be covered with a layer of charcoal to absorb noxious gases. Place the soil on top of the charcoal layer. You may add a pond by nestling a small shallow pan in the dirt. Plant small ferns, grasses, or seedlings; add decaying wood and small animals, such as lizards, if desired. This environment must be kept moist; so keep a glass or a plastic cover on the top.

For a desert terrarium, cover the charcoal with sand and include cactuses and dead twigs instead of moist items. This environment does not need a lid. For a grassland terrarium, use soil and grass seed. Keep it covered.

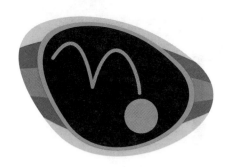

CHAPTER THIRTEEN

Lessons 50-53

Motion

By observing and participating in hands-on activities in this chapter, your student will see for himself the results of force on matter. He will also learn to describe with words and numbers the resulting motion of force on matter.

Materials

The following items must be obtained or prepared before the presentation of the lesson. These items are designated with an * in the materials list in each lesson and in the Supplement. For further information see the individual lessons.

- 2 small model cars similar in shape, size, and material (Lessons 50 and 53)
- 1 small (1"-2" square) piece of oak tag (Lesson 52)

13

Move with Haste!

The following Scripture and discussion could serve as an interesting family devotional time as well as an introduction to the following lessons about movement.

Materials

Have available
• A Bible

Instructions

After reading Exodus 12:33 aloud and discussing the fact that Pharaoh had finally decided to let God's people go, discuss with your family members what it must have been like to see all of the Israelites leaving the land of Egypt. There were so many people that if they were lined up, shoulder to shoulder, heel to toe, they would fill two hundred football fields! And besides people, there were flocks and herds. To make matters more interesting, Pharaoh wanted them to move with haste! Ask your student to think of words that mean "to move with haste." *(run, dart, race, dash)* Yes, God kept His promise to free His people from the hand of Pharaoh. (BAT: 8a Faith in God's promises)

Lesson 50

What Causes Movement?

Text, pages 150-53 • Notebook, page 45

Preview

Objectives

Given proper instruction, your student will be able to

- Tell how long an object moved.
- Tell how far an object moved.
- Indicate the fastest and slowest moving objects in a group of pictures.

Materials

Have available

- 1 stopwatch or a watch with a second hand
- 2 small model cars similar in shape, size, and material*
- 1 tape measure
- Masking tape
- A Write It flip chart

Prepare

- The cars by testing them to make sure that they move straight ahead when pushed.
- The running surface (a large table top or counter works best) by taping a starting line about one foot from one end of the surface.
- The Write It flip chart by writing *Car No. 1* and *Car No. 2.*

Notes

The statement on page 153, "Sometimes the way moving things look depends on where you are," introduces the idea of relative motion. This concept is important to the understanding of motion in the solar system. Emphasize it only as an item of interest to which your student may be able to relate. You may want to read the sentences and discuss the cartoon on that page after you have completed the evaluation.

Finding Out... About Speed and Distance

1. Get

    a stopwatch or a watch with a second hand   two small model cars   a tape measure

2. Have a partner gently push one of the cars when you say "Go." Start your watch at the same time. When the car stops on its own, stop the watch or call out the time. How many seconds did the car move?

3. Measure how far the car moved.

4. Leave the first car where it stopped. Push the other car harder. Time and measure its travel. How far did the second car go? For how long did it move?

5. Record what happened.

152

Lesson

Introducing the Lesson

Introduce the activity. Direct your student's attention to the *Finding Out* activity on page 152. Instruct him to read silently the steps on the page. Then direct him to look at the picture and predict what he thinks happened when the first car was pushed and what happened when the second car was pushed. *(The second car probably moved for a longer time and a longer distance than the first car because the push on it was harder than on the first car.)*

Direct the activity. Allow your student to help gather the materials. Place the materials on a table or on a countertop.

 You may want to invite another child to participate in this part of the lesson.

If you choose to do this demonstration with your student, you should keep time and allow your student to be the driver. Both of you should stand near the starting line. Explain to the driver that he must set the front wheels of Car

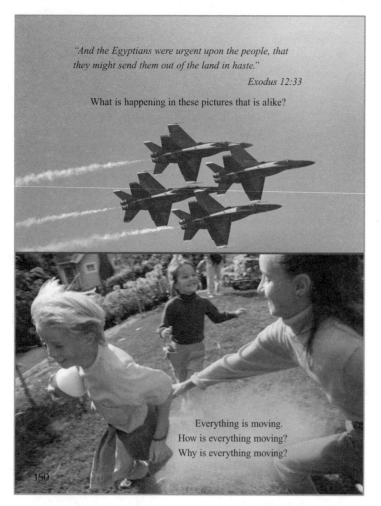

"And the Egyptians were urgent upon the people, that they might send them out of the land in haste."

Exodus 12:33

What is happening in these pictures that is alike?

Everything is moving.
How is everything moving?
Why is everything moving?

150

How Things Move

Scientists use both words and numbers to describe. If they describe a tree, they describe its size with numbers and its color with words. If they describe a car, they describe its speed with numbers and its shape with words. If they describe motion, they use both words and numbers too.

What do they describe about motion using numbers? They describe how far things move by using numbers. They measure distance. They describe how fast things move by using numbers. They measure speed.

151

No. 1 on the starting line and push the car *gently* from that spot when you say "Go." Start the stopwatch when you say "Go" and stop the watch when the car comes to a stop. You may need to have some trial runs, but after a successful run is completed, tell the driver to write on the Write It flip chart the number of seconds Car No. 1 moved. Measure from the starting line to the front wheels of the car and report the number of inches that the car moved. Then direct your student to write the number of inches under *Car No. 1* on the Write It flip chart.

Continue the activity. Follow the same procedure for Car No. 2, but instruct the driver to push that car harder. After your student records the number of seconds and the number of inches that Car No. 2 moved, ask him to tell the differences in the cars' movements by using words like *slow, slower, fast,* and *faster.*

Conclude the activity. If time allows, repeat the demonstration. Lead your student to conclude that he needs to use both words and numbers to describe how things move. Tell him that he will learn more about motion in today's lesson.

Teaching the Lesson

Direct a text activity on pages 150-53. Use the following questions to initiate your student's interest in what he is going to read.

1. How do you describe motion using words?
2. How do you describe motion using numbers?

Continue with discussion questions. After your student completes his silent reading, use the following questions and statements as a guide to discuss the pages he read.

1. Look at the pictures on page 150. What is happening in these pictures that is alike? *(Everything is moving.)*
2. How is each of the items on page 150 moving? *(The planes are moving faster than anything else on the page. The children are running.)*
3. Look out of a window at a tree. Describe the size and the color of the tree using numbers and words. *(Answers will vary.)*
4. Think about your family's car. Use numbers and words to describe the speed and the appearance of the car. *(Answers will vary.)*
5. What information do words give about motion? *(the way things look and the way things move)*

What do you describe about motion by using words? You describe the way things move by using words. You describe how they look to you.

Pretend you are in a moving car and you see a man standing in a field. Would he look as if he were moving? Pretend you are standing in the field and you see a man driving by in a car. Would the man in the car look as if he were moving? Sometimes the way moving things look depends on where you are.

153

6. What information do numbers give about motion? *(how far and how fast things move—distance and speed)*

7. If you were in a moving car and saw a man standing out in his field, would the man look as if he were moving? Why? *(Yes, he would appear to be moving because you are viewing him out of a "moving window" of your moving car; therefore everything that you see from that viewpoint appears to be moving.)*

8. If you were standing in a field and saw a man drive by in a car, would the man in the car seem to be moving? Why? *(Yes, he would look as if he were moving since you would see the whole scene, including the moving car whizzing past you.)*

9. What does the illustration tell you about the way things in motion look? *(The way moving things look often depends upon where you are when you view the moving things.)*

Evaluating the Lesson

Direct the use of notebook page 45. Instruct your student to follow the directions to indicate which pictured objects move fastest or slowest.

For Your Information

Forces do not always change the motion of an object. To cause movement, forces have to be *unbalanced*. If two men push on a door with the same amount of force but in opposite directions, the door will not move. The forces are balanced. Should one man, however, stop exerting force, the forces will become unbalanced momentarily, and the door will swing toward him. To make an object at rest move, you have to exert a little more force on it than whatever force is holding it still.

Lesson 51

The First Law of Motion

Text, pages 154-55

Preview

Objective

Given proper instruction, your student will be able to

- Describe how a passenger reacts to a bus's starting and stopping.

Materials

Have available

- 1 cup
- 1 3" × 5" card
- 1 button or penny

Notes

Before demonstrating Newton's first law of motion in front of your student, you should practice a few times. The key to success is flicking the card sharply in the center of the 3" side. Because the button has no sideways force on it, it will stay still until the card flies out from under it and gravity makes it fall into the cup.

Introducing the Lesson

Direct the activity. To demonstrate Newton's first law of motion, set on a table a cup topped with a 3" × 5" card and a button or a penny. Ask your student what the cup, the card, and the button are doing. *(They are all just sitting there.)* Tell your student that you want to get the card out from under the button without touching or moving the button. Ask your student for ideas about how you can do this. If he has no suggestions, tell him what you plan to do. Ask your student whether he thinks your suggestion will work and if not, why not. *(Your student might say that if the card moves, the button will move with it.)*

Conclude the activity. Quickly flick the card off the cup. Ask your student what he saw. Discuss what you did and lead your student to conclude that three things were sitting still until you hit one of them—the card. Ask your student whether the cup or the button moved sideways. Why? *(no, because you did not flick them)* Tell your student that he will learn in today's lesson more about the influence that something called *force* has on motion.

Why Things Move

Sir Isaac Newton, a scientist from long ago, was interested in motion. He came up with some ideas that describe why things move. He tested and proved his ideas. People today often call his ideas *Newton's laws of motion*.

The first law of motion says that an object keeps doing what it is doing until some force causes a change. A book stays at rest until you lift it. A marble stays at rest until you hit it with another marble. Look at the pictures. Name other examples of this law.

If you are in a car that stops quickly, your body keeps moving forward after the car has stopped. Seatbelts stop you from moving too far forward, but you still move.

154

First Law: An object keeps doing what it is doing until some force causes a change.

155

Teaching the Lesson

Direct a text activity on pages 154-55. Use the following questions to initiate your student's interest in what he is going to read.

1. Who was Sir Isaac Newton?
2. What is Newton's first law of motion?

Continue with discussion questions. After your student completes his silent reading, use the following questions and statements as a guide to discuss the pages he read.

1. Who was Sir Isaac Newton? *(a scientist from long ago who was interested in motion)*

2. What is the first law of motion? *(An object keeps doing what it is doing until some force causes a change.)*

3. Name some other examples relating to Newton's first law of motion. *(Some possible answers are the way your stomach feels when an elevator starts and stops; the way your head pushes back against the seat of an amusement park ride when the ride starts and jerks forward when the ride stops; the way your body seems to keep moving forward when you get to the bottom of a slide.)*

4. Look at the pictures of the bumper cars on page 154. What do you think would take place if a person in a moving car slammed into another car? *(His body would be thrown forward in his seat. The car would stop, but he would not stop immediately.)*

5. What movement would a person experience if he is sitting in a car and is suddenly hit by another car? *(His body would try to stay in the same place, but his head would jerk backward and his body would press back against the seat as if to say, "Hey, I'm not ready to move! I want to stay right here!")*

Evaluating the Lesson

Introduce the activity. Tell your student that you are going to take him for a ride on a bus. Ask him to notice the movement of the passengers as well as his own movement when the bus starts, as it moves along, and when it stops.

Direct the activity. As you ride on the bus with your student, discuss with him briefly some of the movements that can be observed. Ask your student what movements are caused when the bus travels over a bumpy street. *(The people bump up and down too.)*

Continue the activity. Once back home, discuss with your student some of the motions that he observed on the bus. Ask your student what the passengers did when the bus started. *(The passengers leaned back in their seats.)* Why did they do this? *(Their bodies were reacting to the forward motion of the bus.)* Ask your student what the passengers did when the bus stopped. *(They leaned forward in their seats because their bodies were still moving forward when the bus stopped moving.)*

Discuss the use of seat belts in cars. Ask your student to explain how seat belts work and what they protect passengers from.

Conclude the activity. Instruct your student to draw a picture of the passengers on the bus. Allow your student to select which motion to illustrate—when the bus starts, when the bus stops, or when it causes bumping as it rolls along. Tell him to position the passenger's bodies correctly for the motion that he chooses to illustrate. Give your student opportunity to explain his drawing and to tell the rest of the family about his bus ride.

For Your Information

Sir Isaac Newton was born in 1642. He was a sickly child and was not expected to live more than a year. But he survived—living to be 85—and became the most important man in the history of physics. He invented the first reflecting telescope; devised the mathematical system called calculus; studied optics, astronomy, metallurgy, and philosophy; and defined laws of motion, writing definitions that are still used. He was a professor of mathematics at Cambridge, a respected author, and the first scientist to be knighted.

Lesson 52

The Second Law of Motion

Text, pages 156-57 • Notebook, page 46

Preview

Objectives

Given proper instruction, your student will be able to

- Test the force required to move two objects.
- Identify objects that would require the most force to move.

Materials

Have available

- 1 penny
- 1 small (1"-2" square) piece of oak tag*

Lesson

Introducing the Lesson

Introduce an observing activity. Give your student a small piece of oak tag and a penny. Ask your student which is lighter, the piece of paper or the penny. Then ask which would be easier to blow across the desk and why. *(The paper would move more easily and farther because it is lighter than the penny.)*

Direct the activity. Instruct your student to test his prediction by setting both objects side by side near the front edge of the table and then blowing both at the same time. After your student has tested the objects together, you might have him try blowing each one separately to see how lightly he can blow and still get the paper to move and then how hard he must blow to get the penny to move.

Conclude the activity. Ask your student to try to explain what he just observed, thereby stating the two parts of Newton's second law. *(A light thing is easier to move than a heavy thing. The harder you throw, blow, lift, push, or pull, the faster and farther you can move something.)* Tell your student that he will learn more about Newton's second law of motion in today's lesson.

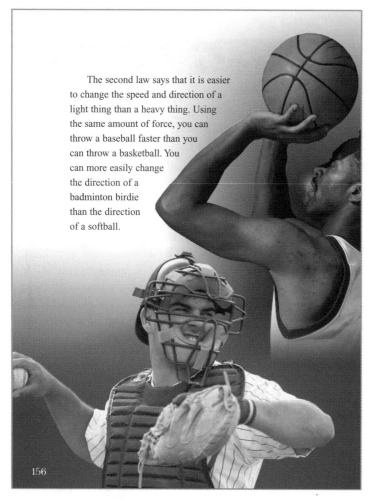

The second law says that it is easier to change the speed and direction of a light thing than a heavy thing. Using the same amount of force, you can throw a baseball faster than you can throw a basketball. You can more easily change the direction of a badminton birdie than the direction of a softball.

156

The second law also says that the more force you use, the faster a thing will change its speed or direction. The harder you pedal your bike, the faster you will change your speed. The harder you throw a basketball, the faster you will change its direction.

A racing car is an example of both parts of the second law of motion. A racing car has a very light body, so it is easy to change its speed and direction. A racing car has a powerful engine. A very powerful engine has more force to make the speed or direction change faster.

Second Law: It is easier to change the speed or direction of a light thing than a heavy thing. And the more force you use, the faster a thing will change its speed or direction.

157

Teaching the Lesson

Direct a text activity on pages 156-57. Use the following questions to initiate your student's interest in what he is going to read.

1. Why can you throw a baseball faster than a basketball?

2. How can a racing car change both speed and direction so easily?

Continue with discussion questions. After your student completes his silent reading, use the following questions and statements as a guide to discuss the pages he read.

1. Which is lighter—a baseball or a basketball? *(a baseball)*

2. If you use the same amount of force, which can you throw faster—a baseball or a basketball? Why? *(the baseball, because it is lighter)*

3. Which is lighter—a badminton birdie or a softball? *(a badminton birdie)*

4. Which can you change the direction of more easily—a badminton birdie or a softball? Why? *(a badminton birdie, because it is lighter)*

5. What will happen if you apply more force to an object? *(The object will change speed or direction faster.)*

6. What parts of a racing car help it to change its speed and direction so easily? *(its light body and its powerful engine)*

7. Think back to the *Finding Out* activity that you did with the two cars. Which car moved faster and farther, the car that was pushed gently or the one that was pushed harder? *(the one that was pushed harder)*

8. Would you choose to throw a tennis ball or a basketball in a ball-throwing contest? Why? *(a tennis ball, because it is lighter than a basketball and could be thrown farther)*

9. State Newton's second law of motion. *(It is easier to change the speed or direction of a light object than a heavy object. The more force you use, the quicker an object will change its speed and direction.)*

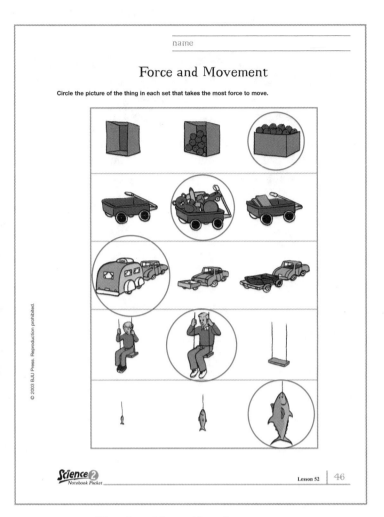

Evaluating the Lesson

Direct a notebook activity on page 46. Instruct your student to circle the item in each group of drawings that would take the most force to move.

For Your Information

A *newton* is defined in physics as the force needed to move a one-kilogram mass one meter per second per second. Since Newton's second law helped scientists develop this unit of force, the unit was named for Newton.

Lesson 53

The Third Law of Motion

Text, pages 158-60

Preview

Objective

Given proper instruction, your student will be able to

- Name the action and the reaction illustrated in a number of photographs.

Materials

Have available

- 1 rubber band
- 1 balloon
- 1 stopwatch or a watch with a second hand
- 2 small model cars similar in size, shape, and material*
- 1 tape measure
- A Write It flip chart
- Masking tape

Prepare

- The cars by testing them to make sure that they move straight ahead when pushed.
- The running surface (a large table or counter works best) by taping a starting line about one foot from one end of the surface and another line one foot beyond the starting line.
- The Write It flip chart by writing *Car No. 1* and *Car No. 2.*

Lesson

Introducing the Lesson

Introduce the activity. Give your student a rubber band and tell him to put it around his thumb and index finger. (*NOTE:* See Figure 53-1.)

Demonstrate as you give the following instructions to your student:

1. Move your thumb and finger apart to stretch the rubber band.
2. Push against the rubber band with the index finger of your other hand.

Direct the activity. Ask your student what he feels when he pushes against the rubber band. *(It feels as if the rubber band is pushing back.)* Explain that your student is actually feeling two pushes: the push that he is giving with his finger and the push that the rubber band is giving against his finger.

Continue the activity. Tell your student that the following demonstration is another way to show the effects of two pushes. Blow up a balloon, hold the neck of the balloon tightly closed, and then direct your student to feel the balloon and tell what is inside it. *(air)*

Instruct your student to hold his hand near the mouth of the balloon as you let a little air escape. Ask your student what he felt. *(The air was seeping out of the balloon.)*

Conclude the activity. Ask your student what he thinks will happen if you let go of the neck of the balloon. *(Your student will probably say from experience that the balloon will zip around the room, letting out air as it goes.)* Let go of the neck of the balloon to see what the balloon actually does. Tell your student that he will learn more about this third law of motion in today's lesson.

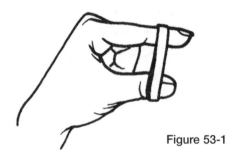

Figure 53-1

The third law says that for every action there is an equal and opposite reaction. That means that when something starts moving, something else moves in the opposite direction. A balloon pushes air out one way. That is an action. The reaction is the crazy zipping of the balloon through the air in the other direction. Can you tell the action and reaction in this example?

Third Law: For every action there is an equal and opposite reaction.

158

Tell the actions and reactions shown in these pictures.

159

Teaching the Lesson

Direct a text activity on pages 158-60. Use the following question to initiate your student's interest in what he is going to read: What is a balloon pushing out of its way as it zips around the room?

Continue with discussion questions. After your student completes his silent reading, use the following questions and statements as a guide to discuss the pages he read.

1. What is the balloon pushing out of the way as it zips around the room? *(air)*

2. Look at the photograph on page 158. What are the actions and reactions? *(The rowers are pushing against the water with the oars, causing the boat to move forward in the water.)*

3. Look at the photographs on page 159. Describe the actions and reactions illustrated here. *(The swimmer's hands and arms push against the water, and the water pushes back against his hands and arms. The exhaust is forced out of the rocket, pushing the rocket up into the air. The bungee jumper is falling, and the rope is pulling him back up. The girl is pushing the swing, and the swing is pushing back.)*

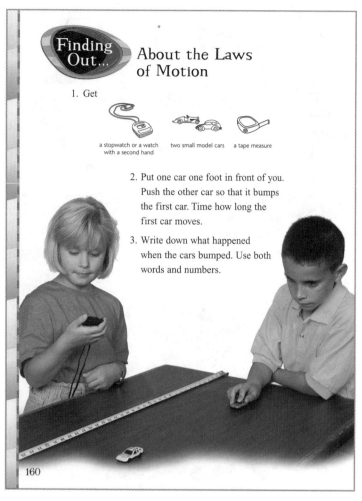

1. Get

a stopwatch or a watch
with a second hand   two small model cars   a tape measure

2. Put one car one foot in front of you.
   Push the other car so that it bumps
   the first car. Time how long the
   first car moves.

3. Write down what happened
   when the cars bumped. Use both
   words and numbers.

160

Evaluating the Lesson

Introduce the activity. Direct your student's attention to page 160. Tell him to read the steps in the box and to look at the picture. Ask your student to tell what he thinks happened when the second car hit the first car. *(The second car stopped, and the first car moved ahead.)* Gather the materials. Allow your student to be the driver, and you be the timer. Set one car (Car No. 1) with its front wheels on the line that you have taped one foot from the starting line.

You may wish to invite another child to conduct this activity with your second-grade child, taking the roles of driver and timer.

Direct the activity. Explain to the driver that he must set the front wheels of his car (Car No. 2) on the starting line. When you say "Go," he should push Car No. 2 so that it hits the back of Car No. 1, which has been placed on the line ahead of the starting line. Start keeping time when the moving car hits the parked car. Stop keeping time when the car that was hit comes to a stop. You may need some trial crashes, but after a successful hit is completed, instruct your student to write on the flip chart the number of seconds that Car No. 1 moved.

Measure from the starting line to the front wheels of Car No. 2 (the car that the driver pushed) and tell your student the number of inches the car moved. Then allow your student to write the number of inches under *Car No. 2* on the Write It flip chart. You should also measure from the second line to the front wheels of Car No. 1 and tell your student the number of inches that it moved. Instruct your student to write the number of inches under *Car No. 1* on the Write It flip chart.

Conclude the activity. After the inches and seconds have been recorded, ask your student to describe what happened when the cars bumped. Instruct him to use both the words and numbers that have been recorded on the Write It flip chart.

As a review of Newton's first law of motion, discuss with your student what would have happened to a person sitting in Car No. 1 and to one sitting in Car No. 2 when the crash occurred. You may want to allow your student to tell of an incident that he experienced or saw.

For Your Information

When two objects are exerting mechanical force on each other, the atoms of each are trying to occupy the space taken up by the other object. But because solids have forces holding the atoms together, the atoms in each object also repel atoms of the other object. When you lean against a wall, for example, the wall is pushing equally hard against you.

CHAPTER FOURTEEN

Lessons 54-55

Ocean Shorelines

These lessons about ocean shorelines emphasize the skills of observation and classification. After studying different kinds of shorelines and beaches, your student will examine sand samples and record his findings.

Materials

The following items must be obtained or prepared before the presentation of the lesson. These items are designated with an * in the materials list in each lesson and in the Supplement. For further information see the individual lessons.

- 1 large map of the United States† (Lesson 54)
- 1 magnifying glass† (Lesson 55)
- Sandpaper swatches of various grades (Lesson 55)
- 1 cup of sand (Lesson 55)

14

The Hurricane Game

Instructions

Your child may be interested in how hurricanes are named. The first hurricane of the year is given an A name like Alice or Andrew, the second is given a B name like Barbara or Bradley, and so forth. All hurricanes used to be named after girls, but now the names alternate between masculine and feminine; one hurricane is given a girl's name, the next is given a boy's name, the next a girl's, etc. Play a "Name-the-Hurricane" game with the members of your family. Allow each family member to take turns in naming hurricanes in alphabetical order from A to Z, alternating between girls' and boys' names. You may wish to list these family hurricane names in a booklet.

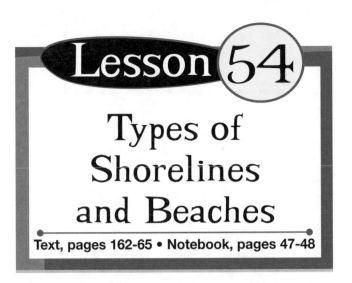

Lesson 54

Types of Shorelines and Beaches

Text, pages 162-65 • Notebook, pages 47-48

Preview

Objectives

Given proper instruction, your student will be able to

- Identify the four types of shorelines.
- Identify the three types of beaches.

Materials

Have available

- 1 large map of the United States*†
- 1 pair of scissors
- Cellophane tape
- Home Teacher's Edition, p. A10

Notes

You may choose from the following methods for getting the cup of sand that you will need in Lesson 55:

Method A Take your student on a field trip to a nearby beach to get some sand.

Method B Purchase the sand from a hardware store or a plant nursery.

Method C Borrow the sand from a sandbox.

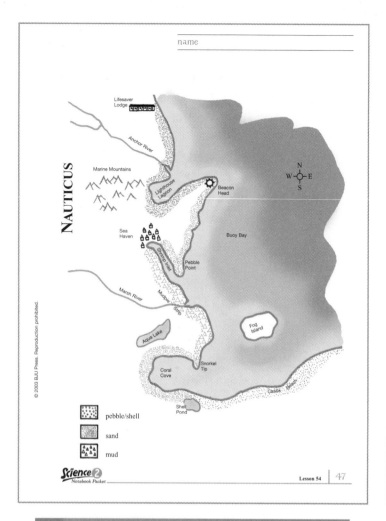

pebble/shell

sand

mud

Lesson 54 | 47

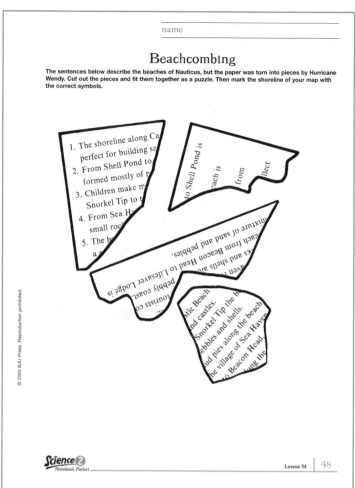

name

Beachcombing

The sentences below describe the beaches of Nauticus, but the paper was torn into pieces by Hurricane Wendy. Cut out the pieces and fit them together as a puzzle. Then mark the shoreline of your map with the correct symbols.

Lesson 54 | 48

Lesson

Introducing the Lesson

Introduce the activity. Discuss with your student any trips to the coast that you have taken as a family. Allow your student to tell about what he enjoyed doing and seeing. Locate on a map the coasts that you have visited.

Direct the activity. Direct your student's attention to notebook pages 47–48. Explain that page 47 is a map of a coastline in an imaginary land called Nauticus. Call attention to the three boxes at the bottom of the page showing the symbols that your student will use to mark the three types of beaches. Explain that page 48 contains a list of beach descriptions of the Nauticus shoreline. Read the directions together; then instruct your student to cut and piece together his instruction list and then to mark his map. The descriptions are printed below for your convenience:

1. The shoreline along Castle Beach to Shell Pond is perfect for building sand castles.

2. From Shell Pond to Snorkel Tip the beach is formed mostly of pebbles and shells.

3. Children make mud pies along the beach from Snorkel Tip to the village of Sea Haven.

4. From Sea Haven to Beacon Head, tourists collect small rocks and shells along the pebbly coast.

5. The beach from Beacon Head to Lifesaver Lodge is a mixture of sand and pebbles.

(*NOTE:* Remind your student that Nauticus is an imaginary place and that the different types of beaches usually do not begin and end so neatly or change so often along a real shoreline.) Tell your student that he will learn more about shorelines in today's lesson.

Have you ever seen an ocean? An ocean is a huge body of water. You cannot see all of it at once. You can see only a little bit of it as you stand on the shore. The ocean is a world of its own, with underwater mountains and valleys and sea plants and sea animals. Since we cannot study the whole ocean at once, let's look at just the shoreline. The shoreline is where the great ocean meets the land.

There are many different kinds of shorelines. Large stones and boulders form *rocky shorelines.*

bluff

rocky

162

marsh

Most *beaches* are sandy. A few are muddy, and a few are covered with pebbles and stones.

Some shores are low, wet edges called *marshes.* They are usually grassy.

Bluffs are high ridges of land or rock along the shore.

sandy

163

Teaching the Lesson

Direct the text activity on pages 162-65. Use the following question and statement to initiate your student's interest in what he is going to read.

1. What is a shoreline?
2. Name four different kinds of shorelines.

Continue with discussion questions. After your student completes his silent reading, use the following questions and statements as a guide to discuss the pages he read.

1. What is an ocean? *(a large body of salt water that cannot be seen all at once)*
2. What is a shoreline? *(where the ocean meets the land)*
3. Look at the photographs on pages 162-63. Identify the four kinds of shorelines shown here. *(rock, beach, marsh, and bluff)*
4. What is it that forms rocky shorelines? *(large stones and boulders)*
5. Name different kinds of beaches. *(sandy ones, muddy ones, beaches covered with pebbles, stones, or shells)*
6. Describe *marshes.* *(low, wet shores that are usually grassy)*
7. Describe *bluffs.* *(high ridges of land or rock)*

8. What can make shorelines change? *(storms or waves; man with his building machines)*
9. What is the name of a severe storm that forms over a large body of water and moves along the coastline, wearing away rock and sand? *(A hurricane forms in the tropical regions of the Atlantic Ocean or Caribbean Sea and moves north; the same type of storm in the Pacific is called a typhoon.)*
10. During a storm, when sand is washed away from a shore by waves or wind, where do you think it goes? *(It either blows to a different coast or goes out into the ocean and settles offshore.)*

With the return of fair weather, the gentler wave action once again begins lifting the sand from the offshore bar and returns it to the beach.

11. Look at the photographs of beaches on page 165. Tell what makes the beaches look different from each other. *(One is sandy, and one is covered with rocks.)*

Sometimes shorelines change. Storms or waves may move sand and mud or wear away land and rock.

Men can change shorelines also. They change the shape of a natural shore or dig out a new harbor. A *harbor* is water that is sheltered by land and is deep enough for ships to float in.

Hundreds of years ago sailors found many good harbors along the East Coast of our country. Big cities usually grow up around good harbors. Why do you think that happens?

164

Beaches

More people know about sandy beaches than about any other kind of shoreline. They like to go there to enjoy the water and the sunshine, to walk along the surf, to play, and to rest. Have you ever been to a beach? What did it look like?

Not all beaches look alike. What makes these beaches look different from each other?

165

---

12. Where do you think new beach sand comes from? *(Sometimes a storm merely shifts sand from one beach to another so that most sand is not new at all.)*

 New sand is formed from rock and mineral fragments that are broken up by water and wind. Much of this sand originates in mountains and is carried to the shore by rivers and streams. It is deposited along the shore and then sorted and distributed by waves and currents.

13. Why do you think cities grew up around harbors on the East Coast? *(Because ships docked in the harbors to unload their cargoes, most of the businesses and trades located near the shores. Communities developed nearby and grew into cities.)*

Evaluating the Lesson

Direct the activity. Display page A10 of the Home Teacher's Edition and ask your student to help you complete the words in the blanks. Start with the four types of shorelines and ask your student to describe each one as he names it. Then proceed to the three kinds of beaches. Your student may refer to pages 162-63 in his textbook if he needs help.

For Your Information

Hurricanes are giant windstorms that can be up to 600 miles in diameter. The accompanying winds have been clocked at speeds of over 200 miles an hour (75 miles per hour is the lowest hurricane velocity). A little over one-third of the hurricanes occur in September, although the hurricane season lasts from June to November. The worst hurricane in United States history hit Galveston, Texas, on September 8, 1900, killing 6,000 people.

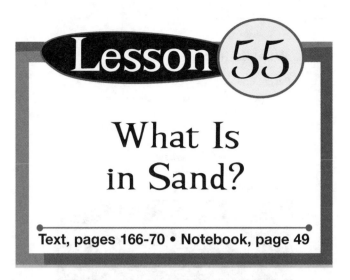

Lesson 55

What Is in Sand?

Text, pages 166-70 • Notebook, page 49

Preview

Objectives

Given proper instruction, your student will be able to

- Identify quartz, basalt, and shells in samples of beach sand.
- Describe beach sand samples by relative amounts of quartz, basalt, and shells.
- Describe the color and shape of each component in each beach sand sample.
- Compare the particle size of beach sand with the size of grains on sandpaper swatches.

Materials

Have available

- 1 magnifying glass*†
- ½ sheet of construction paper (red, orange, blue, or green will work best)
- 1 toothpick
- 1 pencil
- 1 cup of sand (*NOTE:* See *Notes* in Lesson 54.)
- Sandpaper swatches of various grades*

Finding Out... About Sand

1. Get

construction paper | a toothpick | a pencil | a magnifying glass | some sand | your notebook page

2. Pour a few grains of sand on a piece of construction paper. Look at it under the magnifying glass. Use the toothpick to move the grains around. Can you tell which grains are parts of shell, which are quartz, and which are basalt?

3. Record what you see.

"How precious also are thy thoughts unto me, O God! how great is the sum of them! If I should count them, they are more in number than the sand."

Psalm 139:17-18

168

Lesson

Introducing the Lesson

Introduce the activity. Direct your student's attention to the *Finding Out* activity on page 168 and the notebook activity on page 49. Instruct your student to read the instructions orally. Then read the verses from Psalm 139 at the bottom of the page. (Bible Promise: G. God as Friend) Ask your student whether the "sands of the sea" can be counted. Why? *(No; the number is too large to count.)* Explain to your student that this sorting activity will help him to understand the impossibility of counting all the grains of sand on all the beaches in the world. (Bible Promise: I. God as Master)

 You might want to read I Kings 4:29 and Hebrews 11:12.

Sand Study

name _____

Answers will vary.

Put the number in each blank.

1. My sand has _____ grains of quartz.

2. My sand has _____ grains of shell.

3. My sand has _____ grains of basalt.

4. My sand has _____ grains in all.

Answers will vary.

Circle the best answer.

5. My sand has more grains of quartz / shell / basalt than any other kind.

6. My sand has fewer grains of quartz / shell / basalt than any other kind.

7. My sand has more small / medium / large grains than any other size.

Drawings will vary.

Draw and color the shapes.

8. Here are the shape and color of a grain of quartz.

9. Here are the shape and color of a grain of shell.

10. Here are the shape and color of a grain of basalt.

Science 2
Notebook Packet

Lesson 56 | 49

What Is in Sand?

Parts of Sand

What is that grainy material on beaches that sticks to your wet feet? On some beaches it is mostly tiny bits of shell. How do you think shells get broken into such small pieces?

Most sand contains *quartz*. Quartz is a hard, crystal-like material. Look at the close-up picture of sand. Can you see the bits of quartz?

Some sand also has black material in it. The black parts are *basalt*, part of lava rock. Did you know before that there are black beaches? Where do you think such beaches are?

Size of Sand

Some sand has very tiny grains. Some has large grains. Scientists measure the size of sand grains by shaking them through a wire screen. All grains smaller than one-twelfth of an inch fall through. What falls through is called sand.

166

Direct the activity. Place a pinch of sand on your student's piece of construction paper. Instruct your student to examine the sand with his magnifying glass while using the toothpick to help separate and to count individual grains. Then instruct him to record his findings on his notebook page. Caution him to work slowly and count carefully. There will be more grains in a "pinch" of sand than he expects there to be.

> Experiment with the quantity beforehand. Too large a sample will be difficult and frustrating to work with. Even the smallest pinch on your student's piece of construction paper will probably contain enough grains to challenge your second grader.

Teaching the Lesson

Direct a text activity on pages 166-70. Use the following question to initiate your student's interest in what he is going to read: What is sand made of?

Continue with discussion questions. After your student completes his silent reading, use the following questions and statements as a guide to discuss the pages he read.

1. How do you think shells get broken into tiny pieces on a beach? *(Some possible answers include people and animals walking over the shells and the waves and other shells constantly beating against the shells.)*

2. What materials are in sand? *(quartz, basalt, and shells)*

3. What is quartz? *(hard, crystallike material)*

4. What is basalt? *(black material that is part of lava rock)*

5. Where do you think you could find beaches that contain basalt? *(near areas where volcanoes have erupted)*

6. How big are grains of sand? *(smaller than one-twelfth of an inch)*

A Bird on the Sand

This bird lives on seashores. It is small, with long legs and a long pointed beak. It is the sandpiper.

It eats worms, insects, and shrimp. How do you think it gets this food out of the sand?

The sandpiper runs behind the waves that roll back to the sea, looking for food washed up by the water. As it goes it makes a merry piping sound, from which it gets its name.

167

Living by the Shore

People who live on the coasts often try to keep the sand from washing away. They build *breakwaters*.

How do you think breaking up the water helps keep the shore from being worn away?

Some houses along shores are built on stilts. Why do you think the houses are built like that?

169

7. Look at the illustration on page 167. Name the bird and tell what you know about it. *(The sandpiper lives on beaches in the Pacific. These beaches usually have some rocks on the shoreline which serve as resting places for the sandpiper. The sandpiper digs in the sand with its sharp bill, looking for food—insects, worms, and shrimp.)*

8. Describe the kind of beach where this sandpiper could be most comfortable. *(a beach where there are smooth stones or pebbles that it can hop up on to rest and to get the sand out of its claws)*

9. What do you think *breakwaters* are? *(walls or dunes that are built up to keep the sand on the beach from washing away)*

 You may want to compare the breakwater to a high stone wall built in the water at the mouth of a harbor. Breakwaters do what their name suggests: they break the force of huge waves and, therefore, protect the shore.

10. Look at the beach houses on page 169. Why do you think that they are on stilts? *(During storms, sand and water from the beach pass under the house, rather than into the house.)*

"Fear ye not me? saith the Lord: will ye not tremble at my presence, which have placed the sand for the bound of the sea by a perpetual decree, that it cannot pass it: and though the waves thereof toss themselves, yet can they not prevail; though they roar, yet can they not pass over it?"
                                                Jeremiah 5:22

170

Give your student a set of small sandpaper swatches (about five) and ask him to examine the textures. Ask your student to put the swatches in order from fine to coarse and then to study the swatches with his magnifying glass. Ask your student which sandpaper square is most like his homemade sample.

Enrichment

Make available some magnets and small samples of sand containing basalt. Allow your student to experiment with a magnet and the sand to find out if some grains of sand are magnetic.

For Your Information

There are many birds in the sandpiper and snipe family. The *upland plover* lives on dry uplands in the United States and Canada. The *willet* is a large species of sandpiper found on the Gulf Coast and in the western states. Some sandpipers live above the Arctic Circle. The *sanderling*, a three-toed member of the snipe family, nests in the Arctic but winters as far south as the Pacific Islands. All sandpipers are protected by law.

Sand can be found almost everywhere on earth. The sand in some rivers is rich in minerals. Mineral deposits rich in precious metals or stones are called *placers.* The abundant placers in the rivers of California made many a panner for gold wealthy in the 1800s.

11. Read the verse on page 170. What power is being spoken of here? *(God's power)*

Discuss the great power of the sea and its crashing waves and the comparative insignificance of a grain of sand. Point out that God in His wisdom has set up shores of shifting sand to hold back the violence of the sea. Remind your student that the God who created the earth and the seas and the boundaries of both also created men and women and boys and girls and wants them to love and obey Him.

Evaluating the Lesson

Direct a sandpaper activity. Brush a small circle of glue or paste onto the center of your student's piece of construction paper. Instruct your student to make his own sandpaper by spreading the sand onto the glued area. (*NOTE:* You may want to give your student additional sand for this activity.) After the sandpaper circle dries, instruct your student to cut it out.

Lesson 56

Little Things Count

Text, pages 172-73

Preview

Objectives

Given proper instruction, your student will be able to
- Identify some things that can be recycled.
- Participate in a recycling drive.

Materials

Have available
- A picture of the recycling symbol
- Recyclable items such as a newspaper, a glass jar or bottle, and cardboard
- Items made from recycled paper, glass, or cardboard

Lesson

Introducing the Lesson

Show your student a picture of the recycling symbol and ask him if he knows what this symbol means. Then show him the recyclable items. Ask him what he thinks happens to the items when your family is finished using them. Tell him that today you will be studying recycling, one of the ways that we can take care of the wonderful earth God created.

Teaching the Lesson

Direct a text activity on pages 172-73. Use the following questions to initiate your student's interest in what he is going to read.

1. What did God put into our world for us to use?

2. Why is it good to recycle things?

3. What are some things that we can recycle?

Continue with discussion questions. After your student completes his silent reading, use the following questions and statements as a guide to discuss the pages he read.

1. What did God put into our world for us to use? *(resources)*

2. Why should we recycle? *(to save resources, to keep things from being thrown away)*

3. What are two ways that people can recycle? *(take things to a recycling center or put things in a recycling box for city workers to pick up)*

4. What are some things that we can recycle? *(newspaper, glass, and cardboard)* Explain that some people also recycle plastic and aluminum or steel cans.

5. Do you remember what paper is made from? *(trees)* Explain that recycling paper helps us to save trees from being cut down. It also helps to save energy and water.

6. Briefly explain to your student how paper is made. *(The mills turn the recycled paper into a watery mixture called pulp. If recycled paper is not available, then whole trees must be used to form the pulp. To make paper, the pulp is first spread onto screens. Then rollers are used to press the water out, helping the pulp to flatten and dry.)*

 Recycled newspapers (and other recycled paper) can be used to make newsprint, tissue, writing paper, cereal boxes, egg cartons, pencil barrels, grocery bags, tissue paper, construction paper, and paper towels. Used cardboard can be recycled into egg cartons, coffee and drink trays, and seedling pots. If a box or carton is gray on the inside, it is made from recycled materials. Recycled cardboard can sometimes be recycled again.

Little Things Count

Our great God created a beautiful world. In this world He put many resources, or things that we can use. God expects us to use those resources wisely. One way that we can use them wisely is to recycle.

Recycling helps to keep things that we have used from just being thrown away. Old things can be turned into new things. This helps us to save some of our resources.

How can we recycle? In some areas, items to be recycled must be taken to a recycling center. This place has many boxes. Items must be separated and put into their proper boxes. Then they can be recycled.

172

In other places, items at home are put into a special box called a recycling bin. This box is placed at the street next to the trash can. Workers in a recycling truck pick up the items.

What can we recycle? Newspaper is one of the things that we can recycle. We can also recycle glass and cardboard. We help take care of God's earth by recycling. Even little things can make a big difference!

173

Conclude the discussion. Show your student some products made from recycled materials. Point out the label on each product that states that the product is made from recycled materials. Remind him that God has given us the responsibility of taking care of the earth. Discuss with your student the importance of each person doing a little bit of recycling in order to make a big difference. Remind him, too, that recycling is not really beneficial unless we buy products that have been made from recycled goods.

Evaluating the Lesson

Begin a family or neighborhood recycling drive. For a few days, collect newspaper, cardboard, or glass. If possible, extend the recycling drive to include the neighborhood, using your house as the collection point. At the end of the collection time, have your student organize the materials and deliver them to a recycling center.

Enrichment

Follow these steps to make recycled paper at home.

1. Tear about five feet of toilet tissue into pieces. Place it in a mixing bowl and add a handful of lint from a dryer.

2. Add 1½ cups of warm water and 1 tablespoon of laundry starch. Mix well until the pulp is soupy.

3. Place a piece of screen in a rectangular baking pan. Pour the pulp onto the screen and add another cup of warm water. Spread the pulp evenly.

4. Place a towel on a table. Lift the screen with the pulp from the pan, letting the water drain off. Put the screen on the towel.

5. Put another towel on top of the screen. With a rolling pin, remove the excess water.

6. Using a warm iron, press the entire area to remove any remaining moisture.

7. Carefully remove the paper and place it in the sun to dry.

For Your Information

Most of the environmental benefits happen during the pulp-making process rather than during the papermaking. Turning recycled paper into pulp requires less energy and uses weaker chemicals than creating pulp from wood.

Illustration Credits

John Bjerk 110, 134
Matthew Bjerk 4, 8 (top right), 22 (top), 38 (bottom right), 44, 58, 66, 75-77, 82, 104, 112, 114, 141, 162, 169
James Hargis 5-6, 22-23, 28, 59, 73 (bottom), 110, 130-31, 134
Brian Johnson 28
Deborah King 9 (top), 21 (top), 36 (top), 42 (top), 46 (top), 49 (top), 61 (top), 73 (top), 78 (top), 85 (top), 99 (top), 102 (top), 108 (top), 113 (top), 118 (top), 124 (top), 132 (top), 142 (top), 152 (top), 160 (top), 168 (top)
Duane Nichols 8 (bottom)
David Schuppert 26
Lynda Slattery 10-12, 47, 172-73

The following artists are represented by Wilkinson Studios, LLC:

Linda Bittner 94, 138, 167
Robin Brickman 3
Phyllis Pollema Cahill 70, 96
Donna Catanese 92, 129
Mike Dammer 56, 64-65, 109, 153
Bob Masheris 63, 106
Wendy Rasmussen 89, 139
Kate Sweeney 48, 50-52, 117, 120-23
Bobbi Tull 146-47
Nicole Wong 72, 97

Photo Credits

The following agencies and individuals have furnished materials to meet the photographic needs of this textbook. We wish to express our gratitude to them for their important contribution.

Able Stock
Suzanne Altizer
Artemis Images
John Bjerk
Corbis
COREL Corporation
Digital Vision
J.A. Franklin
Dr. Kenneth Frederick
Freedonia Seeds
Getty Images

Toef Hadar
Brenda Hansen
Edwin G. Huffman
Breck Kent
Joyce Landis
Peter LaTourette
Miriam Mitchem
Greg Moss
National Park Service
Susan Perry
Dr. Margene Ranieri

Six Flags Over Georgia
The South Carolina Aquarium
Transparencies, Inc.
University of Idaho Forest Research Nursery
Unusual Films
Ward's Natural Science Establishment
World Bank

Cover
Ryan McVay/Getty Images (tiger); PhotoLink/Getty Images (background)

Front Matter
Unusual Films iii, iv (marble), v (marble); Robert Glusic/Getty Images iv (windmill); Jess Alford/Getty Images iv (cheetahs); PhotoLink/Getty Images v (arm); Corbis v (planes); Pat Powers and Cheryll Schafer/Getty Images v (flower); Susan Perry v (fossil)

Chapter 1
Ryan McVay/Getty Images 2; PhotoLink/Getty Images 5, 7 (top left); John A. Rizzo/Getty Images 7 (bottom right); Kenneth Frederick 7 (background); courtesy of Freedonia Seeds 8; Susan Perry 9

Chapter 2
National Park Service 14; C. Borland/PhotoLink/Getty Images 15; BJU Press Files 16 (left); Jeremy Woodhouse/Getty Images 16 (right); S. Meltzer/PhotoLink/Getty Images 16-17 (bottom); Siede Preis/Getty Images 17 (top); Jack Hollingsworth/Getty Images 17 (bottom right); PhotoLink/Getty Images 17 (bottom left, background); Unusual Films 18, 21; Susan Perry 19 (top left, bottom left), 24, 25 (all); Ward's Natural Science Establishment 19 (right), 20; Russell Illig/Getty Images 27

Chapter 3
Karl Weatherly/Getty Images 30; Joaquin Palting/Getty Images 30-1 (top); Nicola Sutton/Life File/Getty Images 31 (inset); StockTrek/Getty Images 31 (bottom left); Russell Illig/Getty Images 32-33; PhotoLink/Getty Images 33 (top right), 37 (left), 39 (top right), 41 (left); John Bjerk 33 (bottom right); Unusual Films 34, 35 (both), 36, 40, 42 (all); Robert Glusic/Getty Images 37 (right); Lawrence M. Sawyer/Getty Images 38 (left); Geostock/Getty Images 38 (inset); Alex L. Fradkin/Getty Images 39 (left); Arthur S. Aubry/Getty Images 39 (bottom right); Susan Ferry 39 (bottom left); Glen Allison/Getty Images 39 (bottom middle); David Buffington/Getty Images 41 (top right); Corbis 41 (bottom right)

Chapter 4
Unusual Films 44 (both), 45 (both), 46; Joyce Landis 49; PhotoLink/Getty Images 52, 53 (top right, bottom); Karl Weatherly/Getty Images 53 (top left); Corbis 54

Chapter 5
C Square Studios/Getty Images 57 (all); Edwin G. Huffman/World Bank 60 (left); Toef Hadar/World Bank 60 (others); Unusual Films 61; Doug Menuez/Getty Images 62

Chapter 6
PhotoLink/Getty Images 68, 68-69 (main inset), 69 (middle), 71 (left), 75 (left); Andrew Ward/Life File/Getty Images 69; R. Morley/PhotoLink/Getty Images 69 (bottom); Daisuke Morita/Getty Images 71 (right); Unusual Films 74 (left, right), 78; Susan Perry 74 (background); Doug Menuez/Getty Images 75 (right); Jack Hollingsworth/Getty Images 75 (background)

Chapter 7
C Squared Studio/Getty Images 80 (violin), 80-81 (crayons, popsicle); G.K. and Vikki Hart/Getty Images 80 (dog); PhotoLink/Getty Images 81 (rose, family); Geostock/Getty Images 81 (boy); Corbis 82 (top left), 84 (top right, bottom right), 87 (left); Alan and Sandy Carey/Getty Images 82 (inset); Geostock/Getty Images 82 (bottom); Nancy R. Cohen/Getty Images 83 (left); Joyce Landis 83 (all others); PhotoLink/Getty Images 84 (left); Unusual Films 85 (all); Russell Illig/Getty Images 86 (background); Suzanne Altizer 86 (insets); Breck Kent 87 (right), 88 (top left); Karl Weatherly/Getty Images 88 (top right); PhotoLink/Getty Images 88 (bottom); Jess Alford/Getty Images 90 (top); Geostock/Getty Images 90 (bottom left), J. A. Franklin 90 (bottom right); Pat Powers and Cherryl Schafer/Getty Images 91 (bottom right); Miriam Mitchem 91 (others)

Chapter 8
PhotoLink/Getty Images 95, 98 (top left); Susan Perry 98 (top right), 100 (bottom right); Spike Mafford/Getty Images 98 (bottom); Unusual Films 99, 101, 102

(both), 103, (both); Greg Moss 100 (bottom left); Ryan McVay/Getty Images 100 (top right); University of Idaho Forest Research Nursery 104

Chapter 9
R. Morley/PhotoLink/Getty Images 107 (left); PhotoLink/Getty Images 107 (right), 111 (top, bottom), 114 (background); Unusual Films 108, 113; Courtesy of Six Flags Over Georgia 111; Corbis 114 (top, middle, bottom)

Chapter 10
Unusual Films 116, 118; PhotoLink/Getty Images 119 (top); Dr. Margene Ranieri 119 (insets); Susan Perry 124

Chapter 11
C. Sherburne/PhotoLink/Getty Images 126-27 (background); PhotoLink/Getty Images 126 (left), 127 (inset); S. Alden/PhotoLink/Getty Images 126 (inset); Geostock/Getty Images 128 (left); Kim Steele/Getty Images 128 (right); Unusual Films 128 (foreground), 132; Jeremy Hoare/Life File/Getty Images 133

Chapter 12
Breck Kent 136, 137, 141; PhotoLink/Getty Images 140 (both), 144 (left); Susan Perry 142; Bruce Heineman/Getty Images 143 (top); Adalberto Rios Szalay/Sexto Sol/Getty Images 143 (bottom); Digital Vision 144 (right); Geostock/Getty Images 144 (bottom); Frank and Joyce Burek/PhotoLink/Getty Images 145 (turtle); Courtesy: the South Carolina Aquarium 145 (others); Jeremy Woodhouse/Getty Images 148

Chapter 13
Corbis 150 (top); Doug Menuez/ Getty Images 150 (bottom); COREL Corporation 151; Unusual Films 152, 160; Brenda Hansen 154 (top); Unusual Films Courtesy of Six Flags Over Georgia 154 (bottom); Rim Light/PhotoLink/Getty Images 155 (both), Rim Light/Getty Images 156 (bottom); PhotoLink/Getty Images 156 (right); C Indianapolis Motor Speedway (http://www.artemisimages.com) 157; Lawrence M. Sawyer/Getty Images 158; Corbis 159 (left); PhotoLink/Getty Images 159 (background, bottom right); Karl Weatherly/Getty Images 159 (top right)

Chapter 14
John Wang/Getty Images 162 (both), 165 (left); AbleStock 163 (top); Edmond Van Hoorick/Getty Images 163 (bottom); C. Borland/PhotoLink/Getty Images 164; PhotoLink/Getty Images 165 (right); Unusual Films 166, 168; Peter LaTourette 167; Jane Faircloth/Transparencies, Inc. 169; S. Alden/PhotoLink/Getty Images 170

Back Matter
John Wang/Getty Images 174; PhotoLink/Getty Images 175, 177; Steve Cole/Getty Images 176; S. Meltzer/Getty Images 178; Nancy R. Cohen/Getty Images 179; Unusual Films 184

Home Teacher's Edition Cover
Ryan McVay/Getty Images (tiger)
PhotoLink/Getty Images (background)

Supplement

Concepts

Concepts are short statements of scientific knowledge. Although your student will learn about each concept as each lesson is taught, it is not necessary for him to memorize the concept.

Chapter 1

Lesson 1
- What a person believes about the beginning of things is determined by faith.
- Annuals are plants that live for one year.
- Biennials are plants that live for two years.
- Perennials are plants that live for many years.
- A gardener should plan his site before setting up a garden.

Lesson 2
- When planning a flower bed, a gardener considers how long a plant lives, its height, and its coloring.

Lesson 3
- Gardeners can obtain information about plants from a seed package.
- Gardeners can obtain information about plants from a nursery.

Lesson 4
- Gardeners have a monthly plan for taking care of perennial plants.

Chapter 2

Lesson 5
- Scientists use observation to study things about the world.
- There are two main beliefs about how the earth was made.

Lesson 6
- A fossil is a living thing that has been preserved by nature.
- Living things that do not become fossils decay or dissolve.

Lesson 7
- There are several kinds of fossils.

Lesson 8
- Fossils are found in groups.
- Creationists and evolutionists have different beliefs about why fossils are in groups.
- A person who believes the Bible must accept the Creation theory about the fossil clues.

Chapter 3

Lesson 9
- A force is a push or pull.
- Every object in the universe causes a force called gravity.
- Only very large objects, such as planets, moons, and stars, exert enough gravity to be felt.
- Gravity makes things have weight.

Lesson 10
- Magnets cause a force called magnetic force.
- Magnetic force attracts some things.
- Magnetic force repels some things.

Lesson 11
- Mechanical force starts and stops movement.
- Mechanical force can change the direction of a moving object.

Lesson 12
- Surfaces that touch cause a force called friction.
- Friction resists movement.
- There are three kinds of friction: sliding friction, rolling friction, and fluid friction (viscosity).

Chapter 4

Lesson 13
- The human skeleton is made up of bones and cartilage.

Lesson 14
- Bones are grouped by shape.

Lesson 15
- Joints are places in the body where two or more bones meet.
- Most joints allow movement.
- Hinge joints allow up-and-down movement, pivot joints allow back-and-forth movement, and ball-and-socket joints allow movement in all directions.

Lesson 16
- The skeleton gives the body shape and support.
- The skeleton helps the body move.
- The skeleton protects the body.

Chapter 5

Lesson 17
- The earth is round like a ball.

Lesson 18
- People live all around the ball-shaped earth.

Lesson 19
- The earth is surrounded by cosmic space (i.e., space without a top or a bottom).

Lesson 20
- Things below the ground fall to the center of the ball-shaped earth.

Chapter 6
Lesson 21
- Light comes from glowing (luminous) objects.
- Some objects become visible only when light is reflected from them.

Lesson 22
- Light goes out from glowing objects in straight lines.

Lesson 23
- Some things allow light to go through them, whereas other things either partially or completely block light.
- Shadows form when things stop light.

Lesson 24
- The size of a shadow changes with the position of the light source.
- The size of a shadow changes with the position of the object causing the shadow.
- The location of a shadow changes with the position of the light source.
- The location of a shadow changes with the position of the object causing the shadow.

Chapter 7
Lesson 25
- Plants, animals, and people are living things.
- Many living things move on their own.
- Some living things do not move on their own.

Lesson 26
- Living things need food, water, and air.

Lesson 27
- Living things respond to their environments.
- Getting food and taking care of young are animal behaviors.

Lesson 28
- Living things make new living things.
- Some living things make eggs.
- Some living things make babies.

Lesson 29
- Living things grow.
- In some ways, the growth of plants and the growth of animals are similar.
- In some ways, the growth of plants and the growth of animals are different.

Chapter 8
Lesson 30
- A unit can be an amount for measuring.
- Measuring is the act of comparing a unit to something to see how many of those units correspond to that thing.

Lesson 31
- Inch, foot, yard, centimeter, and meter are some standard units for measuring distance.

Lesson 32
- Scientists sometimes measure length in order to classify.

Lesson 33
- Scientists sometimes measure length in order to identify.

Chapter 9
Lesson 34
- The earth rotates, or spins, around and around.
- Rotation of the earth causes a time of light and a time of darkness.
- Each cycle of light and darkness is one day.

Lesson 35
- The earth is divided into twenty-four time zones.
- All the time pieces in each zone have the same time.

Lesson 36
- The earth revolves around the sun.
- The earth faces the sun at a slant, or tilt.
- The seasons occur because the earth revolves and is tilted.

Lesson 37
- A year is one complete cycle of weather changes, or seasons.
- The earth rotates $365\frac{1}{4}$ times in a year.

Chapter 10
Lesson 38
- Each muscle has a name.
- Muscles are made of long, thin threads.
- Muscles are voluntary or involuntary.
- There are three kinds of muscles: skeletal, smooth, and cardiac.

Lesson 39
- Muscles control movement.
- Muscles work together.
- Muscles need exercise.

Lesson 40
- Smooth muscles move things such as food in the body.

Lesson 41
- Cardiac muscles move blood through the heart.
- Blood vessels carry the blood to parts of the body.

Chapter 11
Lesson 42
- Scientists learn about the center of the earth by studying volcanoes.

Lesson 43
- Scientists cannot easily learn about the center of the earth because they cannot see it.
- Scientists learn about the center of the earth by studying volcanoes and earthquakes.

Lesson 44
- The earth has three layers: crust, mantle, and core.
- The earth's crust is thin.
- The mantle and core are thicker and hotter than the crust.

Lesson 45
- The earth's crust is made of oceans, continents, and islands.

Chapter 12

Lesson 46
- A habitat is where an organism lives.
- Everything around an organism is its environment.
- A biome is an area with the same organisms and environment.

Lesson 47
- Soil, sunlight, and water help determine environments.

Lesson 48
- Wind helps determine which plants and animals live in a place.
- The direction and speed of wind can be determined.
- Water is the most important part of an environment.

Lesson 49
- All living things in an area are a community.
- All living things of one kind are a population.

Chapter 13

Lesson 50
- Everywhere things are moving.
- All movement starts with a force.
- Scientists use words and numbers to describe movement.

Lesson 51
- An object keeps doing what it is doing until an unbalanced force causes a change.

Lesson 52
- It is easier to change the speed and direction of a light object than of a heavy one.
- The more force you use, the faster the object will change its speed or direction.

Lesson 53
- For every action there is an equal and opposite reaction.

Chapter 14

Lesson 54
- Rock, beach, marsh, and bluff are types of shorelines.
- Pebble, sand, and mud are types of beaches.
- Beaches differ in sand color and in the presence and size of rocks and pebbles.

Lesson 55
- Ocean beach sand is composed of varying amounts of quartz, basalt, and shells.

Environmental Lesson

Lesson 56
- We need to be wise stewards of God's creation.

Materials List

Chapter 1
Lesson 1
- A Write It flip chart*†
- A *SCIENCE 2 Notebook Packet*†
- A three-ring binder*

Family Time 2
- 1 garden magazine for each family member*
- Scissors
- 1 piece of construction paper for each family member*
- Glue

Lesson 2
- A Write It flip chart

Lesson 3
- 1 package of flower seeds*
- A Write It flip chart

Lesson 4
- 1 spray mist bottle
- Crayons
- Scissors
- 1 stapler
- A Write It flip chart

Chapter 2
Family Time 5
- Appendix, pp. A1-A3*†
- Glue
- 1 manila file folder*
- Clear Con-Tact paper*
- Scissors
- 1 metal brad*
- Tape
- 1 resealable plastic bag or envelope
- Small colored rocks or buttons

Lesson 5
- 1 box of instant pudding*
- Enough milk to prepare the pudding
- 1 large bowl
- A mixer (optional)
- 1 large spoon
- Individual spoons (optional)
- A Write It flip chart

Lesson 6
- A fossil collection*†
- 1 can of food

Family Time 7
- 2 cups flour
- 1 cup salt
- 2 cups water
- 4 teaspoons cream of tartar
- 2 tablespoons cooking oil
- Food coloring (optional)

Lesson 7
- The play dough made during Family Time 7
- The fossil collection*†
- Small plastic animals*
- Stiff leaves, such as holly leaves*
- Some dead insects*
- Rubber cement*
- 2 paper cups

Lesson 8
- 1 quart or half-gallon jar
- Several small containers with different kinds of sediment in each—small pebbles, fine-grained sand, coarse sand*
- Magazines and brochures showing various land forms, rocks, and fossils*
- Poster board (optional)*
- 8 sentence strips
- Appendix, p. A4
- Some construction paper
- A Bible
- An encyclopedia or reference book written from an evolutionist viewpoint

Chapter 3
Family Time 9
- 1 large baby food jar*
- A rubber glove*
- 1 long chicken bone (thigh or leg)
- $\frac{3}{4}$ cup of white vinegar
- 3 tablespoons of salt
- Masking tape

Lesson 9
- Scales (postage scales or food scales)*

Family Time 10
- Poster board*
- Felt-tip pens or crayons in a variety of colors

Lesson 10
- 1 large bar magnet with poles marked*†
- 1 small bar magnet*†
- 1 small paper bag
- Small items to test: eraser, plastic button, penny, staples, nail

Lesson 11
- 1 empty cardboard half-gallon milk carton*
- Scissors

Lesson 12
- 1 metal cookie sheet
- 2 tall, clear glasses
- Water
- Corn syrup*
- 2 marbles*
- A stopwatch or watch with a second hand
- Round objects: a marble, a smooth round pencil
- Flat objects: a wooden block, a spoon, a coin, an eraser
- A Write It flip chart

Chapter 4

Lesson 13
- The chicken bone in the vinegar-salt solution prepared in Family Time 9
- 1 long chicken bone (thigh or leg)
- 1 large baby food jar*
- $\frac{1}{2}$ cup of water
- 1 tablespoon baking soda
- 1 rubber glove*
- 1 measuring cup
- 1 tablespoon

Lesson 14
- 1 chicken skeleton*
- 1 shoebox
- Appendix, pp. A5-A9

Lesson 15
- No materials needed

Lesson 16
- 1 metal brad
- 1 glue stick
- Scissors

Chapter 5

Lesson 17
- Models or pictures of model cars, airplanes, ships, furniture, or houses
- Some disc-shaped objects (a record or CD, a Frisbee, a plate, a plastic lid)
- Some ball-shaped objects (a rubber ball, a grapefruit, an orange, a ball of yarn or string, a Ping-Pong ball)
- 1 globe*†
- Appendix, p. A10
- Cellophane tape

Lesson 18
- 1 globe*†
- Cellophane tape or masking tape
- Appendix, p. A11

Lesson 19
- 1 ball
- A Write It flip chart
- 1 3" × 5" card

Lesson 20
- 1 Styrofoam ball, 2 inches or more in diameter*
- 1 pencil

Chapter 6

Lesson 21
- 1 shoebox
- 1 index card
- Cellophane or masking tape
- Small book or toy that will fit inside the shoebox
- 30 pieces of 9" × 11" construction paper*
- 30 M&M candies*

Lesson 22
- 1 large bowl or cake pan
- 1 marble*
- Water
- 1 ball
- 1 candle
- Matches
- 2 dusty chalkboard erasers*
- Hole puncher
- Clay*
- 1 flashlight
- 3 4" × 6" cards

Family Time 23
- 1 large sheet of drawing paper for each family member*
- Pencil
- Any type of film or filmstrip projector*
- 1 sheet of black construction paper for each family member*
- 1 sheet of white construction paper for each family member*
- Glue
- Masking tape

Lesson 23
- A Write It flip chart
- 1 strip of transparent acetate*
- 1 strip of waxed paper
- 1 strip of aluminum foil
- Opaque materials such as cardboard, a pie tin, a brick, and a book
- Translucent materials such as onionskin paper, toilet tissue, gauze, and frosted glass or plastic
- Transparent materials such as clear glass or plastic
- 6 baby food jars with lids*
- Any two of the following transparent liquids: water, ginger ale, white vinegar, light corn syrup*
- Any two of the following translucent liquids: apple juice, tea, strawberry pop, lemon juice*
- Any two of the following opaque liquids: milk, strong coffee, soy sauce, grape juice*

Lesson 24
- 1 ruler
- Clay*
- 1 flashlight

Chapter 7

Lesson 25
- Crayons
- Felt-tip pens
- A Write It flip chart

Lesson 26
- 2 resealable plastic bags
- 2 paper towels
- 6-8 bean seeds*
- Masking tape
- 1 felt-tip pen
- Cellophane tape
- 1 green rubber glove*

Family Time 27
- A Bible

Lesson 27
- A Write It flip chart

Lesson 28
- A Write It flip chart
- 12 magazine pictures of different animals*
- 12 4" × 6" cards
- A Bible

Lesson 29
- Baby record book and/or baby photographs of your student
- 1 current photograph of your student
- 1 bathroom scale
- 1 growth chart*
- Appendix, p. A12
- 1 egg carton
- Scissors
- Tape
- Glue
- 4 chenille wires*
- Crayons
- A Write It flip chart

Chapter 8
Lesson 30
- 1 package of paper clips
- Appendix, pp. A13-A17

Lesson 31
- A Write It flip chart
- 1 4" × 6" card*
- 1 one-foot ruler
- 1 centimeter ruler
- 1 tape measure
- 1 piece of poster board*
- 1 yardstick
- 1 meter stick*
- Cellophane or masking tape

Lesson 32
- 1 one-foot ruler
- 1 centimeter ruler
- 1 pencil
- 1 paper plate or plastic meat tray

- Large assortment of buttons
- 10 rocks ranging from about $\frac{1}{8}$" to more than 10" in diameter*

Lesson 33
- 1 one-foot ruler
- 1 centimeter ruler
- Appendix, pp. A18-A21

Chapter 9
Lesson 34
- 1 globe*†
- 1 flashlight
- Plastic tack*
- 1 large paper plate (10" × 12")
- 1 small paper plate (6" × 8")
- Metal brads
- 1 black or dark blue crayon
- A Write It flip chart

Lesson 35
- 4 electric or spring-wound clocks*
- 1 Judy Mini-Clock*†
- 1 basketball or volleyball*
- 1 large United States map*†
- 2 sheets of construction paper

Lesson 36
- 1 basketball or volleyball*
- 1 globe*†
- A Write It flip chart
- Appendix, p. A22

Lesson 37
- Several calendars (If possible, obtain at least one calendar for a year whose number is divisible by four—1996, 2000, 2004.)*
- 4 index cards or paper strips for labeling
- Construction paper
- Scissors
- A piece of drawing paper

Chapter 10
Lesson 38
- A watch with a second hand
- 1 skein of yarn, any color*
- A thin piece of raw steak or chicken*
- 1 darning needle*
- 1 microscope slide*†
- 1 cover slip (small square piece of glass or plastic)*†
- Red and blue food coloring
- Rubbing alcohol
- 1 small bottle (baby food jar, olive jar, etc.)
- 1 tablespoon
- 1 magnifying glass*†
- 1 pencil

Lesson 39
- A rag doll*
- A piece of drawing paper
- Crayons

Lesson 40
- 1 pair of paper lips made of construction paper
- 1 small bowl or butter tub
- 1 cardboard tube (from a paper towel roll)
- 2 balloons
- 1 vacuum cleaner hose
- 2 dishpans or medium-sized bowls
- 1 sponge
- 1 bucket
- 1 paper circle
- Masking tape

Family Time 41
- A Bible

Lesson 41
- 1 box of round toothpicks*
- 1 thumbtack
- 1 stopwatch or watch with a second hand
- 1 red crayon
- 1 blue crayon

Chapter 11

Lesson 42
- Play dough (*NOTE:* See Lesson 7 for the recipe for homemade play dough.)

Lesson 43
- A volcano made of play dough* (*NOTE:* See Lesson 42.)
- 1 box of baking soda
- 1 bottle of vinegar
- Red and yellow food coloring
- A picture of Mount St. Helens*
- 1 ball, any size

Lesson 44
- 1 globe*†
- 1 recipe of play dough, divided and tinted three colors (*NOTE:* See Lesson 7.)*
- 1 two-foot length of thread
- 1 apple*
- 1 knife
- Crayons

Lesson 45
- 1 globe*†
- 1 nickel
- 1 shallow dishpan
- Sand for the dishpan*

Chapter 12

Family Time 46
- Appendix, pp. A23-A25
- Laminating film or clear Con-Tact paper (optional)*
- 1 manila file folder*
- Glue
- 1 metal brad
- Tape
- Stiff cardboard the size of the spinner
- 1 envelope
- 1 resealable plastic bag
- 1 colored button for each player

Lesson 46
- A few old magazines that include pictures of outdoor places
- 1 piece of poster board*
- Glue
- Scissors
- Felt-tip pens or crayons
- A Write It flip chart
- The "Spin an Animal Home" game that was prepared in Family Time 46

Lesson 47
- 6 live earthworms, available from a bait-and-tackle shop or from your backyard*
- 1 foil pie plate
- 2 paper towels
- 1 small piece of aluminum foil
- Some dirt or sand
- A Write It flip chart

Lesson 48
- 2 small pieces of paper
- One foot from an old nylon stocking
- Wire coat hanger
- Rubber cement or glue
- 4 colored stakes*

Lesson 49
- A location in your yard or neighborhood that contains at least one anthill
- A piece of string

Chapter 13

Family Time 50
- A Bible

Lesson 50
- 1 stopwatch or a watch with a second hand
- 2 small model cars similar in shape, size, and material
- 1 tape measure
- Masking tape
- A Write It flip chart

Lesson 51
- 1 cup
- 1 3" × 5" card
- 1 button or penny

Lesson 52
- 1 penny
- 1 small (1" to 2" square) piece of oak tag*

Lesson 53
- 1 rubber band
- 1 balloon
- 1 stopwatch or a watch with a second hand
- 2 small model cars similar in shape, size, and material
- 1 tape measure
- A Write It flip chart
- Masking tape

Chapter 14

Lesson 54
- 1 large map of the United States*†
- Scissors
- Cellophane tape
- Appendix, p. A10

Lesson 55
- 1 magnifying glass*†
- $\frac{1}{2}$ sheet of construction paper (red, orange, blue, or green will work best)
- 1 toothpick
- 1 pencil
- 1 cup of sand (*NOTE:* See *Notes* in Lesson 54.)
- Sandpaper swatches of various grades

Bible Action Truths

The quality and consistency of a man's decisions reflect his character. Christian character begins with justification, but it grows throughout the lifelong process of sanctification. God's grace is sufficient for the task, and a major part of God's gracious provision is His Word. The Bible provides the very "words of life" that instruct us in salvation and Christian living. By obeying God's commands and making godly decisions based on His Word, Christians can strengthen their character.

Too often Christians live by only vague guidance—for instance, that we should "do good" to all men. While doing good is desirable, more specific guidance will lead to more consistent decisions.

Consistent decisions are made when man acts on Bible principles—or Bible Action Truths. The thirty-seven Bible Action Truths (listed under eight general principles) provide Christians with specific goals for their actions and attitudes. Study the Scriptures indicated for a fuller understanding of the principles in Bible Action Truths.

Thousands have found this format helpful in identifying and applying principles of behavior. Yet there is no "magic" in this formula. As you study the Word, you likely will find other truths that speak to you. The key is for you to study the Scriptures, look for Bible Action Truths, and be sensitive to the leading of the Holy Spirit.

1. Salvation-Separation Principle
Salvation results from God's direct action. Although man is unable to work for this "gift of God," the Christian's reaction to salvation should be to separate himself from the world unto God.

a. **Understanding Jesus Christ** (Matthew 3:17; 16:16; I Corinthians 15:3-4; Philippians 2:9-11) Jesus is the Son of God. He was sent to earth to die on the cross for our sins. He was buried but rose from the dead after three days.

b. **Repentance and faith** (Luke 13:3; Isaiah 55:7; Acts 5:30-31; Hebrews 11:6; Acts 16:31) If we believe that Jesus died for our sins, we can accept Him as our Savior. We must be sorry for our sins, turn from them, confess them to God, and believe that He will forgive us.

c. **Separation from the world** (John 17:6, 11, 14, 18; II Corinthians 6:14-18; I John 2:15-16; James 4:4; Romans 16:17-18; II John 10-11) After we are saved, we should live a different life. We should try to be like Christ and not live like those who are unsaved.

2. Sonship-Servant Principle
Only by an act of God the Father could sinful man become a son of God. As a son of God, however, the Christian must realize that he has been "bought with a price"; he is now Christ's servant.

a. **Authority** (Romans 13:1-7; I Peter 2:13-19; I Timothy 6:1-5; Hebrews 13:17; Matthew 22:21; I Thessalonians 5:12-13) We should respect, honor, and obey those in authority over us.

b. **Servanthood** (Philippians 2:7-8; Ephesians 6:5-8) Just as Christ was a humble servant while He was on earth, we should also be humble and obedient.

c. **Faithfulness** (I Corinthians 4:2; Matthew 25:23; Luke 9:62) We should do our work so that God and others can depend on us.

d. **Goal setting** (Proverbs 13:12, 19; Philippians 3:13; Colossians 3:2; I Corinthians 9:24) To be faithful servants, we must set goals for our work. We should look forward to finishing a job and going on to something more.

e. **Work** (Ephesians 4:28; II Thessalonians 3:10-12) God never honors a lazy servant. He wants us to be busy and dependable workers.

f. **Enthusiasm** (Colossians 3:23; Romans 12:11) We should do all tasks with energy and with a happy, willing spirit.

3. Uniqueness-Unity Principle
No one is a mere person; God has created each individual a unique being. But because God has an overall plan for His creation, each unique member must contribute to the unity of the entire body.

a. **Self-concept** (Psalms 8:3-8; 139; II Corinthians 5:17; Ephesians 2:10; 4:1-3, 11-13; II Peter 1:10) We are special creatures in God's plan. He has given each of us special abilities to use in our lives for Him.

b. **Mind** (Philippians 2:5; 4:8; II Corinthians 10:5; Proverbs 23:7; Luke 6:45; Proverbs 4:23; Romans 7:23, 25; Daniel 1:8; James 1:8) We should give our thoughts and minds to God. What we do and say really begins in our minds. We should try to think of ourselves humbly, as Christ did when He lived on earth.

c. **Emotional control** (Galatians 5:24; Proverbs 16:32; 25:28; II Timothy 1:7; Acts 20:24) With the help of God and the power of the Holy Spirit, we should have control over our feelings. We must be careful not to act out of anger.

d. Body as a temple (I Corinthians 3:16-17; 6:19-20) We should remember that our bodies are the dwelling place of God's Holy Spirit. We should keep ourselves pure, honest, and dedicated to God's will.

e. Unity of Christ and the church (John 17:21; Ephesians 2:19-22; 5:23-32; II Thessalonians 3:6, 14-15) Since we are saved, we are now part of God's family and should unite ourselves with others to worship and grow as Christians. Christ is the head of His church, which includes all believers. He wants us to work together as His church in carrying out His plans, but He forbids us to work in fellowship with disobedient brethren.

4. Holiness-Habit Principle

Believers are declared holy as a result of Christ's finished action on the cross. Daily holiness of life, however, comes from forming godly habits. A Christian must consciously establish godly patterns of action; he must develop habits of holiness.

a. Sowing and reaping (Galatians 6:7-8; Hosea 8:7; Matthew 6:1-8) We must remember that we will be rewarded according to the kind of work we have done. If we are faithful, we will be rewarded. If we are unfaithful, we will not be rewarded. We cannot fool God.

b. Purity (I Thessalonians 4:1-7; I Peter 1:22) We should try to live lives that are free from sin. We should keep our minds, words, and deeds clean and pure.

c. Honesty (II Corinthians 8:21; Romans 12:17; Proverbs 16:8; Ephesians 4:25) We should not lie. We should be honest in every way. Even if we could gain more by being dishonest, we should still be honest. God sees all things.

d. Victory (I Corinthians 10:13; Romans 8:37; I John 5:4; John 16:33; I Corinthians 15:57-58) If we constantly try to be pure, honest, and Christlike, with God's help we will be able to overcome temptations.

5. Love-Life Principle

We love God because He first loved us. God's action of manifesting His love to us through His Son demonstrates the truth that love must be exercised. Since God acted in love toward us, believers must act likewise by showing godly love to others.

a. Love (I John 3:11, 16-18; 4:7-21; Ephesians 5:2; I Corinthians 13; John 15:17) God's love to us was the greatest love possible. We should, in turn, show our love for others by our words and actions.

b. Giving (II Corinthians 9:6-8; Proverbs 3:9-10; Luke 6:38) We should give cheerfully to God the first part of all we earn. We should also give to others unselfishly.

c. Evangelism and missions (Psalm 126:5-6; Matthew 28:18-20; Romans 1:16-17; II Corinthians 5:11-21) We should be busy telling others about the love of God and His plan of salvation. We should share in the work of foreign missionaries by our giving and prayers.

d. Communication (Ephesians 4:22-29; Colossians 4:6; James 3:2-13; Isaiah 50:4) We should have control of our tongues so that we will not say things displeasing to God. We should encourage others and be kind and helpful in what we say.

e. Friendliness (Proverbs 18:24; 17:17; Psalm 119:63) We should be friendly to others, and we should be loyal to those who love and serve God.

6. Communion-Consecration Principle

Because sin separates man from God, any communion between man and God must be achieved by God's direct action of removing sin. Once communion is established, the believer's reaction should be to maintain a consciousness of this fellowship by living a consecrated life.

a. Bible study (I Peter 2:2-3; II Timothy 2:15; Psalm 119) To grow as Christians we must spend time with God daily by reading His Word.

b. Prayer (I Chronicles 16:11; I Thessalonians 5:17; John 15:7, 16; 16:24; Psalm 145:18; Romans 8:26-27) We should bring all our requests to God, trusting Him to answer them in His own way.

c. Spirit-filled (Ephesians 5:18-19; Galatians 5:16, 22-23; Romans 8:13-14; I John 1:7-9) We should let the Holy Spirit rule in our hearts and show us what to say and do. We should not say and do just what we want to, for those things are often wrong and harmful to others.

d. Clear conscience (I Timothy 1:19; Acts 24:16) To be good Christians, we cannot have wrong acts or thoughts or words bothering our consciences. We must confess them to God and to those people against whom we have sinned. We cannot live lives close to God if we have guilty consciences.

e. Forgiveness (Ephesians 4:30-32; Luke 17:3-4; Colossians 3:13; Matthew 18:15-17; Mark 11:25-26) We must ask forgiveness of God when we have done wrong. Just as God forgives our sins freely, we should forgive others when they do wrong things to us.

7. Grace-Gratitude Principle

Grace is unmerited favor. Man does not deserve God's grace. However, after God bestows His grace, believers should react with an overflow of gratitude.

a. Grace (I Corinthians 15:10; Ephesians 2:8-9) Without God's grace we would be sinners on our way to hell. He loved us when we did not deserve His love and provided for us a way to escape sin's punishment by the death of His Son on the cross.

b. Exaltation of Christ (Colossians 1:12-21; Ephesians 1:17-23; Philippians 2:9-11; Galatians 6:14; Hebrews 1:2-3; John 1:1-4, 14; 5:23) We should realize and remember at all times the power, holiness, majesty, and perfection of Christ, and we should give Him the praise and glory for everything that is accomplished through us.

c. Praise (Psalm 107:8; Hebrews 13:15; I Peter 2:9; Ephesians 1:6; I Chronicles 16:23-36; 29:11-13) Remembering God's great love and goodness toward us, we should continually praise His name.

d. Contentment (Philippians 4:11; I Timothy 6:6-8; Psalm 77:3; Proverbs 15:16; Hebrews 13:5) Money, houses, cars, and all things on earth will last only for a little while. God has given us just what He meant for us to have. We should be happy and content with what we have, knowing that God will provide for us all that we need. We should also be happy wherever God places us.

e. Humility (I Peter 5:5-6; Philippians 2:3-4) We should not be proud and boastful but should be willing to be quiet and in the background. Our reward will come from God on Judgment Day, and men's praise to us here on earth will not matter at all. Christ was humble when He lived on earth, and we should be like Him.

8. Power-Prevailing Principle

Believers can prevail only as God gives the power. "I can do all things through Christ." God is the source of our power used in fighting the good fight of faith.

a. Faith in God's promises (II Peter 1:4; Philippians 4:6; Romans 4:16-21; I Thessalonians 5:18; Romans 8:28; I Peter 5:7; Hebrews 3:18–4:11) God always remains true to His promises. Believing that He will keep all the promises in His Word, we should be determined fighters for Him.

b. Faith in the power of the Word of God (Hebrews 4:12; Jeremiah 23:29; Psalm 119; I Peter 1:23-25) God's Word is powerful and endures forever. All other things will pass away, but God's Word shall never pass away because it is written to us from God, and God is eternal.

c. Fight (Ephesians 6:11-17; II Timothy 4:7-8; I Timothy 6:12; I Peter 5:8-9) God does not have any use for lazy or cowardly fighters. We must work and fight against sin, using the Word of God as our weapon against the Devil. What we do for God now will determine how much He will reward us in heaven.

d. Courage (I Chronicles 28:20; Joshua 1:9; Hebrews 13:6; Ephesians 3:11-12; Acts 4:13, 31) God has promised us that He will not forsake us; therefore, we should not be afraid to speak out against sin. We should remember that we are armed with God's strength.

Bible Promises

A. Liberty from Sin—Born into God's spiritual kingdom, a Christian is enabled to live right and gain victory over sin through faith in Christ. (Romans 8:3-4—"For what the law could not do, in that it was weak through the flesh, God sending his own Son in the likeness of sinful flesh, and for sin, condemned sin in the flesh: that the righteousness of the law might be fulfilled in us, who walk not after the flesh, but after the Spirit.")

B. Guiltless by the Blood—Cleansed by the blood of Christ, the Christian is pardoned from the guilt of his sins. He does not have to brood or fret over his past because the Lord has declared him righteous. (Romans 8:33—"Who shall lay anything to the charge of God's elect? It is God that justifieth." Isaiah 45:24—"Surely, shall one say, in the Lord have I righteousness and strength: even to him shall men come; and all that are incensed against him shall be ashamed.")

C. Basis for Prayer—Knowing that his righteousness comes entirely from Christ and not from himself, the Christian is free to plead the blood of Christ and to come before God in prayer at any time. (Romans 5:1-2—"Therefore being justified by faith, we have peace with God through our Lord Jesus Christ: by whom also we have access by faith into this grace wherein we stand, and rejoice in hope of the glory of God.")

D. Identified in Christ—The Christian has the assurance that God sees him as a son of God, perfectly united with Christ. He also knows that he has access to the strength and the grace of Christ in his daily living. (Galatians 2:20—"I am crucified with Christ: nevertheless, I live; yet not I, but Christ liveth in me: and the life which I now live in the flesh I live by the faith of the Son of God, who loved me, and gave himself for me." Ephesians 1:3—"Blessed be the God and Father of our Lord Jesus Christ, who hath blessed us with all spiritual blessings in heavenly places in Christ.")

E. Christ as Sacrifice—Christ was a willing sacrifice for the sins of the world. His blood covers every sin of the believer and pardons the Christian for eternity. The purpose of His death and resurrection was to redeem a people to Himself. (Isaiah 53:4-5—"Surely he hath borne our griefs, and carried our sorrows: yet we did esteem him stricken, smitten of God, and afflicted. But he was wounded for our transgressions, he was bruised for our iniquities: the chastisement of our peace was upon him; and with his stripes we are healed." John 10:27-28—"My sheep hear my voice, and I know them, and they follow me: and I give unto them eternal life; and they shall never perish, neither shall any man pluck them out of my hand.")

F. Christ as Intercessor—Having pardoned them through His blood, Christ performs the office of High Priest in praying for His people. (Hebrews 7:25—"Wherefore he is able also to save them to the uttermost that come unto God by him, seeing he ever liveth to make intercession for them." John 17:20—"Neither pray I for these alone, but for them also which shall believe on me through their word.")

G. Christ as Friend—In giving salvation to the believer, Christ enters a personal, loving relationship with the Christian that cannot be ended. This relationship is understood and enjoyed on the believer's part through fellowship with the Lord through Bible reading and prayer. (Isaiah 54:5—"For thy Maker is thine husband; the Lord of hosts is his name; and thy Redeemer the Holy One of Israel; The God of the whole earth shall he be called." Romans 8:38-39—"For I am persuaded, that neither death, nor life, nor angels, nor principalities, nor powers, nor things present, nor things to come, nor height, nor depth, nor any other creature, shall be able to separate us from the love of God, which is in Christ Jesus our Lord.")

H. God as Father—God has appointed Himself to be responsible for the well-being of the Christian. He both protects and nourishes the believer, and it was from Him that salvation originated. (Isaiah 54:17—"No weapon that is formed against thee shall prosper; and every tongue that shall rise against thee in judgment thou shalt condemn. This is the heritage of the servants of the Lord, and their righteousness is of me, saith the Lord." Psalm 103:13—"Like as a father pitieth his children, so the Lord pitieth them that fear Him.")

I. God as Master—God is sovereign over all creation. He orders the lives of His people for His glory and their good. (Romans 8:28—"And we know that all things work together for good to them that love God, to them who are the called according to his purpose.")

FOSSIL FIND

START

You find a fossil right away! Take 1 rock.

What do you call a living thing preserved by nature?

You found a petrified fossil. Take 1 rock.

What theory says God made the earth?

Things buried _____ become fossils.

What theory says the earth made itself?

Stop to record your findings.

You dropped a fossil. Lose 1 rock.

Where on the earth are fossils found?

You've found a rare fossil! Take 1 rock.

What kind of fossil comes from tree sap?

You're digging in the wrong place. Take 0 rocks. Lose 0 rocks.

What theory says the earth has changed by itself many times?

What kind of fossil is a living thing that turns to rock?

Which theory must a person who believes the Bible accept?

What happens to a living thing trapped by mud or sand?

What might you see in a piece of amber?

Lunch

break!

What kind of fossil is a thin mold?

You ran too fast and fell down. Go back 2 spaces.

What theory says the earth was changed at the curse and the Flood?

You dropped your shovel and broke your molds. Lose 2 rocks.

What kind of fossil is made when mud fills a mold or imprint?

Name the kind of fossil that is just the image of a living thing.

What kind of rocks are fossils found in?

Stop to talk to another digger.

Your fossil drops into a stream. Lose 1 rock.

What is a kind of frozen fossil?

You lost your ax. Lose 1 rock.

Name a kind of fossil that is an actual preserved living thing.

What does the evolution theory say about how the earth has changed?

You found your ax. Take 1 rock.

What does the Creation theory say about how the earth has changed?

Which theory must a Christian believe?

END

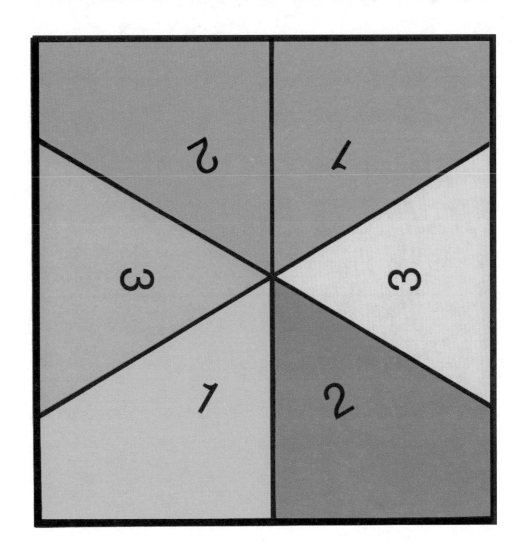

Fossil Find

Fossil Clues

1. Things buried quickly can become fossils.

2. Fossils form from living things.

3. Fossils show how the earth has changed.

4. Many fossils are found in groups.

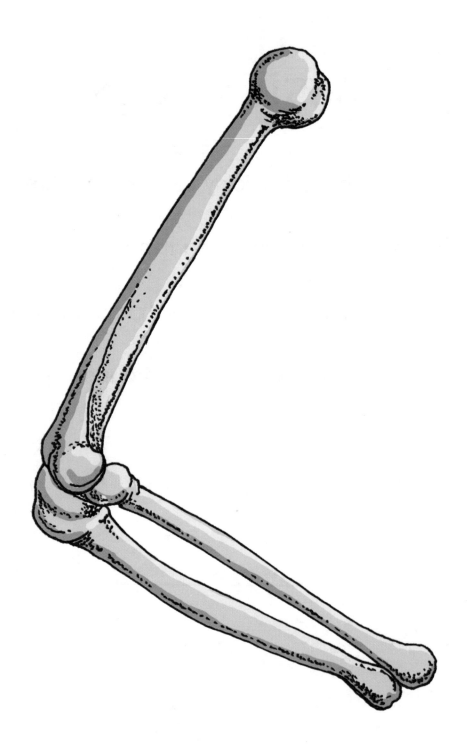

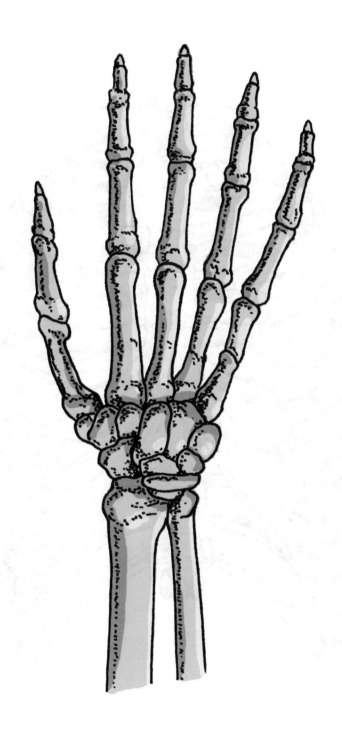

(S)

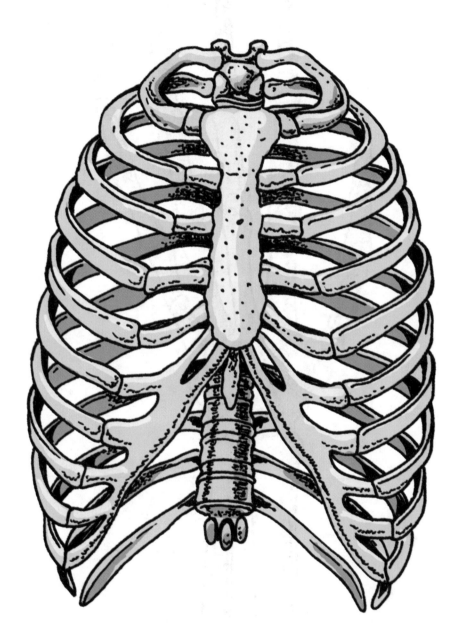

(F)

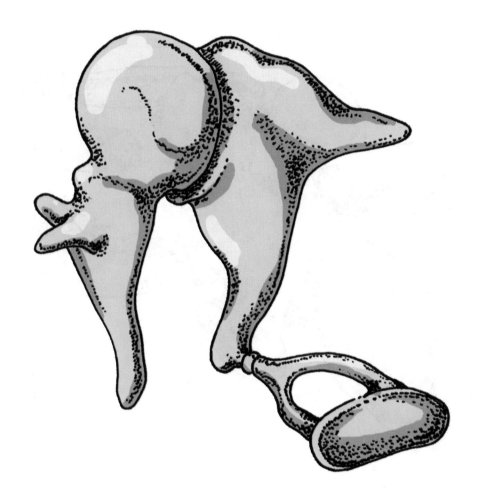

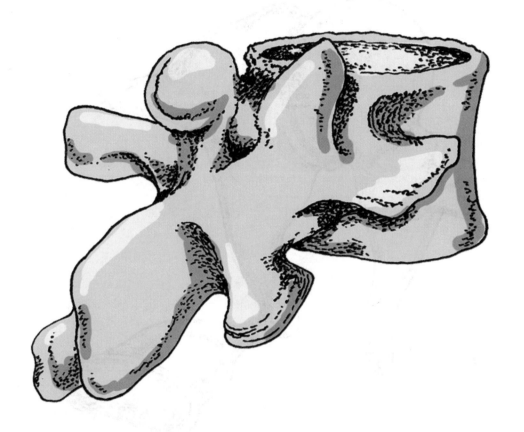

(l)

Shorelines

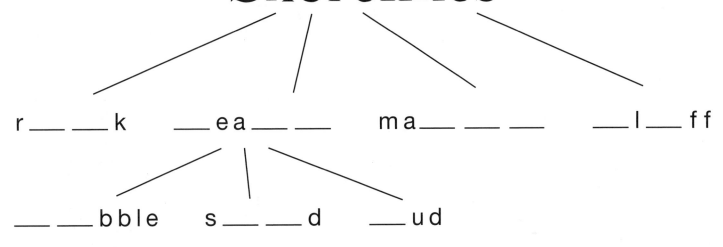

r __ __ k   __ e a __ __   m a __ __ __   __ l __ f f

__ __ b b l e   s __ __ d   __ u d

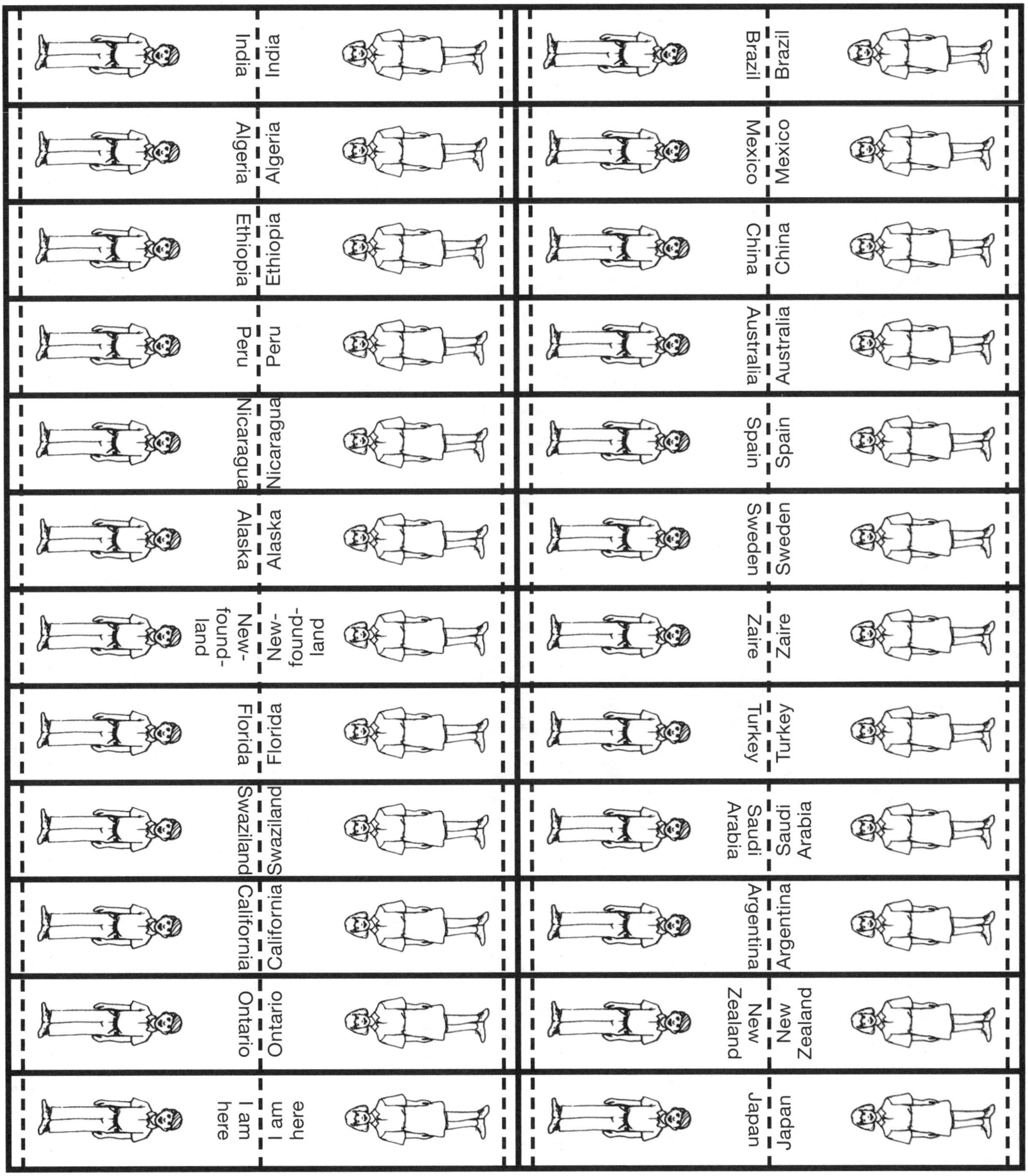

India | India
Algeria | Algeria
Ethiopia | Ethiopia
Peru | Peru
Nicaragua | Nicaragua
Alaska | Alaska
New-found-land | New-found-land
Florida | Florida
Swaziland | Swaziland
California | California
Ontario | Ontario
I am here | I am here

Brazil | Brazil
Mexico | Mexico
China | China
Australia | Australia
Spain | Spain
Sweden | Sweden
Zaire | Zaire
Turkey | Turkey
Saudi Arabia | Saudi Arabia
Argentina | Argentina
New Zealand | New Zealand
Japan | Japan

Class Album Sheet

Name: _____

Height: _____ inches   Height: _____ inches

Weight: _____ pounds   Weight: _____ pounds

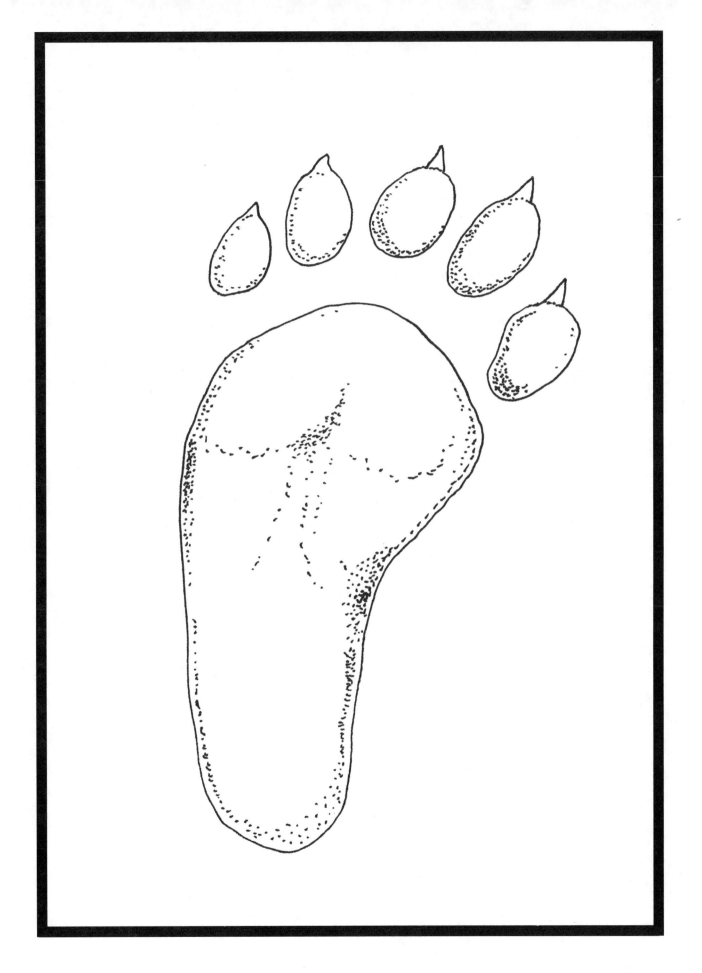

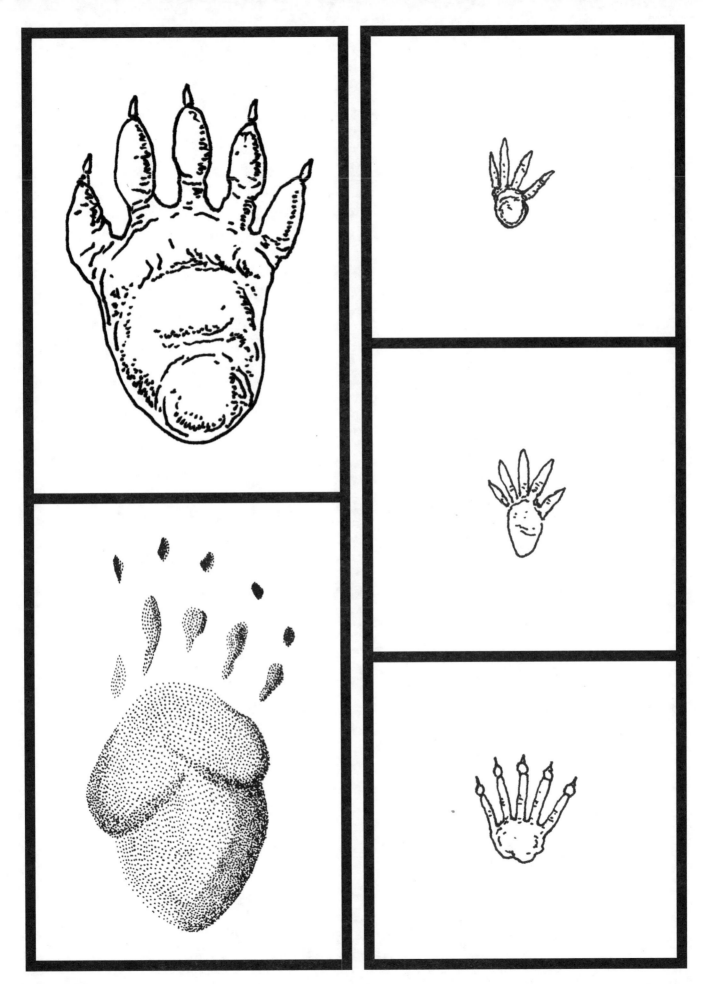

Science 2
Home Teacher's Edition

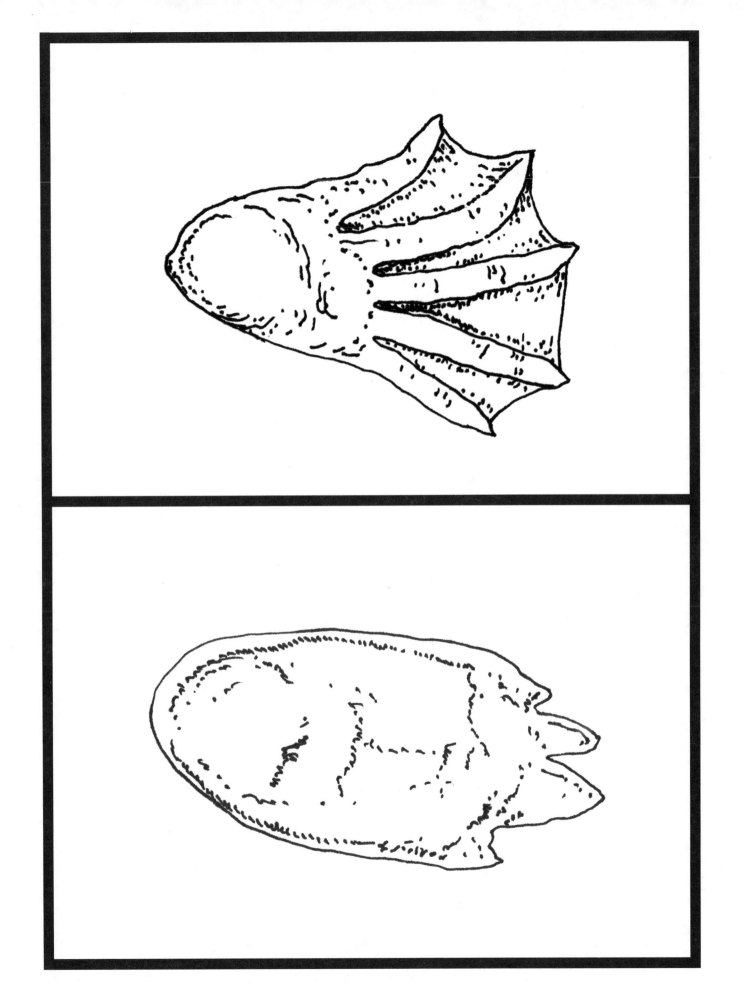

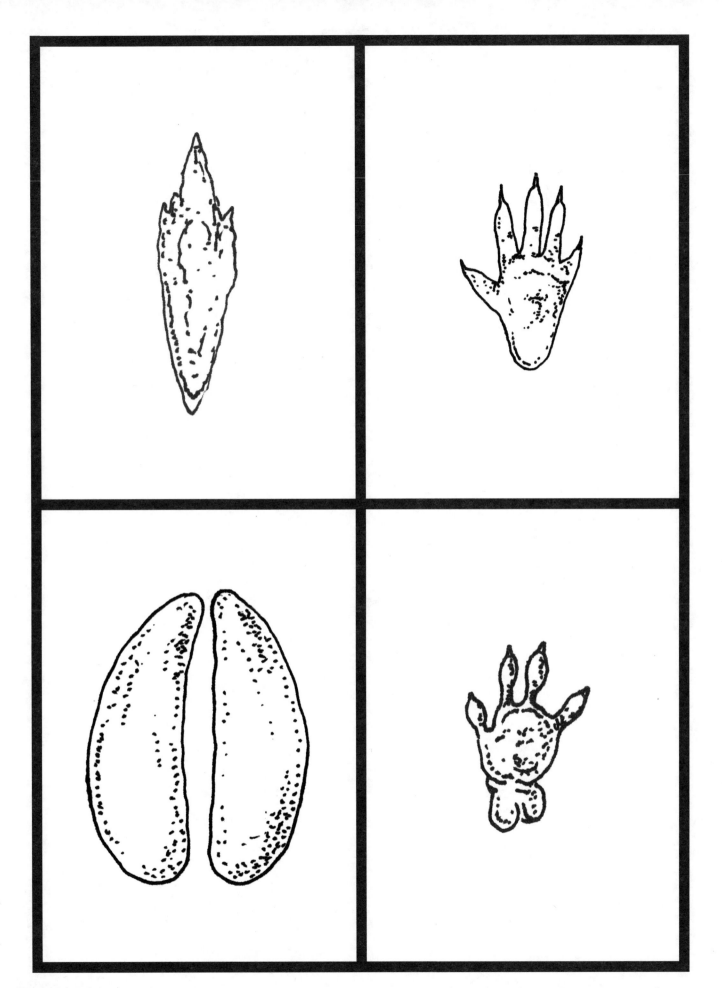

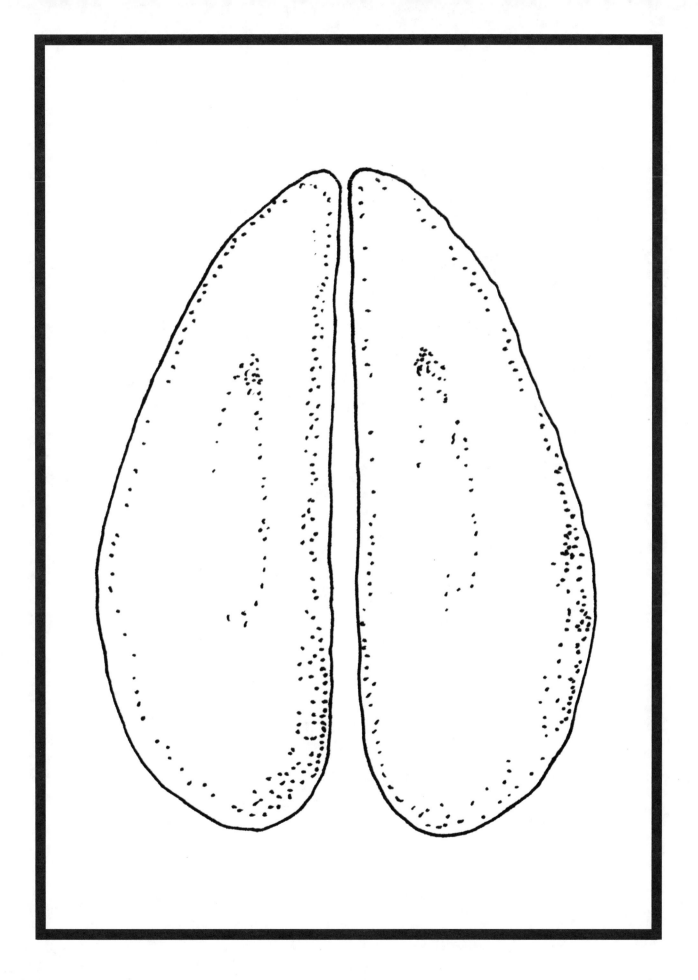

Field Guide

If the print has two large toes, the size makes the difference.

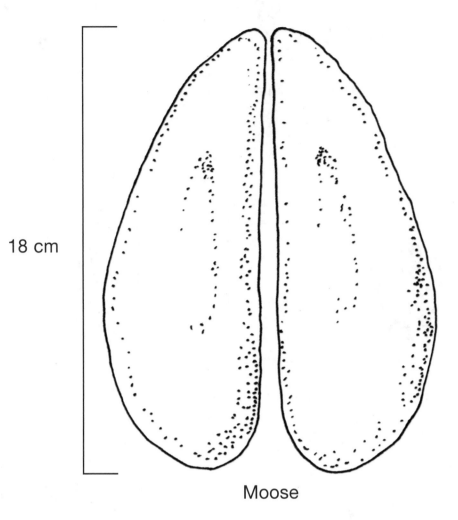

18 cm

Moose

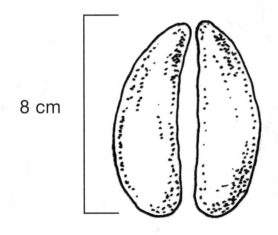

8 cm

White-tailed deer

If the print has long, thin toes with claw marks at the end, the size makes the difference.

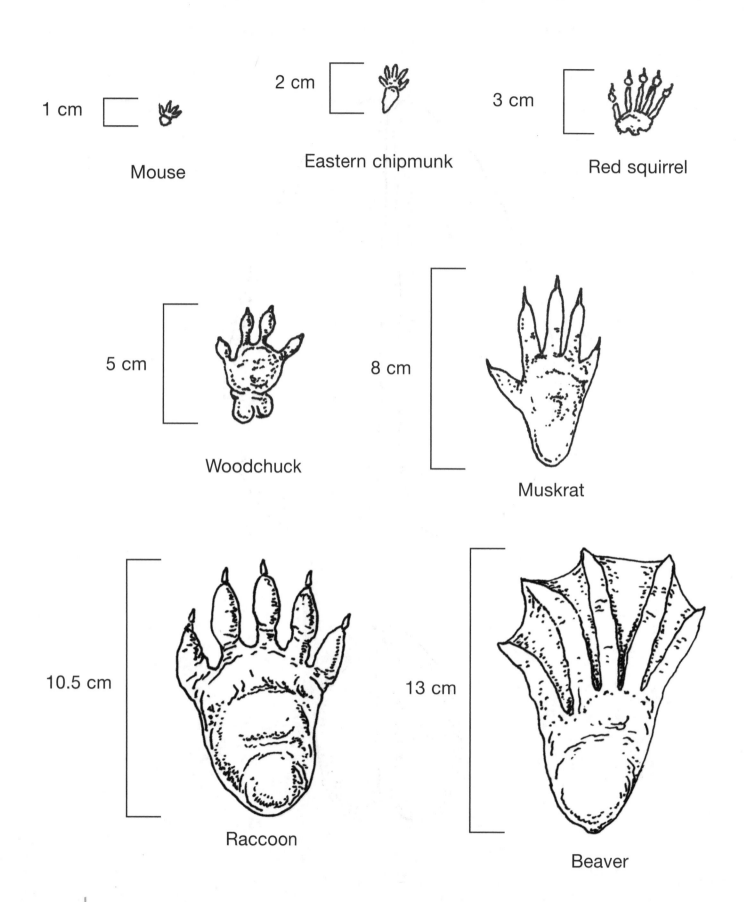

1 cm — Mouse

2 cm — Eastern chipmunk

3 cm — Red squirrel

5 cm — Woodchuck

8 cm — Muskrat

10.5 cm — Raccoon

13 cm — Beaver

If the print has oval toe marks across the top of the pad, the size makes the difference.

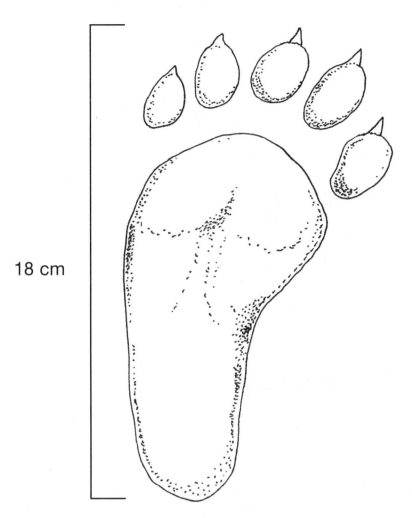

18 cm

Black Bear

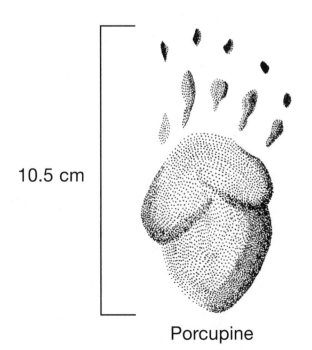

10.5 cm

Porcupine

If the print has a large heel and four toe marks, the size makes the difference.

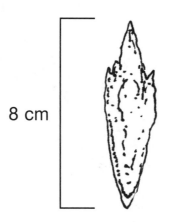

8 cm

Cottontail Rabbit

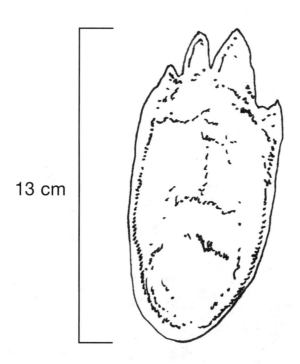

13 cm

Snowshoe Hare

summer
winter
spring
fall

summer
winter
spring
fall

summer
winter
spring
fall

summer
winter
spring
fall

FREE Animal Home

FREE Animal Home

FREE Animal Home

FREE Animal Home

FREE Animal Home

START

FREE Animal Home

FREE Animal Home

Spin an ANIMAL HOME

FINISH

FREE Animal Home

Answers for "Spin an Animal Home"

START
sagebrush—desert
mountain trout—fresh water
shark—ocean
oak tree—forest
prairie dog—grasslands
rubber tree—jungle
frog—fresh water
barrel cactus—desert
coral—ocean
moose—forest
jackrabbit—grasslands
saguaro cactus—desert
woodpecker—forest
water lily—fresh water
jellyfish—ocean
boa constrictor—jungle
white-tailed deer—forest
gopher—grasslands
gila monster—desert
minnow—fresh water
sand dollar—ocean
chipmunk—forest
gorilla—jungle
prairie chicken—grasslands
dolphin—ocean
tarantula—desert
striped bass—fresh water
parrot—jungle
black bear—forest
scorpion—desert
short grass—grasslands
toucan—jungle
seaweed—ocean
zebra—grasslands
roadrunner—desert
octopus—ocean
hemlock tree—forest
monkey—jungle
elk—grassland
starfish—ocean
sidewinder rattlesnake—desert
whale—ocean
banana tree—jungle
antelope—forest
mallard duck—fresh water
buffalo—grasslands
FINISH

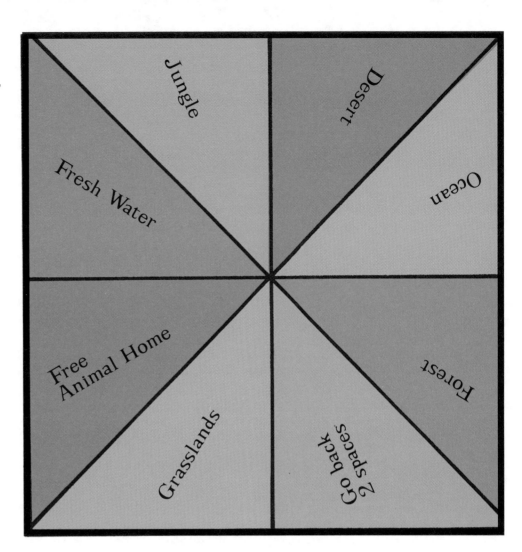

Science 1 Start your student on the path of scientific inquiry with an introduction to the senses, heat, sound, animals, and heavenly bodies—presenting God as Creator of all things.

Science 2 Present God's earth and His creation clearly as your student studies bones, plants, the shape and movement of the earth, natural forces, and shorelines.

Science 3 Direct your student's natural curiosity by helping him describe what God has created. Through studies of classification of animals, the solar system, skin, photosynthesis, birds, mass, and weight, your student will increase his knowledge of the world God made.

Working Together

Whether you have been teaching for many years or are just getting started, your comments are vital in helping us maintain our standard of excellence. In fact, most of the improvements in our materials started with good advice from consumers. So after you have put our products to the test, please give us your thoughtful comments and honest assessment.

And thanks for your valuable help!

Book Title _____ Grade level_____

Material was ☐ used in classroom. ☐ used in home school. ☐ examined only.

How did you hear about us?

_____
_____
_____

I liked

_____
_____
_____

I'd like it better if

_____
_____
_____

How did our material compare with other publishers' materials?

_____
_____
_____

Other comments?

_____
_____
_____

Fold and tape. DO NOT STAPLE
Mailing address on the other side.

BJU PRESS
Greenville, SC 29614

(OPTIONAL)
☐ Dr. ☐ Miss ☐ Mrs. ☐ Mr. _____
School _____
Street _____
City _____ State ____ ZIP_____
Phone (_____) _____
E-mail _____

TAPE SHUT–<u>DO NOT STAPLE</u>

BUSINESS REPLY MAIL
FIRST-CLASS MAIL   PERMIT NO. 344   GREENVILLE, SC

POSTAGE WILL BE PAID BY ADDRESSEE

BJU PRESS
TEXTBOOK DIVISION
1700 WADE HAMPTON BLVD.
GREENVILLE, SC 29609-9971

please fold

- -

please fold

- -